CUBAN
NATURE

Property of
Menlo Park, CA
94027

CUBAN NATURE

Roberto Gutiérrez Domech
Manuel Rivero Glean

Translated by
Josefina Ezpeleta Laplace

Updated, Corrected, and Expanded Edition
2 Regional Maps
4 Paleogeographical Maps
15 Territorial Maps
32 Separate Color Photographs
A Physical-Geographical Map of the Island

Editorial José Martí

Original title in Spanish: *Minigeografía de Cuba*
Edition: Lourdes Tagle Rodríguez
        and Israel Fernández Pujol
Design: Enrique Mayol Amador
Electronic composition: Liuba Paramónova

Map in cover courtesy of the Archivo Nacional de Cuba
[Cuban Public Record Office], map number 754 through
Bachelor José Macle Cruz

General Geographic Map 1:4 000 000 courtesy of Digital
Cartography Agency. GEOCUBA LA HABANA

ISBN 959-09-0176-X

INSTITUTO CUBANO DEL LIBRO
Editorial JOSÉ MARTÍ
Publicaciones en Lenguas Extranjeras
Calzada No. 259 entre J e I, Vedado
Ciudad de La Habana, Cuba

ACKNOWLEDGMENTS

Minigeografía de Cuba, published now by José Martí Publishing House with the new title *Cuban Nature*, has relied on the exhaustive and meticulous revision of Lourdes Tagle Rodríguez. She has known how to imbue the book with a new attribute: clarity without ambiguity.

The translation has been carried out thanks to the intellect and love of Josefina Ezpeleta Laplace, who has taken the hard task as a matter of honor.

We owe a sincere debt of gratitude to the members of the Martel Speleological Group of Cuba, with whom we have shared many years of exploration along the length and breadth of the country.

We offer our appreciation for this collective book to everyone: Those mentioned, those who we remember without mentioning, and those that we do not even remember because there are many contributors. We are beholden to all.

THE AUTHORS

PROLOGUE

In my opinion, the writer of the prologue of a book truly assumes a great responsibility. It is, therefore, my pleasure to write these lines because I share the enthusiasm of the authors of *Cuban Nature*. Oftentimes, we are in need of a specific datum or of concise geographical information and in order to obtain it we must navigate through thick tomes chockfull of details, only to find that the piece we are searching for is submerged in the depths of other issues. For this reason, a book like this is essential.

Cuban Nature minimizes such unsuccessful searches. If one needs to know some data about the position of Cuba, refer to Chapter 1. If one requires information regarding its geological formation or its relief, it is found in Chapter 2. Chapters 3 to 5 were written to find data related with climate or biota. In Chapter 6 one may find information regarding a specific locale if you were to travel through our territory and wish to find out some information about it. Also, very useful small maps which include main roads and inhabited places are included. And, of course, the last chapters offer data about economy and society, main productive fields of the country, and environment-related affairs. All this is written in straightforward language and it is smartly illustrated.

I have known the authors for a long time. When the year 1959 dawned, we met as we embarked on life's adventure by founding a group for speleological exploration along with Mario Hernández and Alberto Martínez. We were then beginners and newcomers to high-school at the Instituto de Segunda Enseñanza in Vedado. From that time on, our weekends and holidays were linked to Cuban nature while we explored caves, climbed mountains, and walked around valleys. These adventures not only bonded us as brothers, but also fostered in our minds our love for Nature. A love we have always proudly proclaimed. I am not referring to a contemplative type of love, but to a "belonging feeling" which has led us to defend Nature as part of our own legacy. In writing *Cuban Nature*, Roberto Gutiérrez and Manuel Rivero have pervaded each page with that feeling. Therefore, the reading of this book is not a faded journey through large innocuous databases, but a personal involvement in landscapes much like what the authors have repeatedly done. It is not a simple inquisitiveness regarding this or that flashy fact, but a rational sought-out inquiry into each aspect of the wonderful world of our isles and their seas.

Today, it is almost impossible to talk about economy, development or society without mentioning environment, conservation, and protection. The simple juxtaposition of words or ideas leads us nowhere. Unfortunately, hunger does not understand "rational use of resources." In the same vein, it is not easy to consider "sustainable development" together with "protection of the environment" in the context of a national economy fraught with an endemic recession. Sometimes, economists and decision-making persons have to place the need to feed and to give shelter to a community above the weighing of the few choices available to them in order to preserve a wild forest or a threatened species. We need not mention the vandalism that exists hand-in-hand with the production of capital in some countries. The alternatives are limited. Ironically, man, the cause of his own problems, threatens the extinction of his own species.

The protection of Nature and, consequently, of the human race, cannot be solved either at governmental level or at international forums. These venues help to create awareness and to develop programs. But, as far as I am concerned, education is the basis of everything.

When economists and business persons alike are raised in an environment where nature is an essential category; when decision-making persons know for a fact the irreparable consequences of their actions; when the ethics of these ideas are embodied by all and not the criteria of a few; then, we will be more cautious in our pronouncements towards the natural environment. I am pleased to introduce the importance of geography and the significance of this small book because I am sure it will convey the love for Nature and its cultivation to a large number of people. Thus, advancing the cause of the race against death in a single-mindedness of wills. To paraphrase the poet, only love generates wonderment and only love perpetuates it.

MANUEL A. ITURRALDE-VINENT

CONTENTS

INTRODUCTION

It is an arduous task to attempt to summarize in a few pages the economic and physical-geographic characteristics of a territory as complex as that of the Cuban Archipelago. Its geological conditions and location on the border of many geographical zones of the planet turn it into a mosaic of landscapes. Such a task is always in danger of omission, cast aside in favor of something more important, or superficially dealt.

Current considerations, data and knowledge regarding the geography of Cuba have been updated. We are aware that there is a considerable level of information in almost all of the fields. This level may be perfected and generalized for more extensive purposes. But, for our purposes, the information needs to be interesting for tourists, for scholars who are in search of a specific datum, and for the eager reader who is looking for a cursory knowledge of the country.

A book of this kind cannot be exclusively based on the direct and personal knowledge of its authors regarding each described issue or outstanding theme. Therefore, in order to attain the comparative purposes of the book the following sources were used: Information from the *Nuevo Atlas Nacional de Cuba* [New National Atlas of Cuba] issued in 1988 by the Academy of Sciences; textbooks by the notable geographers Salvador Massip and Antonio Núñez Jiménez; Núñez Jiménez's most recent contributions, *El Archipiélago* [The Archipelago] and *Bojeo;* the Multimedia Encyclopaedia *Todo de Cuba [All about Cuba];* geological information from the geologist and admirable researcher Manuel Iturralde-Vinent.

It stands to reason that our humble cumulative experience of over twenty-five years in the research of geo-sciences has born the idea for this book. In addition, we render our admiration to the knowledge acquired from the experience of numerous technicians and nature professionals, and to those who specialize in the subject matters we cover. With this same gratitude, we mention numbers of amateur speleologists, who in their modesty and anonymity, collaborate in accomplishing several projects and who spend their free time extending the knowledge base of the Cuban Archipelago.

The English edition is the outcome of the revision, correction, expansion and updating of the Spanish edition.

In order for this book to be accessible to the general public, its language and style have been revised while maintaining the accurate objectivity of a science book. Due to recent changes in the very specialized fields of botany and zoology, some less than exact facts in the taxonomy and nomenclature of the wild biota have been rectified. The chapter dealing with the economy of the country has been expanded and updated. A paragraph named "Society" has been added and thoughtful attention has been given to the historical evolution of the Cuban population. This section has been updated with official figures up to the year 1997, reflecting the modest but firm economic growth of Cuba.

Likewise, the photographic and cartographic illustrations have been improved and diversified, thanks to the generous collaboration of institutions and people who are near and dear to us.

CHAPTER I

GEOGRAPHICAL SITUATION OF THE CUBAN ARCHIPELAGO

The Republic of Cuba is made up of numerous groups of isles, islets, and keys, namely, an archipelago. This archipelago includes the Isle of Cuba, its largest one in surface area, followed by the Isle of Youth (former Isle of Pines), and 4194 isles, islets and keys. The latter are arranged in four archipelagos north and south of the main isle, encompassing 4010 isles (some of them larger than other territories of the Lesser Antilles which are considered nations), as well as other little islets not included in this grouping. This definition of the Cuban territory must include the Cuban insular shelf comprised between 34°57' and 74°6' western longitude west of Greenwich, and between 23°18' and 19°47'30" northern latitude (Núñez Jiménez, 1965).

The Cuban Archipelago is the largest of the Caribbean-Antillean region. It is specifically located north-westernmost of the Caribbean Sea basin in the Greater Antilles.

Cuba is bounded in the north by the Straits of Florida, the Nicholas Channel, and the Old Bahamas Channel, which separate our territory from Florida, the southernmost state of the United States of America, and from the archipelagos of Bahamas, Bermuda and the Virgin Islands.

To the south, Cuba is bounded by the Yucatan Basin and the Straits of Colón, which separate it from Central America and from the isle of Jamaica. To the west, its border is defined by the Yucatan Channel located between the archipelago and the Yucatan Peninsula in Mexico, as well as by the Gulf of Mexico. The Windward Passage separates Cuba, furthest east, from the isle Hispaniola or Quisqueya whose western part is the Republic of Haiti.

The emergent part of Cuba is comprised to the east between 74°8'3", geographical coordinates of Quema-

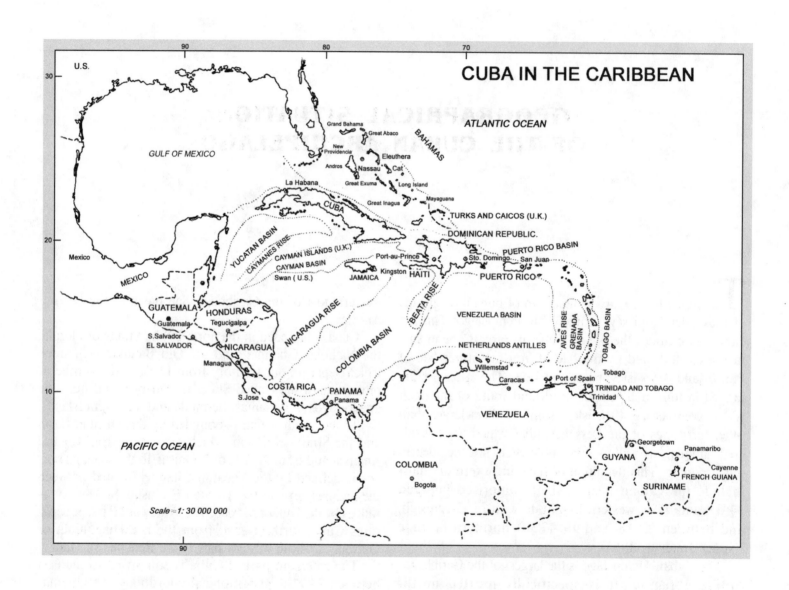

dos Point, in the Maisí region; to the west at 84°57'7" western longitude, corresponding to San Antonio Cape; and to the north between 23°17'9" in Cruz del Padre Key, north of the province of Matanzas, and 19°49'38" northern latitude in Inglés Point.

The Isle of Cuba, the largest territory of the Cuban Archipelago, the insular Caribbean or the Antilles, has a surface area of 105,007 sq km. The measured length between its western extremity in San Antonio Cape and its eastern one in Quemados Point is 1250 km. Its greatest width from north to south is 191 km between Taralagos (or Tararacos) Beach, about 1 km east southeast of Prácticos Point at the northern coast of Camagüey, and Camarón Grande Point in the southeastern part of Granma. Its narrowest width is 31 km, measured from Del Río Inlet, south of Mariel Bay at the north of La Habana province, and Majana Inlet, in the southern coast of the same province. The total length of its rough coasts is 5746 km; 3209 km of which belong to the northern littoral, and 2537 km to the southern one.

The Isle of Youth is the second broadest isle of the Cuban Archipelago, with a surface area of 2200 sq km; followed by the Romano and Coco cays with a surface area of 926 and 370 sq km respectively, both located in the Sabana-Camagüey (or Jardines del Rey) Archipelago.

One of the distinctive features of Cuba is its double insularity as noted by the Cuban geographer Antonio Núñez Jiménez in his book *El Archipiélago* [The Archipelago]. "Cuba is twice over an island. In the first place, it is surrounded by sea, and secondly because its insular shelf is separated from the shelfs of the North and South American continents, and from the rest of the Caribbean islands," states this explorer.

According to the Soviet school, regarding the zonal principle of physiographic regional division, Cuba lies in the seasonally wet subzone of the tropical zone (charac-terized by the interrelation between temperature and humidity, which rules its hydric regime, its vegetation, and soils), of the intertropical belt (of a higher regional consistency than the former one, extending in the direction of the parallels, and characterized by its thermic conditions).

In accordance with the azonal principle of this same school, there are in the American continent the following groups of countries:[1] The Mountain Ranges (in North America); the Arctic Islands (to the north of Canada); the regions east of Mountain Ranges (in North America); the American Mediterranean (where the Bahamas and Antilles are located); the Andes; and the regions east of the Andes.

The American Mediterranean is made up of the physical-geographic countries of Central America and the Antilles, and the Cuban Archipelago belongs to it. The Antilles, in turn, are divided into two physical-geographic provinces: The Greater Antilles, and the Lesser Antilles and the Bahamas. The last provincial unit includes two sub-provinces: The Bahamian-Cuban Plains, where the western and central regions of Cuba are found, up to the basins of the Cauto and Mayarí rivers; and the mountains of the Greater Antilles, comprising the orographic group east of the Cauto and Mayarí rivers (Nipe-Sagua-Baracoa and Sierra Maestra), and those of Hispaniola (Dominican Republic and Haiti).

The American Mediterranean is also shaped by the Gulf of Mexico in its northwestern region, and by the Caribbean Sea in its southeastern region. The bottom of this (Mediterranean) sea is extremely rough. The largest part of the insular territories is raised heights from the submarine relief. Furthermore, three islands of the Greater Antilles, Cuba, Hispaniola and Jamaica, are separated by

1. The word "country" is used as a hierarchical category of the physical-geographical regionalization, and not as a republic.

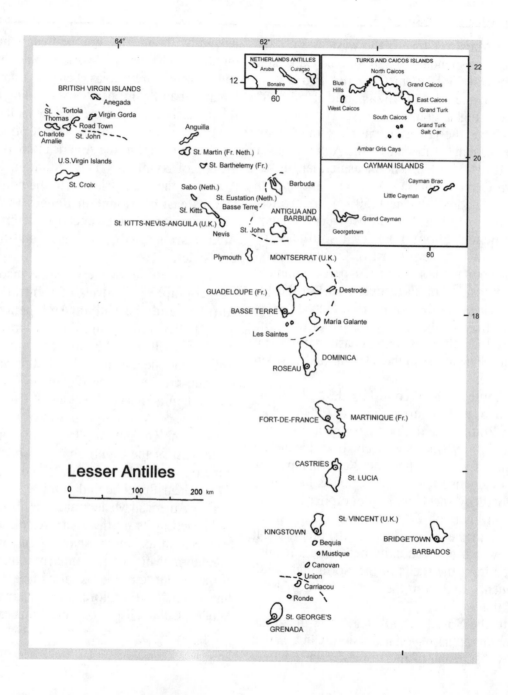

BRITISH VIRGIN ISLANDS

Anegada

St. Thomas Tortola Virgin Gorda
Road Town
Charlote Amalie St. John

U.S.Virgin Islands

St. Croix

Anguilla

St. Martin (Fr. Neth.)

St. Barthelemy (Fr.)

Sabo (Neth.) Barbuda
St. Eustation (Neth.)
Basse Terre
St. Kitts ANTIGUA AND BARBUDA
St. KITTS-NEVIS-ANGUILA (U.K.)
Nevis St. John

Plymouth MONTSERRAT (U.K.)

GUADELOUPE (Fr.) Destrode
BASSE TERRE
María Galante
Les Saintes

DOMINICA
ROSEAU

FORT-DE-FRANCE MARTINIQUE (Fr.)

CASTRIES
St. LUCIA

St. VINCENT (U.K.)
KINGSTOWN
Bequia BRIDGETOWN
Mustique BARBADOS
Canovan
Union
Carriacou
Ronde
St. GEORGE'S
GRENADA

NETHERLANDS ANTILLES
Aruba Curaçao
12 Bonaire
60

TURKS AND CAICOS ISLANDS
North Caicos
Blue Hills Grand Caicos
East Caicos
West Caicos Grand Turk
South Caicos
Grand Turk
Salt Car
Ambar Gris Cays
20

CAYMAN ISLANDS
Cayman Brac
Little Cayman
Grand Cayman
Georgetown
80

64° 62° 22

18

Lesser Antilles

0 100 200 km

Los Caimanes Basin, whereby the Yucatan Basin opens between Cuba and the Yucatan Peninsula.

Nevertheless, the relief of the Mediterranean sea shapes an orogenic unit with the Andes and the western North American mountain ranges. A continental base lies to the north of Cuba, stretching on to the Bahamas and the Florida Peninsula. Nature has linked the furthermost southwest region of Cuba with a submerged crest and valley system which runs parallel to the eastern coast of the Yucatan Peninsula, with outcroppings in the isle of Cozumel. These territories represent a very ancient continental crust. The mountainous groups in the east of the Cuban Archipelago are part of Los Caimanes Ridge, whose subcontinental base allows it to set a geologic-geographical link with Central America (Honduras and Guatemala).

The Cuban Archipelago is bounded to the north by the Straits of Florida, which separate it from the peninsula of the same name. The shortest distance between the island of Cuba and the North American territory is 140 km, separating Caleta de Raíces Inlet, west of the mouth of the Jaruco River in La Habana, and Sand Cay, southwest of Key West. In the south, the Caribbean Sea separates the Isle of Youth from the Cayman Islands with a distance of 275 km. Also in that same direction, the Straits of Colón comprise the 146 km expanse of sea between Cruz Cape in Granma province and Rosehall in neighboring Jamaica. The mountains of that country, blue in color due to their distance, can be seen from the peaks of the Sierra Maestra Range, and even from Los Pretiles, a natural vantage point located in one of the highest marine terraces in the south of the Maisí region. The Winward Passage in the east separates Cuba from Hispaniola, and its shortest distance is 83.5 km between a point located north-east of Ovando Bay and Mole St. Nicholas Cape in Haiti. As a result of this, on very clear days, Mole St. Nicholas Cape can be seen from Maisí Point or Quemados Point, our eastern extremost tip. To the west, the distance

between San Antonio Cape in Pinar del Río, and Contoy Isle in the Mexican territory is 210 km.

The shortest distance separating Cuba from a foreign territory is just the 22 km between Confites Key, north of Cuba, and Lobo Cay in the Bahamas Archipelago.

The northernmost and southernmost parallels of Cuba are: 23°16'34" at Cruz del Padre Cay, north of the province of Matanzas, and 19°49'32" at Inglés Point, close to Cruz Cape, in Granma. The western and eastern tips are respectively located in the meridians 84°57'11" at San Antonio Cape and 74°7'55" at Quemados Point, Maisí.

ADVANTAGES AND DISADVANTAGES OF THE GEOGRAPHICAL SITUATION OF CUBA

The geographical position of Cuba has been, and will be a catalytist for different political, economic and military indicators. Yet, this geographical position must not be exaggerated when considering the socioeconomic conditions of the country and the correlation between political/economic and regional/international forces in every past era.

During the 15th century, the northernmost coast of the largest of the Antilles crossed paths with the vessels of Christopher Columbus. Yet, this course of events did not work in the island's favor since the conquest and colonization of its terrritory began shortly after than that of its neighboring island Hispaniola. Following the discovery of the open spaces and the wealth of Central and South America, the Cuban island became a compelling link for maritime trade between the Spanish metropolis and the New World. Cuba's valuable forests were razed in subsequent centuries in order to outfit and repair the Crown vessels and later, to make room for the harvest of sugar cane.

Since the Spanish dominion was entrenched in the Antillean island until the mid-nineteenth century, that island remained, temporarily, on the border of the bloody and lenghty imperialist struggle waged by the developing European powers to take possession of the other Caribbean islands. These islands were, in turn, divided among England, France, Holland, and later, the United States of America.

Although Cuba's geographical position and other political and economic factors delayed its independence from the Spanish colonial yoke, its proximity to the developing imperialist power of the American continent thrust it towards a condition of mediatized republic or a semi-colony of this new metropolis.

In 1959, Cuba had a rebirth as the First Free Territory of America (a situation unrelated to its geographical predestination). A people's revolution took place headed by a generation embodying the historical legacy of Simón Bolívar, José Martí, Julio Antonio Mella and other noteworthy anti-imperialist combatants. These men led the national struggle towards true political and economic independence, confronting face to face the geographical predestination which would have otherwise determined the fate of a nation, a small country with scant energy resources, an underdeveloped country bounded by sea by the most powerful imperial force in the planet.

At present, the geographical position of Cuba is one connected to the political ambitions of its people and leaders: The preservation of its ecosystems and natural resources; the tropically moderate climate; the plenitude of its coastal ruggedness (beaches, coral reefs and bays); and the high education of its population. This lends itself to concerns regarding nature tourism; international maritime trade; extraction of mineral resources; and industrial and farming production.

CUBA IN THE CARIBBEAN-ANTILLEAN REGION

Due to its geographical position, Cuba was the initial stepping stone for the exploration and conquest of a part of the American territories. During the first third of the 16th century, expeditions towards Mexico, Florida and some to Peru departed from the largest of the Antilles.

In 1519, Major Pilot Antón de Alaminos, an emissary of Hernan Cortés, conqueror of the New Spain (Mexico), whose charge was to ship gold and impart news of the American exploits to the Spanish Crown, discovered and used the route of the New Bahamas Channel. Driven by the Gulf Stream, he crossed the Straits of Florida due north, up to the Bahamas Islands, and then due eastward towards Spain.

As a result of this course of action, this route was chosen over that of the Old Bahama Channel, located between the northern coast of Cuba and the Bahamas Islands. Thereby, Santiago de Cuba Bay lost its relative importance and Havana Bay became the most important harbour enclave between the New and the Old World.

Shortly after, the Crown and trading groups and financiers form the peninsula realized the dangers which pirate attacks posed to the transport of American loot between the Mexican port of Veracruz and Seville. San Cristóbal de La Habana (former name of Havana city) was attacked by French corsairs in 1537. Jacques de Sores, a French corsair took the young village of Santiago de Cuba in 1554 and three years later, he destroyed the village of Havana.

The defeat of the Spanish Armada by the English Navy in 1588, forced King Phillip II to order the strengthening of the trade enclaves in the West Indies. Thus, Havana, Cartagena, Portobelo, Trujillo and Veracruz were fortified. The fleet and merchandise from all of the strongholds assembled in the main fortress and as convoy headed for the

Spanish ports. This method of fleet transport established since 1561, turned San Cristóbal de La Habana into the most important center of maritime traffic in the New World. This model of protection imparted on the transport of the fabulous American riches weakened during the second half of the 17th century, although it continued to be maintained until the next century.

In spite of pirate attacks to its villages and ports, the island of Cuba grew in population and importance. The Spanish monarchy not only organized defenses and militia in several Cuban villages, but also it counterattacked. The Spaniards organized two punitive expeditions: One from Santiago de Cuba towards the Bahamas, where bases fortified by the English were destroyed; and the other from Havana to Charleston, which belonged to the French monarchy. Furthermore, Cuban pirate attacks were launched in New York and Boston, then British territories.

From 1767 on, the military authorities in Havana were in charge of naval forces protecting the Florida Peninsula. From 1800 on, The General Captain of Cuba, who then resided in Havana, was also the General Captain of Florida. Later, during the 19th century, the Floridian territory was under the administrative jurisdiction of the province of Havana.

Due to its strategic location with respect to American commercial routes and its natural riches, the island of Cuba was coveted by the English. In 1740, a Jamaica-launched fleet by Admiral Vernon blockaded but did not attack the port of Havana. One year later, this same admiral landed troops in Guantánamo Bay, where he founded the Cumberland colony. From there, the troops attempted to move forward towards Santiago de Cuba, but were not able to reach it. In 1762, a powerful English war fleet with more than twenty-two thousand men in two hundred ships, attacked and took Havana, the strongest military bastion of the New World. With this course of action, the English

sought to control all trade crossing the Antillean seas. One year later, the Spanish command abdicated to England the Florida Peninsula in exchange for the village of Havana. This shows the significance not only of the geographical position of Cuba as a whole, but also that of Havana, in particular. One of the immediate outcomes of the English stay in Havana was the increased fortification of this village, along with the villages of Matanzas and Santiago de Cuba.

When Spanish and French interests coincided with those of Great Britain, several military reinforcements were sent from Cuba between the years 1764 and 1779. Reinforcements were sent to sustain Gallic positions in North America, particularly Louisiana as well as to support the struggle of the Thirteen Colonies against the English. In 1717, Spanish authorities conferred the title of Bullwark of the West Indies to Cuba, therein acknowledging its strategic value.

The Count of Arana, having signed on behalf of Spain in 1783 the treaty that legalized the independence of the Thirteen Colonies, attested to the Spanish king the advantages of solely ruling the islands of Cuba and Puerto Rico when he said: "... and above all, we will enjoy all the advantages purveid by America, without the burdens of their possesion" (Núñez Jiménez, 1982).

During the 18th century, politicians, public officials and military personnel serving under the Spanish Crown, emphasized in their public documents and in both open and private discussions the strategic importance for trading with the largest island of the Antilles.

In his work, *Ensayo político sobre la isla de Cuba* [Political Essay about the Island of Cuba], in 1829, Humboldt emphasized the importance of Cuba's geographical location, over and above its territorial riches. Prior to this, in 1817, José Antonio Miralla, an Argentinian, dedicated to inter-American trade, noted: "The island of Cuba, due to its geographical location, seems destined by nature to be the universal depository for all the trading nations ...."

Afterwards, Domingo del Monte in 1844, José María de la Torre in 1854, and Rodríguez Ferrer in 1876, all pointed out in one form or another the advantage of the geographical position of the so-called "Key of the Gulf."

The developing North American empire did not delay in recognizing the territorial position of the Caribbean island, and since then has not ceased its attempt to take possession of it, or at least, to exert influence over its political and economic affairs.

In 1823, the United States President John Quincy Adams laid the groundwork for the need to annex Cuba in order to maintain and ensure the continuance of the North American Union. That same year, Thomas Jefferson wrote:

"... the addition of Cuba to our Confederation is exactly what it needs in order to round off our national power and take it to its highest interest level" (Núñez Jiménez, 1982).

The strategic position of the Cuban Archipelago has been coveted by powers near and far. The Cuban geographer and encyclopaedist Antonio Núñez Jiménez in his book *El Archipiélago* [The Archipelago] (Chapter XXIII), compiled a detailed list of perspective threats to this area. These concerns are currently included in the Helms-Burton Law of the United States Government. Due to its extraterritorial character, this North American law violates all commercial treaties and international rights, and it has disregarded the nation as well as all the governments and peoples of the world, including its allies.

CHAPTER II

GEOLOGICAL AND GEOMORPHOLOGICAL FEATURES OF CUBA

Since the formation of the Earth, its complex dynamics have subjected it to both sudden and slow, uninterrupted changes. These changes were brought about by geological processes which, in turn, oppose and complement each other within the customary process of internal and external geodynamics. These movements comprise the cyclical tendencies toward uplift of the Earth's crust, resulting in the unevenness of some terrain. These elevated areas then experience the effect of erosive agents such as rain, snow, ice, and wind. These agents cause the erosion and subsequent displacement of fragments and detritus from elevated areas to lower ones, where such deposited detritus may begin to form rocks over the course of millennia. Within this very same constant transformation process, many different geological formations arise whereby rocks may emerge as magma from the inner layers of the earth by way of subaerial or underwater volcanoes. These rocks will refill depressions or, in turn, form elevated places which will be eventually eroded.

To these vertical movements, one must add the unquestionable horizontal shifts of diverse parts of the Earth's crust which are named plates. These plates have undergone through constant changes during the life of the planet Earth thereby striking a balance between land and sea, eventually configuring and positioning continents and islands. Since the World's geologic evolution is not finished, these changes have not stopped, nor will they stop, and Cuba is also experiencing these transformations.

GEOLOGICAL HISTORY OF CUBA

In order to analyze the geological evolution of the territory which is currently known as the Republic of Cuba, one needs to understand that the current geographical structure of this archipelago was not always the same. In different stages of its development, some of the rocks that now conform its subsoil were not then formed. They were either in the process of being deposited or were then part of structures found in other locations of the globe.

The study of the geology of Cuba documented by Iturralde in 1988, is the study of the successive "geographies" of Cuba. For this reason, there are four stages in the geological evolution of our archipelago, even if the geographical concept of Cuba loses its present interpretation. These stages are the following: Paleozoic-Jurassic; Jurassic-Cretaceous; Cretaceous-Paleogene (Eocene); and Paleogene (Eocene)-Holocene.

The main characteristics of these stages are based on a model of geological evolution according to the most up-to-date concepts with regard to the continental drift, and according to criteria endorsed by the majority of the specialists who study the geology of Cuba.[2]

PALEOZOIC-JURASSIC STAGE

During this stage, Cuba or "ProtoCuba," (Iturralde, 1988) was part of a huge continent named *Pangaea* by Alfred Wegener—the German author of the continental drift theory. This continent comprised, among others, territories of the current continents of North America, South America and Africa.

This vast territory began to break up in the course of the Triassic Period within the Mesozoic Era, due to the formation of a narrow and lengthened depression. This depression began extending from the European Mediterranean Sea to the North Atlantic Ocean, and bringing about the following movement of continental masses: To the southeast, which would later become South America and Africa; to the north, which would become North America; besides the creation

2. The criteria of Iturralde (1988) and our own observations, which in general coincide with his, are mainly used to explain each stage because we consider them more accessible to the objectives of this book.

of an Euroamerican Mediterranean sea. During the Jurassic Period, the general tendency to movement and the evolution of the depression continue until the subsequent formation of the North Atlantic Ocean.

Even though the exact location of "ProtoCuba" has not been accurately established yet, its existence within the vast territory of *Pangaea* is accepted. This is due to the presence, in part of Cuba, of a typical folded substratum of continental massifs, the remains of a sialic rock massif —aluminum-silicate in nature—characteristic of places where there are depths greater than forty kilometers. For instance, these are: *Gneiss*, at El Guayabo, in the Guaniguanico Mountain Range; marble and quartz rocks in La Trampa Hill, in Bacunayagua and San Adrián, north of La Habana and Matanzas; and *calcifiro* at Menéndez and Socorro beaches, north of Matanzas and Villa Clara, among other places. These rocks were part of the emergent surface of *Pangaea*, and today are found outside their original bedding place mixed with younger sediments. Sialic rocks in oceanic basins have little or no thickness to speak of.

Thin detritus material such as sand and gravel, coming from the erosion of continental massifs form sedimentary and metamorphosed-sedimentary rocks which are found in the Guaniguanico Mountain Range, in the Guamuhaya Mountains, in the regions of La Asunción in Baracoa and in the Isle of Youth. This detritus seems to come from a sector of *Pangaea* named *Caribaea* by Rutten and Bucher (Iturralde, 1988), due south of "ProtoCuba." Evaporite rocks found north of the province of Ciego de Ávila are indicators of the continental feature of the substratum.

In addition to the acknowledged evidence regarding the continental feature of the folded substratum of Cuba which is presently considered part of the geological structure known as the Bahamas Shelf, there is added evidence from *Pangaea*. In inner *Pangaea*, during the Upper Jurassic stage, a sea was formed during the breaking up of the continent. Aside from rocky beds of chemical and biological origin, sediments coming from the erosion of the highest territories were first deposited on the continental slope. These sediments later sunk to the bottom to join the remains of rocky massifs lying on the bottom of the newly forming narrow sea. For this reason, remains of the ocean crust of the American Mediterranean Sea, Jurassic Age, have proven to be part of the foundation, that folded substratum corresponding to the time of the fracture of *Pangaea*.

The rocks forming the ocean crusts are named simatic, because they are made up of ferromagnesian rocks and, therefore, are more dense in nature than the sialic ones. These rocks from the abyss are similar in composition to the components of the upper part of the mantle. They are mostly harzburgite, lherzolitte, serpentine, pyroxenite, amphibolite, gabbro, diorite, dolerite, basalt and andesite. They usually appear in combination and for this reason they are referred to as ophiolite association, ophiolite complex, or merely, ophiolite. These dark, blackish-green colored rocks form a longitudinal belt around the island of Cuba, and outcrop in the Cajálbana Plateau in Pinar del Río; from Guanabacoa to Jaruco, in La Habana and Ciudad de La Habana provinces; from Santa Cruz del Norte to Matanzas; from Motembo to Chambas, in the provinces of Villa Clara and Ciego de Ávila; from Esmeralda to Lugareño, in Camagüey; from Puerto Padre in Las Tunas to Banes in Holguín; and from Cueto in Holguín province to farther to the east of Baracoa in Guantánamo. These rocks are generally mixed due to the displacements they have undergone which cause them to be found in their current positions.

JURASSIC-CRETACEOUS STAGE

In this stage, the American Mediterranean Sea probably had reached its maximum width. At the same time, a process of compression began between parts of *Pangaea* which today form the North and South American continents. This process was closely linked with the formation of the South Atlantic Ocean. In that era, an archipelago made of volcanic islands was formed, which so resembled the volcanic archipelagos of the Pacific Ocean that a genetic relationship may well be established between the two.

According to Iturralde (1988), the Atlantic Ocean coasts are, generally, low-lying, descending with a smooth slope to the ocean bottoms; they do not have volcanoes; however, earthquakes do occur. On the other hand, the Pacific Ocean coasts have a steep relief, and the slopes descending to the sea depths have very complicated configurations. In comparison to the Atlantic Ocean, there are numerous volcanoes, and earthquakes are very frequent. That is why it is known as the "Fire Belt of the Pacific."

In western Pacific, it is common to find the continental shelf, the continental slope, the marginal sea, the archipelago of volcanic islands and the abyssal basin between the continent and the ocean. An analysis of maps and graphs of that region (for instance, the archipelagos or islands of Papua New Guinea, New Caledonia or Sajalin) will identify the basis for its similarity with Cuba.

Along the northern coast of Cuba, the remains of the southern edge of the Bahamas Shelf and its continental slope may be found. During the Jurassic-Cretaceous Period, limestone, dolomite and some evaporite were deposited along this northern coast. These deposits belonged to shallow sea waters resembling a submerged shelf, much like the one now present in the Bahamas. The rocks have a thickness of about ten or more kilometers, and lie almost horizontally, just slightly disturbed. Such rocks outcrop in the north coast of Villa Clara and Camagüey provinces, and they have been drilled to make wells in Francés, Fragoso and Coco Keys, as well as in the territories of Chambas and Morón. In these territories, limestone are also present but, in this case, bearing microfossils and ammonites characteristic of deeper waters. This is referred to as the Cayo Coco sequence. The deposits accumulated in the low lands that bounded the shelf on the south side during the Cretaceous Period appear in the Meneses, Jatibonico, Cubitas and Gibara mountain ranges, in the provinces of Sancti Spíritus, Ciego de Ávila, Camagüey and Holguín, as well as in Pan de Guajaibón (a mogote) and Sierra Azul Range which are part of the Guaniguanico Mountain Range in the province of Pinar del Río.

In the central and eastern territories noted above, these deposits are made up of limestone and dolomite with rudists and microfossils, characteristic of shallow sea waters. This is named the Remedios Sequence.

The stratum sequence in this edge or peripheral zone of the shelf is deformed by folds and faults, and they often superpose themselves, as opposed to the salient features in the inner part of that shelf structure.

During the Cretaceous Period, the continental slope of the Bahamas Shelf occupied a latitudinal position corresponding to the current one of the island of Cuba. To the north, the deposited rocks in that slope resemble those from the Remedios Sequence, whereas to the south, they are more similar to those from oceanic bottoms. These strata are characterized predominantly by limestone, radiolarites, and the presence of sandstones, aleurolites and argillites containing fossil remains of ammonites and microplankton typical of deep marine waters connected to the ocean. These rocks are named Las Villas Sequence, and they extend from the uppermost of the Upper Jurassic Period until the Upper Cretaceous Period, although the

corresponding strata to part of this period are missing because this zone was emergent during that geological time.

The rocks from Las Villas Sequence outcrop in Cantel, Martí, Máximo Gómez and Menéndez Beach, in Matanzas; from Motembo to Chambas, in Sancti Spíritus and Ciego de Ávila provinces; from Esmeralda and Lugareño to the Camaján Range in the province of Camagüey; and south to heights of Gibara in Holguín province.

Several specialists in the field point out that the transition between the sialic crust of the Bahamas Shelf represented by arkoses and other rocks to the north and the oceanic crust of the marginal sea, made up of basalts and radiolarites to the south, may be found in the boundaries of the continental slope.

The ophiolite association or complex is found south of the slope. This complex represents the relics of a marginal sea which separated the continent from the archipelago of volcanic islands whose rocks extend through a considerable part of the current Cuban territory.

Unlike the Pacific region, continental massifs are found in the southern area of Cuba, such as those of the Guaniguanico Mountain Range; those from the Isle of Youth; and those from the Guamuhaya Mountains. These massifs are construed to be the remains of the subcontinent *Caribaea*, previously mentioned.

The existence of an archipelago of volcanic islands during the Cretaceous Period is a fact duly examined by all of the researchers of the territory, inasmuch as it has the same rocks along the length and breadth of the Cuban territory. Nevertheless, there are places where these rocks can only be found by drilling wells through thick layers of younger deposits.

The volcanic arc rocks are visible in La Palma or Consolación del Norte in Pinar del Río province, as well as in Bauta and Madruga, to the west and east of La Habana respectively; in nearby Jovellanos in Matanzas province;

and between Aguada de Pasajeros in Cienfuegos and Ciego de Ávila province. These rocks are also apparent in the south-central region of Camagüey, between Puerto Padre and Banes in Las Tunas and Holguín provinces, respectively. The presence of volcanic arc rocks extends towards the easternmost part of the island with visible outcrops in the valleys of the Nipe, Cristal and Baracoa mountain ranges.

Rocks that are well represented in Cuba from among the rocks of the archipelago or volcanic arc group are the volcano-sedimentary and intrusive rocks. The former ones are formed as a result of the action of sub-aerial or submerged volcanoes and their erosion thereof, and they are found in a crystalline or fragmentary form. Among these rocks there are a large variety of lavas, tuffs, tephroids and tuphites often intercalated with limestone, sandstones, marls and other appropriate sedimentary rocks.

Although intrusive rocks may have the same mineralogical composition of volcano-sedimentary ones, they crystallize in the inner part of the Earth, and therefore, they are always crystalline rocks, without glass, and with a more homogeneous composition.

Tuff, tephroid, and in lesser degree, basaltic and andesite lavas, intercalated with limestone, silicites, and so on, predominate in Pinar del Río province, thus indicating a submarine origin.

In La Habana, Ciudad de La Habana and Matanzas provinces, among volcano-sedimentary rocks, tuffs, tephroids and tuphites (pyroclastic) are very common, similarly intercalated with limestone and silicites, which also indicate a submarine origin in a relatively deep sea. Lavas are scarce, and andesite rocks predominate. These volcano-sedimentary rocks located on the western part of Cuba are very folded and faulted, both of which have masked their original position.

The sequences in the central region of Cuba have undergone fewer transformations and hence, they have been studied with greater ease. It is there, at the bottom of the sea, where the first volcanic activity took place along fissures whence basalt and andesite-basalt lavas broke out reaching powerful accumulations when several active fissures collided as they did in Guáimaro, Camagüey. These eruptions were partially explosive in nature, producing considerable amounts of ash and other fragmentary materials which were deposited in the most depressed zones of the submarine relief forming pyroclastic rocks in the periphery of volcanic centers and appropriate sedimentary ones in its borders.

The bottom sea had a rough relief, as it is shown by the presence of reef limestone over lavas, forming close to the surface.

According to the composition of the lavas and their intercalation with sedimentary rock sequences, it may be supposed that eruptions through fissures and submerged volcanoes took place, and even some of these volcanic buttes gave rise to keys and islets.

In Eastern Cuba, volcano-sedimentary rocks are seldom studied because they have been notably altered by tectonism and metamorphization. In addition, the volcanism was submarine in nature and andesite lavas were intruded with powerful deposits of pyroclastic and sedimentary rocks.

With few outcroppings, the intrusive rocks in Cuba are arranged latitudinally in elongated bodies ranging from Cumanayagua in the province of Cienfuegos to Cacocum in Holguín. The rocks found in these areas are primarily gabbros, diorites, granodiorites and quartz-diorites. In the same area granites and sienites are present in smaller amounts, although one may find pegmatites, porphyries and aplites.

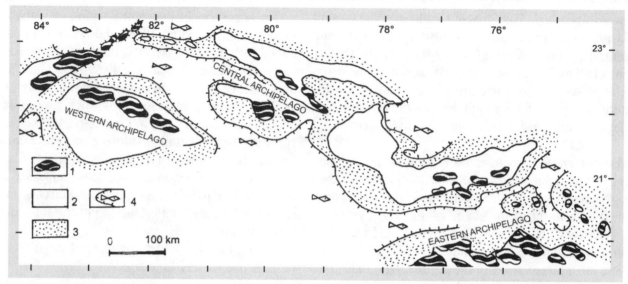

Paleogeographic map from the Upper Eocene. Current geographical coordinates of the Cuban territory are given as reference.
Emergent lands: 1. Mountainous; 2. Flat. Submerged lands: 3. Insular Shelf; 4. Submarine Depressions. (According to Iturralde, 1988.)

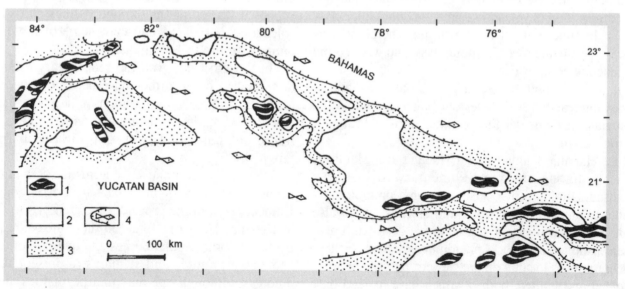

Paleogeographic map from the Oligocene. Current geographical reference. Emergent lands: 1. Montainous; 2. Flat. Sumerged lands:
3. Insular Shelf; 4. Submarine Depressions. (According to Iturralde, 1988.)

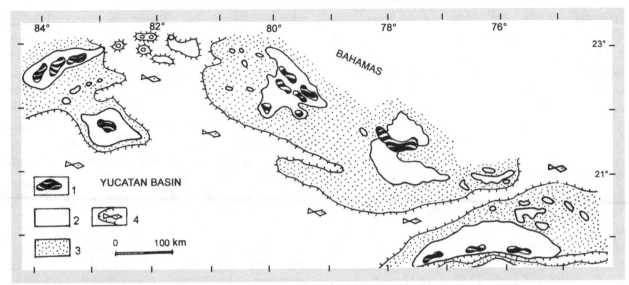

Paleogeographic map from the Middle Miocene. Current geographical reference. Emergent lands: 1. Montainous; 2. Flat. Sumerged lands: 3. Insular Shelf; 4. Submarine Depressions. (According to Iturralde, 1988.)

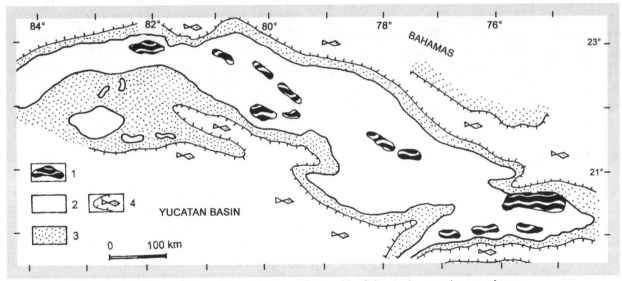

Paleogeographic map from the Pliocene. Current geographical coordinates of the Cuban territory are given as reference. Emergent lands: 1. Mountainous; 2. Flat. Submerged lands: 3. Insular Shelf; 4. Submarine Depressions. (According to Iturralde, 1988.)

These intrusive rocks have radioactive elements whose emergence, disappearance or transformation determine their age. With these rocks it is possible to use absolute dating methods as opposed to relative dating methods established by fossils. The potasium-argon method is one such method which has been used to date some Cuban samples. It determines age as far back as seventy to eighty four million years, with a three to ten million year margin of error.

If we were to compare the similarities between the Cuban volcanic arc and those of the Pacific Ocean, we would find that south of the rocks which belong to the Caribbean Archipelago of volcanic islands, one must find the remains of a fault or an oceanic abyssal basin that have not been found in Cuba. To the south of the outcrops of volcanic rocks, there are accumulations of huge thickness of young sediments which form the insular shelf of the Cuban Archipelago and may have apparently buried the volcanic rocks.

As it has been mentioned before, the fracture of *Pangaea* brought about the movement of some sialic blocks which did not migrate towards South America, and they were left behind, thereby forming the microcontinent known as *Caribaea*. It is difficult to define the form and dimension of the blocks because they have undergone significant transformations. At present, the remains of this micro-continent are the massifs of Guaniguanico, Guamuhaya and those found due north of the Isle of Youth.

CRETACEOUS-PALEOGENE (EOCENE) STAGE

This stage is probably one of the most dynamic stages in the geological evolution of Cuba, inasmuch as the geological and geographical elements, similar to those formed in the western Pacific Ocean during the Jurassic-Cretaceous stage, underwent radical transformation because of intense compressions. These compressions decreased an extensive territory comprising hundreds of thousands of square kilometers into a folded belt, where the sequences of the continental margin, of the marginal sea and those of the archipelago of volcanic islands, piled up one on top of another. During this stage, the folded substratum of Cuba was consolidated. Furthermore, the large structures observed may be still differentiated, and it is possible to accomplish the paleogeographic reconstruction based upon the rocks, which have remained as "witnesses."

Apparently, the Bahamas Shelf had a similar shape to the current one, although its southern border was placed farther to the north, coinciding with the present Old Bahamas Channel. It has proved extracting samples of sediments from deep water in drilled wells in that zone, corresponding to the Paleocene and Middle Eocene geological periods, over Cretacic rocks from shallow bottoms.

A depression known as Frontal Depression is found south of the Bahamas Shelf. It is formed over the substratum, where the mentioned Cayo Coco, Remedios and Las Villas Sequences are deposited, which constituted the periphery of the shelf. Fragments of the most ancient rocks that made up the substratum of the depression are found in such depression. Apparently, those fragments were broken off from the rough scarpments formed by the fast sinking of the shelf border, and went together with the general compression of the substratum.

Nowadays, the Frontal Depression is refilled of olistostromic deposits or merely olistostromes. They took form when large rocky masses (allochthonous), which are horizontally slipped at different speeds from south to north over others that were *in situ* (autocthonous; in this case is the bottom of the depression), and generated by compression forces, mixed with others and between themselves in a very complex way. This confused situation becomes greater when the bad weather agents erase complete layers, and transform and hide others. In this period, south of the Frontal Depression, an existence of a group of isles and keys named Northern Archipelago is pointed out; it should move northwards throughout the filling process of this depression and its remains are found in olistostromes. This movement is calculated in 3 mm/atm, the same magnitude than that of the Frontal Depression destruction.

During the Cretaceous-Eocene period, in the context of the current Cuban territory, some very complex structures still formed, such as the superimposed basins. They are named so, because they had formed over the deformed substratum of the Cretaceous volcanic islands, and over the back of the allochthonous one that was horizontally moved in order to refill the Frontal Depression.

This structure started to develop from an emerged territory. It is characterized by the thickness of its sediments and the abundance of rudists, among other fossils. Rudists were pelecypod mollusks that made up true banks and reefs like the present coral ones.

The sedimentation cadence is another feature of the sediments in the superimposed basins, which is known as *flyschoides* sequence. It is owing to frequent earthquakes going together with ascending and descending movements of the lands that brought about gentle folds and faults.

The existence of a southern archipelago south of these basins is known as an intuition. Its clues are found today in the Isle of Youth and in the Guamuhaya massif, while its remains, made up of metamorphosed rocks, are among Middle Eocene and younger sediments, both of which refill the superimposed basins.

It seems to have existed a huge marine depression named Yucatan Basin, south of ProtoCuba, where, in spite of the difficulties in its study because of its depth and structure, some geophysical (seismic) research have revealed the existence of an horizontal bedding of sediments from the Upper Eocene and younger, deposited over a more ancient either submarine or subaerial submerged relief that must correspond to the period at which we refer.

In the eastern utmost tip of the current island of Cuba, in a part of Hispaniola, Jamaica and Puerto Rico, as well as in the present territories of the Grand Cayman Ridge and Nicaragua Rise, an archipelago of volcanic islands spread, and its remains have been found. One must take into account that during the Cretaceous-Eocene stage, the mentioned territories possibly were up to 200 km farther to the west than at present.

The volcanic rocks from the Paleocene-Middle Eocene in Cuba are found, above all, in the Sierra Maestra Mountain Range and in the southern hillside of the Nipe-Cristal-Baracoa mountainous group; in a lesser degree also their remains appear in the subsoil of the Cauto, Camagüey and Las Tunas plains, and even, so far as in La Habana, pyroclast rocks are found.

From the Middle Eocene, volcanism became weaker, until its disappearance; since then, there are no traces of volcanism in Cuba and ProtoCuba.

PALEOGENE (EOCENE) HOLOCENE STAGE

In the history of the geological development of Cuba, this period is characterized by noteworthy differences with the foregoing ones. First of all, because the folded substratum structures are relatively steady in their position with reference to the nearest continental masses, like North America, South America and to the seas of the surroundings. In second place, because during this stage the shape of the Cuban Archipelago and of some of the neighboring islands of the Greater Antilles would be shaped in a relatively definite way.

From the subaerial emergence of elevated regions (but isolated among them like isles), where the folded substratum outcropped—made up of rocks that took form before the Upper Eocene, it means, more than forty-five million years ago—mainly in the current territories of Guaniguanico, Guamuhaya, and so others, an intense erosion process was leveling the territory and depositing the detritus that went from those elevated places. These detritus were deposited in the coasts of those isles until to shape extensive and deep beds of "covering" sediments that joined the isles and covered some areas of the outcropping substratum. The emergent territories are identified by the presence of materials made up in subaerial conditions, such as alluvial sands, clays, tuffs, fossilliferous soils, sediments of detritus from the slopes of the elevations, and so forth. They differentiate from those formed in marine conditions, in which limestone, marls and other organogenic rocks showing shells, corals and other marine fossils in an usual way, abound.

Generally, these regions cannot be noticed because other environs are superposed over already consolidated rocks, even with a constituted relief, and of the erosion action, which can mask and sometimes erase entire beds of rock. The sea advance movement above raised territories is named *marine transgresion* or merely *transgresion,* and the back movement, *regression.* These forward and backward sea movements were very frequent in the Early Eocene Period, where the vertical and horizontal tectonic movements predominated, unlike preceding stages, in which tension and compression movements prevailed. These last movements brought about large folds and faults making possible the slide of those folds over its own strata; these processes are named *overthrusts,* a concept of very complex comprehension and polemic interpretation by the specialists.

The vertical shifts allow the occurrence of marine origin sediments in different positions. They are clear examples of the dynamics and the vigor of the tectonics in the last stages of the geological evolution of Cuba. As a result of this course of action, carbonated rocks of that genesis may be observed in so different places, like in the La Habana-Matanzas southern plain; the Morón plain, north of Ciego de Ávila; the Camagüey southern plain; the elevations north of La Habana and Ciudad de la Habana, between Mariel and Matanzas; the Escaleras de Jaruco, the Camoa and the Somorrostro Hills and the Anafe Plateau at La Habana; the hills known as Pan de Matanzas and El Palenque at Matanzas province; in the subsoil of some keys from the Sabana-Camagüey Archipelago and of the Zapata Peninsula; and in other places, known because wells have been drilled with different purposes. Sediments of marine genesis, but with different geological age, appear also in elevated hills in the northern side of the Sierra Maestra Mountain Range, and in the Cabo Cruz, Guaso and Maisí Plateaus.

During this epoch (Upper Eocene-Holocene or Recent) these tectonic movements—or neotectonic movements, as the tectonic efforts are known after the formation of the folded substratum—brought about the faulting of the territory in many blocks, divided or limited by some of the most important faults of Cuba, from the viewpoint of its present formation. These faults have, as a whole, a southeast-northeast direction and a varying size shift of their edges.

The Pinar Fault constitutes the southern border of the Guaniguanico Mountain Range, and it extends practically towards the territory of La Habana. It was active between the Eocene and the Oligocene, and its eastern edge registered a shift about 30 km - 40 km to the northeast.

The Trocha Fault, that affects the territories of Ciego de Ávila and Camagüey, was active between the Oligocene and the Miocene. It has brought about a shift between 10 km and 20 km of the territory of Camagüey, from its original position, to the northeast. Meantime, the Camagüey

Fault, which divides the province of the same name, has moved its eastern edge between 20 km and 30 km. The Nipe-Guacanayabo Fault, which has such name because of the bay and gulf to where it is spreaded, has caused a similar movement in same direction.

The Oriente Fault follows by one side the course of the northern wall of the Los Caimanes Basin, from which is part the known Bartlett Trench, and by the other side, borders the south coast of the provinces of Granma, Santiago de Cuba and Guantánamo. The south limb of this fault has had eastwards shifts so big as 100 km - 200 km. As a matter of fact, the current territories of Hispaniola and Puerto Rico underwent a shift to the east, and Jamaica to the south, brought about by the formation of the Los Caimanes Basin. These movements are not unknown in the world, and the measurements taken in diverse regions of the globe show vertical—ascending or descending—and horizontal movements (above of all, in zones of evident seismic activity) about some millimeters per atmosphere (mm/atm) and even some centimeters per atmosphere (cm/atm). When these movements take place in our days, they are imperceptible, and just we may have them thanks to the effective measurements some specialists carry out. For instance, eastwards shifts from 0.4 cm/year to 2 cm/year along the Oriente Fault have been calculated, which is, from the geological viewpoint, a highly "fast" movement.

In fact, from the e nd of the Eocene period Cuba presented itself as follows:

- A western archipelago, which included the territories of Pinar del Río, the Isle of Youth and surrounding zones, with a varied relief and indiscriminately submerged or emerged areas.
- A central archipelago that occupied the territories from Matanzas to Holguín. It mainly were made up of flat lands with some mountainous massifs, like the hills of

Trinidad and Sancti Spíritus belonging to the present Guamuhaya Mountains.

- An eastern archipelago, included between the Los Caimanes Basin and a Mediterranean channel named *Nipe-Guacanayabo,* corresponding the last one with emergent lands and their insular shelf, located in the present eastern Cuba. In this archipelago, a mountainous relief—the Cristal-Baracoa Range (the Bartlett Land)—is observed. It is possible that this archipelago had spread until the Miocene, in the position occupying today Jamaica and Hispaniola, in shallow waters and some small isles, till the Oriente Fault took place and brought about the movement of its own edges.

These archipelagos, each one with its insular shelf, were separated by channels and deep water navigable channels that replace themselves for lowlands, sometimes marshy, along the Oligocene and Middle to Upper Miocene. A considerable part of the territory emerged during the Pliocene, while during the Pleistocene, a large part of this lands were cyclically submerged owing to the oscillations of the level of the seas, brought about by the glaciations took place in that period. In short, one may affirm: The Cuban territory just reached its present shape about one million years ago.

VOLCANISM

In some stages throughout the geological history of Cuba the volcanic activity was noteworthy; they happened during the Cretaceous and the Early-Paleogene periods.

During the last period of the Mesozoic Era an arc of volcanic islands developed south to the oceanic basin, known by the common name of *Zaza zone.* This arc outcrops along the Cuban territory, but has the highest noteworthiness in central Cuba and Camagüey. Furthermore, outstanding outcrops are found in Bahía Honda, Pinar del Río and in Auras, Holguín and in the Nipe-Cristal-Baracoa region, in the northern-eastern utmost tip of the island of Cuba. Probably, this volcanic arc took form over a melanocratic pre-Cretaceous basement, represented by the rocks of the ophiolitic and possibly, amphibolitic complex.

In the zone of the El Purial Range, in Guantánamo, the sequences appear metamorphosed *(Instituto de Geografía* [Institute of Geography], 1988).

The Cretaceous volcanic arc is divided into two principal complexes: A volcano-sedimentary complex and another intrusive one.

In a profile of the first one, it may be differentiated: Pyroclastites having medium composition, intercalated with layers made up of andesitic and basaltic lavas, agglomerates and cilicites. Over these rocks are found limestones from Lower Cretaceous (Albian); more above, there are insertions of andesite-dacitic tuffs and lens of biogenic limestone from Upper Cretaceous (Turonian). The top of this sequence is occupied by volcano-sedimentary rocks from Upper Cretaceous (Santonian) with lens of biogenic limestone from Upper Cretaceous (Lower Campanian). These rocks are cut by magmatic bodies arranged in the same direction of the arc, but with a greater development between Cienfuegos in central Cuba towards Las Tunas in eastern Cuba.

These magmatic or intrusive bodies are mainly composed of granodiorites, quartz-diorites, diorites, plagiogranites and scanty granites. In the nearness of Guáimaro, Camagüey, an alkaline magmatism with hornblendic and aplitic sienite bodies displays.

The metamorphic complex named Mabujina is observed towards the southern edge of the island of Cuba. Apparently, it is the basement of the own volcanic arc. It has a very complex structure, and its contacts, both with the Escambray metamorphic complex (Guamuhaya Mountains) and with the Zaza zone, are tectonic along steep faults. This Cretaceous volcanic arc was active until Upper Cretaceous (Lower Campanian) and after that, a generalized uplift brought about during which superimposed basins developed (formed also in the Upper-Maastrichtian Cretaceous) with sinorogenic, molasse and olistostromic deposits. The rocks of the volcanic arc and its cover underwent intense overthrusts that moved them from their original positions.

A Paleogene volcanic arc with a Paleocene-Middle-Upper Eocene age was superposed over the Cretaceous volcanic arc in the eastern region; it spread, with a variable width, about 200 km throughout the southern edges of Granma, Santiago de Cuba and Guantánamo provinces, shaping the chief mountain range of the country, Sierra Maestra, and the south edge of the Nipe-Cristal-Baracoa elevations.

Two structural complexes differ in this volcanic arc. The first one is an andesite-basaltic, mainly a lavatic complex—with a Paleocene-Eocene age—that displays in the Sierra Maestra Mountain Range, above all north of the Turquino Pike, where a great concentration of volcanoes as well as a pyroclastic dacitic-rhyolithic part of the same age that is observed in the group of the Nipe-Cristal-Baracoa elevations, has registered. The other one, from both mountainous zones, is a carbonated-tuffite-like structural complex from Middle Eocene. Both complexes are cut by dikes and intrusive bodies of diabases and even plagiogranites, which attain different sizes. The occurrence of this stage of volcanic development is not only expressed by lavas and intrusive rocks, but also by the finding of volcanic ash, associated with the mentioned rocks, and sometimes in places so far as the province of La Habana, where they have been found between marine rocks from Lower Eocene.

The Paleogene volcanic arc has its own cover, represented by a formation of *flyschoide* terrigenous molasse of Middle-Upper Eocene age.

After this last age, no volcanism signals are found in the Cuban territory, and unlike relative close countries of the region, Cuba is free from volcanic activity since historic times.

TECTONISM

There were numerous movements in different parts of the territory of ProtoCuba until the constitution of the current one. In addition to these, the tectonic movements that had an effect on the local structures between themselves, and between them and the regional geological structures, have registered times of great intensity, and the shifts were about 150 km. This datum should not astonish us since, in Europe and specifically in the Alps, "horizontal" movements about 300 km - 400 km have been registered.

Essentially, it may be said that until Middle-Upper Eocene, due to the orogenic periods (or orogeny), like the Laramian orogeny (named *Cuban orogeny* for its preponderant action in the geological evolution of Cuba), there were movements that attained great magnitudes. These movements brought about the faulting, dragging or horizontal sliding, and overthrust or superposition of large stony layers, aside from tilted faults associated to these overthrusts that are indicators of a "tectonic style" named *Alpine* or *typical-Alpine*, because it was in the Alps where it was studied first in detail.

In the Nipe-Cristal-Baracoa Mountains lies an example of an allochthonous rocky layer (it is away from its original position), where a layer is identified in an ophiolite massif of some 2500 sq km, whose thickness attains 1000 m from the summit of the elevations to the bottom of the valleys. The rocks from the autochthonous one (it is in its original position) outcrop, represented by sandstones and conglomerates from Cretaceous to Paleocene.

The enlightenment of this complex geological movement has been a reason of bitter discussions inasmuch as its recognition requires an exhaustive analysis of the bedding of the rocks of the different parts of the overthrust region. The analysis always are accomplished starting from the trends of the specialists and the knowledge and comprehension level that one has about an specific matter, in order to find the dragging signals, and the traces either in the surface or in the subsoil, and the inversion of the stratigraphic sequence that bring about these movements.

A more known and established example (once understood), but no less polemic for its acceptance, is the case of the Guaniguanico Mountain Range. There, the overthrusts have caused the occurrence of nappes that sometimes "ride" in more than one generation of movements, bringing about inverse stratigraphic sequences, observable only after very detailed research.

The San Carlos area in the Los Órganos Range is an example, among many, because the Luis Lazo valley (or San Carlos valley) is a window where the autochthonous layer outcrops among the allochthonous one, represented by the Mesa and the San Carlos Ranges, both of which are constituted by more ancient rocks than those they lie over.

The Cretacous-Eocene Stage was very dynamic to the effect of these horizontal shifts of tectocnic layers, with regard to the diversity in shapes and sizes. These overthrusts are:

- The rocks of the ophiolitic association moved over the Bahamas continental margin.
- The associations of the Cretaceous volcanic arc slipped over the ophiolitic complex, and in some cases, went forward up to the continental margin.
- These same associations overthrusted the southern sialic massifs (Isle of Youth and Guamuhaya).
- The above mentioned massifs internally broke off, forming smaller layers which shifted one on top of another.

The rocky sequences piled up on account of these movements, and the zone they occupied diminished in almost two thirds of its area, to attain about 179,000 sq km, the area today occupies the folded substratum.

After this geological epoch, there have been, above all, vertical movements—with oscillations or not—, defined as having a Germanic style. This a lot more up-to-date process has been put on top over existing layers and rocky complexes, bringing about the formation of sinked or elevated tectonic blocks, known as *grabens* and *cuasigrabens* or *horsts* and *cuasihorsts,* respectively. They have masked, in many times, the character of the previous ones. Other common neotectonic movements are those of horizontal distension.

The posorogenic cover began to develop in the upper part of the Upper Eocene in most of the existing territory. In the Middle Eocene it continued its development in the rest. These covering deposits are not in correspondence with the existing zonations, and they cover the most ancient structures until Cuba reached its present shape. Furthermore, these covering deposits were formed in a tectonic environ having relative calmness.

Some calculus about the intensity of neotectonic movements show vertical shifts to 0.08 mm/year in the Miocene Period, and to 0.02 mm/year in the Oligocene.

The tectonic movements do not happen, as it is understood, without causing any reaction—both physic and social—, because they bring about varied-intensity earthquakes. At present times, in our archipelago, both horizontal and vertical tectonic movements occur, but they have slow speed, which impedes their detection. For instance, in 1964 in Alaska an earthquake brought about, in just a few seconds, a land shift of 9.4 m in vertical direction, and 21 m in the horizontal one. It means a speed about 1 m/s, in contrast with lifting movements in some Japanese coasts and in the own Cuban territory.

There is an historical record of earthquakes in Cuba since 1524. Therefore, one may affirm that the most unstable region from a tectonic viewpoint is Santiago de Cuba, where, at least, one earthquake per year may occur. In this region, the two most intense remembered earthquakes took place in 1766 and in 1852; both were IX degree earthquakes in the MKS-1964 scale, and brought about the partial destruction of the city. The strongest earthquake recorded in Cuba took place in 1880 in the western zone, and had effect on Candelaria and San Cristóbal.

MINERAL RESOURCES

The great geological variability of Cuba and its position in the tropical zone of the globe made possible the formation of diverse sorts of mineral ores, both metallic and non-metallic, endogenous and exogenous. The Cuban subsoil has also petroleum and gas strata, with unlike characteristics *(Instituto de Geografía* [Institute of Geography], 1988). At present times, Cuban and joint ventures concern with their prospection.

Beds of massive sulfur with copper have developed in the rocky complexes of the northern continental margin, related with the subvolcanic basic magmatism in the western region of the archipelago. Likewise, petroleum and gas strata are found in that sector, in the La Habana-Matanzas regions (Boca de Jaruco field, Varadero and Cárdenas), as well as dolomite, gypsum, anhydrite and bauxite deposits in the hills of Sierra Azul-Pan de Guajaibón in the El Rosario Range, province of Pinar del Río.

Deposits of chromite, copper and gold appear in the basic and ultrabasic rocks belonging to the ophiolitic belt of the former oceanic basin. Exogenic laterite beds with nickel, iron and cobalt have developed in some zones, formed in weathering crusts from serpentinized ultrabasic rocks. The major nickel reserves of the territory and one of the biggest of the world are found in the Nipe-Cristal-Baracoa region.

The rocky complexes of the volcanic arcs contain copper and manganese beds, as well as little iron and molybdenum deposits and gold veins. Gold with antimony is found in the metamorphic massif of the Isle of Youth.

Copper deposits in veins, having a great development of the terrigenous-carbonated complexes, are found in the regions of the Los Órganos Range and Guamuhaya Mountains, like those of Matahambre (by the way, economically exhausted nowadays), in the first of these orographic groups. Lenticular polimetallic deposits (lead, zinc, cooper, iron), and even those of wolfram and gold have also been discovered in these regions.

The non-metallic mineral beds are found in all the structure-facial zones of the Cuban Archipelago. Deposits of marble and kaolin, and quartz displays are notably known in the Isle of Youth, and those of the last mineral in the Guamuhaya hills, as well as limestone and dolomitic limestone (used as ornamental rocks and for covering in construction) beds in Real Campiña, Cienfuegos, and other of ultrabasic rocks, used with the same purpose. Felspar beds are known in Sancti Spíritus and Holguín.

There are important deposits of bentonite in La Habana, and also of zeolitic rocks, formed by hydrothermal alterations in the volcano-sedimentary sediments of volcanic arcs.

Neogene limestone and other carbonated rocks are commonly used as construction stones and raw material for cement production in La Habana and Cienfuegos. In some places, over the above mentioned rocks, phosphorite beds are formed. Accumulations of quartz sand and clay are found in Quaternary deposits. The last one is used to produce red ceramics, or heat-resistant (special) ceramics. Tuff, foundry sands, minerals for abrasive purposes and others, are in these same deposits.

There are also high-grade petroleum and gas strata in the Majagua-Ciego de Ávila zone (Majagua field), which contribute with a considerable part to national production. Throughout the territory there are places where petroleum is displayed, like the so-called "tar pits" and gas spouts, some of them used by the resident people in their neighborhoods. In this respect, accumulations of bituminous rocks also have been found, and their study demonstrates the possibility of extracting the petroleum they have through industrial processes requiring technological investments not used in the country up to date.

PRESENT GEOLOGICAL ERAS AND PERIODS IN CUBA

In order to describe, just briefly, the very complex geological history of the Cuban Archipelago and its principal stages, as well as the fossil remains characterizing each of them, one needs to attend to the accumulated geological knowledge starting since the past century, when its subsoil became interesting for the first time.

Geology (*geos* = land; *logos* = study) is the science that studies the globe in a more direct way, although to do that, it may make use of other sciences, like physics, chemistry, biology, and even mathematics. That is why it is not an exact science. It has been, and still is, very polemic since it was conceived as such, clearing obstacles imposed by the obscurantism and the lack of a dialectic analysis of the world's truth.

The origin of our common house—the Mother Land—has been a notably discussed subject by several specialists. They have established some concepts in the discussions, such as the Earth is an spheroid made up of several concentric rocky spheres in different physical stages of the matter, whose temperature and density increase towards its inner part. The outer layer of the globe is called *lithosphere* and it shares its surface with the *hydrosphere*. In both layers life develops thanks to the presence of a gaseous layer: *The atmosphere.*

The lithosphere is constituted by minerals (inorganic elements or chemical combinations), built up by natural processes, endowed with both defined and constant physical and chemical characteristics, and also by rocks, which are bodies made up of mineral aggregates linked among them by permanent cohesion forces.

The lithosphere, since the formation of the Earth, has underwent countless changes, because of the opposite action of internal geodynamic forces (in general, volcanism, plutonism, tectonics) and the external geodynamic ones (meteorization, erosion, transport and deposit, by different agents).

All the processes that have taken place in the geological evolution of the planet have remained as records in the rocks forming the Earth's crust (lithosphere); above all, in the bedded sedimentary rocks. These rocks are like huge sheets of a book showing the large history of the world—its age is calculated between 600 and 3000 million years—and of the different animals and plants that preceded and shared with the man the history of the planet. The volcanic or plutonic rocks that are found in association with the sedimentary strata allow to set up correlations in each specific place and in a planetary scale.

The dating set up by the fossils of animals and plants captured in the stony pages of the earthly history book names relative dating. The igneous rocks have the property of decomposing, acquiring, transferring or turning a few minerals in others in the course of time. Measurement of this geological time names absolute dating, and the uranium/lead, potasium/argon, and rubidium/strontium methods are some of them.

The geological time can not be measured, therefore, in weeks, months or years, not even in centuries. This time has been divided and subdivided into units that have a lot more prolonged length, whose more generalized divisions are two eons: Criptozoic Eon *(kryptos* = hidden; *zoon* = life) and Phanerozoic Eon *(phaneros* = visible or evident; *zoon* = life).

The first eon is not represented in Cuba; it occupies, according to calculus, much more than two thirds of the geological time of the Earth. Although life relics have been observed in rocks of this eon, it has not been possible to identify any species, genus, family or anyother biological category.

The Phanerozoic Eon has divided into three eras: Paleozoic Era *(palaeos* = ancient; *zoon* = life), also named Primary Era; Mesozoic Era *(mesos* = medieval; *zoon* = life), known likewise as Secondary Era; and Cenozoic or Tertiary Era *(kainos* = recent; *zoon* = life). The existence of a Quaternary Era is sometimes accepted inside the Cenozoic Era, and often, as an independent one.

The Paleozoic Era is not represented in Cuba, and it is only known from other lands the profusion of invertebrates like trilobites—that have made famous this era—, crinoids, brachiopods and others, as well as the presence of armored fishes and the first fishes with lungs, sharks, amphibians, labyrinthodont-type reptiles and luxuriant plants, in some of the periods in which this geological time span is divided.

The Mesozoic Era is divided into three periods: the Triassic, not observed in Cuba; the Jurassic, lasting more than fifty million years, since one hundred seventy million years ago; and the Cretaceous, with a similar span of the foregoing, until seventy million years ago.

The Cenozoic Era is divided into two periods: Paleogene and Neogene. The Paleogene lasted forty million years, since seventy million years ago, and it is divided into turn in the periods or epochs named Paleocene, Eocene and Oligocene. Meanwhile, within the Neogene, there are the Miocene and Pliocene epochs, with an approximate span of twenty million years. The Quaternary Era is divided into the Pleistocene, about one or two million years of age, and the Holocene or Recent Period. (See Table 1).

Table 1. Geochronology of well-represented geological and glacial eras, periods and epochs in Cuban Archipelago. (Based on Iturralde-Vinent, 1988)

Era	Span, in Million Years		Period	Epoch	Tectonic Epoch		General Changes of Earthly Climate
Cenozoic	6 5±31	1.8	Quaternary (Q)	Holocene (Q4) Pleistocene (Q1-3)	Alpine		Glacial era
		22	Neogene (N)	Pliocene (N2) Miocene (N1))			
		41	Paleogene (P)	Oligocene (P3) Eocene (P2) Paleocene (P1)			Warm era
Mesozoic	170±5	70	Cretaceous (K)	Upper (J3) Lower (K1)		Kimmeridgian	
		55-60	Jurassic (J)	Upper (J3) Middle (J2) Lower (J1)			
	230±10	40-45	Triassic (T)	Upper (T3) Middle (J2) Lower (J1)			Glacial P.

MAIN FOSSILS OF THE CUBAN TERRITORY

The most ancient fossils of Cuba belong to the Jurassic Period of the Mesozoic Era, and they are the *Piazopterix branneri* fern (originally described as *Phlebopteris cubensis),* which proves the existence of emergent territories, and a pelecipod or lamellibranch mollusk named *Trigonia (Vaugonia) kromelbeini,* corresponding to Lower-Middle Jurassic. The bedrocks where these fossils are found are denominated San Cayetano formation, and they are restricted to the Alturas de Pizarras[3] Range in the Guaniguanico Mountain Range, province of Pinar del Río.

The fauna was very abundant during the Upper Jurassic. Cephalopod mollusks (close to squids and octopus) known as ammonites, very important to the world stratigraphy,

3. The name of this range means "slaty hills" because of their composition, mainly slates. *Trans.*

stand out. A large number of genera have been found in Cuba, and among them it may be mentioned: *Perisphinctes, Vinalesphinctes, Ochetoceras, Cubaochetoceras, Aspidoceras* and so forth, reaching more than two hundreds. In the Jurassic seas of Cuba or ProtoCuba also lived another mollusks, like nautiloids and belemnites; fishes like *Gyrodus macrophthalmus cubensis, Caturus deani, Sauropsis woodwardi, Eugnathides browni* and *Leptolepis euspondylus*, some of them with teeth adapted to feed on shells; and even some of the big marine reptiles of that epoch, like the plesiosaurs and ichthyosaurs that were widespread in all the seas of the world. As a matter of fact, in the first half of the century in Cuba were described some species of ichthyosaurs, i.e.: *Ichthyosaurus torrei, Sphaerodontes caroli, Criptocleidus cuervoi, C. cuervoi quesadai* and *C. cuervoi caroli.*

Remains of bones and fragments of skulls, seemingly belonging to some of the land dinosaurs that inhabited the continents and may suggest the emergent character of any part of either the current territory of Cuba or the nearness of an emerged land named *Caribaea*, have been also found. Even, the presence of a flying reptile, a pterosaur named *Nesodactylus hesperius,* has been published. All of these findings have accomplished in the Guaniguanico Mountain Range in Pinar del Río.

Cuban Jurassic seas also sheltered numerous protozoans (calpionelids, radiolarians and scanty foraminifera) constituting stratigraphic indexes.

During the Cretaceous time, even though there are clues of emergent lands, it is hard to study the fossil remains that have been possible to recover. However, the marine fossils are still abundant and some new forms were developed, such as the rudists, large pelecypod mollusks that lived in shallow waters forming banks like the present reefs. In this stage, the ammonites kept as one of the most abundant groups; although, on the whole, these Cretaceous cephalopods were very different than the Jurassic ones. Remains of echinoderms, corals and fishes may also be found. The planctonic foraminifera began to occupy a significant place like index fossils, and the calpionelids, nannoconids, calcisferulids and other protozoans stayed as such.

Remains of the large dinosaurs that existed in the continents during the Cretaceous, have not been found in Cuba. At the end of this period, the largest reptiles, the ammonites and other many groups, disappeared in such a drastic way that it has given reason to numerous apocalyptic hypothesis.

Remains of marine fossils are still the most abundant ones during the Paleogene, and numerous species of echinoderms, mollusks (gasteropods and pelecypods), corals, fishes, and sharks above all—*Striatolamia macrota, S.* sp., *Carcharodon auriculatus,* and *Isurus* sp. species—have been identified.

There are many microfossils, and among them the foraminifera stand out; some of them develop a giantism process, and attain up to 10 cm width. Radiolarians, ostracods, discoasterids, coccolitoforids and other microorganisms became very abundant.

Some recent discoveries in sediments from Lower Miocene, in the Zaza zone, Sancti Spíritus province, prove the existence of emerged zones during this period. Remains of land turtles, saurs (that inhabited non-marine waters), a still unnamed primate and a sloth (*Imagocnus zazae*) have been found in that zone. Remains of pollen and spores of angiosperms have been only collected from the vegetation of these lands, as well as carbonized vegetable pieces. El Chorrillo, a petrified forest located in Camagüey, where numerous remains of completely silicified trunks have been found, deserves mention aside.

From the Neogene, the macro- and micro-fossils of marine animals species are very similar to the present ones.

Maybe the only difference is that in the Miocene seas inhabited the *Carcharodon megalodon,* a huge shark into whose mouth comfortably would fit ten people, and others like *Carcharhinus obscurus, Galeocerdo contortus, Hemipristis serra,* and *Negaprion brevirostris.*

The echinoderms are notably well-represented with diverse genera like *Clypeaster, Antillaster, Eupatagus, Echinolampas, Schizaster, Haimea* and many others. The mollusks, both pelecypods and gasteropods, were abundant in an important proportion, standing out *Chlamys, Chione, Lucina, Cardium, Cypraea, Hyotissa* and other genera. Among the corals, examples of *Montastrea* and *Acropora* genus may be denoted.

Both planctonic and benthonic foraminifera are found in such a way that in some rocks may be collected hundreds of thousands, in fragments that attain few grams. Both radiolarians and ostracods are still important stratigraphic indexes.

In this stage sirenians also inhabited in Cuban seas, like dugongs or manatees, and a seal, *Monachus tropicalis,* whose offals are very difficult to locate, and they only appear by chance in quarries and wells.

Cuba, with its present shape, gave shelter to a wealthy biota during the Quaternary Era. Some of the representatives of that fauna and flora are known because their remains laid down in caves or elsewhere—where they died or where they were dragged to—in spite of the hardness the tropical climate imposes. These remains have allowed to know that in the country inhabited examples of all the orders of reptiles, 13 orders of birds and 7 of mammals, up to reach 131 vertebrate species.

Since the discovery in the last century of fragments of bones belonging to a giant sloth in the surroundings of the Ciego Montero spa in the province of Cienfuegos, successive findings have been taking place. Not only this toothless animal named *Megalocnus rodens* and others of smaller size like *Mesocnus browni, Mesocnus torrei,* and *Acratocnus antillensis;* but also some arboreal sloths like *Microcnus gliriformis* and others, have been found.

In the Cuban territory the rodents were abundant, mainly hutias of diverse genera like *Capromys, Macrocapromys, Boromis;* insectivorous such as the *Solenodon cubanus* or "almiquí" that has survived till now; and little predators like *Nesophontes,* which today would be confused with a rat in its external appearance.

The role of predators, by any reckoning, was played in this fauna by the big birds, whose remains have been discovered mainly in caves. Owls, like *Tyto noeli* and *T. riveroi;* long-eared owls that attain a man size with 1.20 m - 1.30 m height, like *Ornimegalonix oteroi* and *O. acevedoi;* the major falcon that had ever existed in any place of the globe, *Tytanohierax borrasi;* and the gigantic-size vulture *Antillovultur varonai.* In a fortuitous way, other birds, which maybe have abund, have exhumed, though their remains are very hard to find, because of their habitat and the Cuban climate. Very complete remains of a crane, *Grus cubensis,* associated with toothless animals, rodents and other rapacious birds mentioned yet, were found in a very important fossiliferous deposit, in Pío Domingo cavern at the Los Órganos Range.

Among the vertebrates, one species of canid, *Cubacyon transversidens,* and one of primate, *Paralouatta varonai,* have been described, though remains allowing to predict the existence of more species of apes have appeared.

The reptiles were represented by several genera, extinguished yet, like *Geochelone* or *Testudo,* among the chelonians; and *Crocodylus cubensis,* among the saurs. Remains of the Cuban boa, *Epicrates angulifer,* appear associated with all of the Pleistocene vertebrate remains, a fact that proves their age in the Cuban territory.

The bats were particularly abundant; 29 species have been studied, from which 27 survive. As a curiosity, in this group one must denote that during the Pleistocene in Cuba lived a vampire species: *Desmodus rotundus*.

THE RELIEF OF CUBA

The stage of formation of the Cuban relief in the megablock named Cuba of the "Cuban microplate"—as it has been defined the part of the Caribbean-Antillean territory made up of the tectonic megablocks: Yucatan Basin, Gran Cayman Ridge and the already mentioned of Cuba—started in the Paleogene. At that time, as a fundamental trend, vertical movements began, and the horizontal ones notably diminished, which led to the modification and the "rearrangement" of the Alpine-typical tectonic structures created during the orogenic stage of that territory.

Positive morpho-structures that attain considerable size were formed during the Eocene and the Oligocene; they were in turn modified or rejuvenated during the Neogene. The analysis of the deposits demonstrates the existence of emergent territories with small elevations and undulated plains, as well as peripheral and inner basins.

Morpho-structural and hipsometric steps have been differentiated in the Cuban territory in order to distinguish the mesoforms from the mountainous relief. If we were to consider that there are no high mountains in the country, the following may be distinguished: Medium-sized-mountains, those that are between 1500 m and 2000 m high; low-mountains, which are between 1000 m and 1500 m; small-mountains, between 500 m and 1000 m, and very-small-mountains, which range from 300 m to 500 m of altitude.

On the other hand, the plains—mainly differentiated—because of its genesis, have been cataloged as marine plains, having terraced surfaces and being from sea level up to 100 m - 120 m; abrasive and abrasive-denuded plains, between 80 m - 90 m and 100 m - 120 m; and abrasive and abrasive-erosive plains, between 40 m - 45 m, 50 m - 60 m and 75 m - 80 m of altitude.

A large period of emersion and tectonic stability took place since the Upper Oligocene until the Middle Miocene. During that time the relief was denuded, and wide flat and wavy plains were formed, as well as some groups of small elevations. The most ancient leveling surfaces found and also preserved in the current relief in the Cuban territory belong to that same age. These denuded genesis surfaces were fragmented by uplift movements at the end of the Miocene and Pliocene stages, and they were elevated as blocks at different heights, preserving their relics in the highest parts of the mountainous massifs.

Thereby, during the Oligocene, they were shaped as morpho-structures, with similar frontiers to the present ones: The Guaniguanico Mountain Range in the province of Pinar del Río; the Guamuhaya massif (mistakenly called Escambray in adopting the name of some elevations of Santa Clara, located 20 km south-southeast from this city in the central zone of the island of Cuba); the Camagüey mesoblock in the region of the same name; the Gran Piedra Range (part of the Sierra Maestra Mountain Range) in the province of Santiago de Cuba, and others.

The Pinar del Río Southern Plain, the Agabama Plain in the central territory, the Cauto and the Nipe-Alto Cedro Plains in diverse areas of the eastern region were conformed as negative morpho-structures, among others.

New tectonic and lithologic morpho-structures were defined during the Upper Miocene and the Pliocene, the most ancient ones were reactivated, and new leveling surfaces were formed. The last ones occupy the periphery and the intermediate parts of the mountainous systems, the summits of the groups of hills and the denuded and high abrasive plains of the center of the archipelago.

The magnitude of the tectonic movements and the position of sea level determined at that time the formation of the morpho-structural categories of mountains, hills and plains in the mainland and of the deep faults, depressions, insular chains and the insular shelf in the oceanic bottoms. Thereby, it may be distinguished the following genetic types:

· Systems of *horst* and blocks in overthurst layers, like the Guaniguanico Mountain Range. The most ancient leveling surfaces from Lower Miocene are preserved like relics devoid of sediments or like wavy surfaces at intermediate levels. They are closely related with the development of karst and the formation of its most typical forms: Mogotes, poljes, dolinas, lapiaz and large polygeneration systems of caverns.

· Systems of *horst* and massive blocks corresponding with elevated bodies of ultrabasic rocks, such as the Cajálbana Plateau (or highland), the Sierra Alta de Agabama Range, and the Nipe-Sagua-Baracoa Mountains.

· Systems of antiform dome-block mountains, like the Guamuhaya Mountains, elevated in the Upper Miocene, dome-shaped, with a complex inner structure, a concentric arrangement. The ancient levels of the summit of the mountains preserve deluvial sediments being residues from surfaces having higher altitude, more ancient than the current ones.

· Systems of stepped *horst* mountains, like the Jatibonico Range between Sancti Spíritus and Ciego de Ávila provinces, linked to moderate neotectonic uplifts.

· Systems of stepped blocks in monoclinals and intrusions, like the Sierra Maestra Mountain Range in Granma and Santiago de Cuba provinces, linked to intense neotectonic uplifts.

· Systems of stepped *horst* in foldings and monoclinals, like the Gran Piedra Range in Santiago de Cuba, fractured during the neotectonic stage in transverse-diagonal units with a northeastern direction. Also of this type, but corresponding to neotectonic uplifts later than the Lower Miocene that involved fragments of the neoautocthonous covering, are the Sierra del Cristal Range, the Toa and Baracoa Crests, and the Guaso Plateau in the provinces of Holguín, Santiago de Cuba and Guantánamo, respectively.

· Systems of block hills in complex folding, corresponding with intense uplifts in former strongly faulted structures, like the El Purial Range in Guantánamo. Through the design of the fluvial net, the new faults and folds become apparent.

From the genetic and morphological viewpoint, there are three types of elevations *(Instituto de Geografía* [Institute of Geography], 1988):

· Tectonic-erosive elevations, in which the chief genetic agent is their endogenous active character, but they have been considerably transformed by the morpho-genetic processes. They originated over massive cristallyne rocks, easily denuding, like the La Cañada Range in the Isle of Youth; the Cubanacán Hills in the central region; the San Felipe Hills in La Habana, and others.

· Tectonic-structural elevations that owe their origin to small uplifts and to the morphologic expression of their passive inner structure, like the hills of the .Alturas del Norte de La Habana-Matanzas region; the Sierra Morena Range and the Mogotes de Jumagua in Sagua la Grande zone; and the Bamburanao-Jatibonico Range in the provinces of Sancti Spíritus and Ciego de Ávila; or, because of their active inner structure, like the Cunagua Hill in Camagüey.

• Lithologic-structural and petrogenic elevations, residual hills that were caused by differential erosion, in which sometimes their internal structure is expressed. They elevate a few tens of meters over the denuded plains that surround them, and their upper levels are the most ancient remains of them.

MAIN MOUNTAINOUS SYSTEMS AND PLAINS

As a whole, the territory of the Cuban Archipelago is flat in its four-fifth parts. In a descending order of importance, the group of elevations are the eastern region, the central and the western one.

From the west to the east, the main positive and negative morpho-structures are included in the *Occidental* [Western], *Central* and *Oriental* [Eastern] macroregions.

OCCIDENTAL [WESTERN] MACROREGION

Llanura Cársica de [Karstic Plain of] *Guanahacabibes.* This plain is distinguished by the occurrence of naked karst and covered with fine soil layers. It lies in the province of Pinar del Río and occupies its westernmost part.

Llanura [Plain] Guane-Mantua. This plain has a bigger thickness of sandy soils, and lies at the same province of the foregoing, in its western utmost tip.

Llanura Meridional de [Southern Plain of] *Pinar del Río.* This plain is extended from San Juan y Martínez to Candelaria, with a carbonated substratum and normal thickness of alluvio-deluvial soils, where the best fields of the excellent Cuban tobacco are found.

Guaniguanico Cordillera [Mountain Range]. This mountain range is also in the province of Pinar del Río, in which two large orographic groups differ: The Sierra de los Órganos and Sierra del Rosario Ranges. The scarps and general alignments of the mountainous areas and valleys of this group follow the general trend of the faulting of the territory, limited to the south by the Pinar Fault that has a clear expression in the topography.

In the Sierra de los Órganos Range the famous cone and tower karst is found, whose genetic processes brought about the existence of mogotes, poljes and other valleys and caves in a number over four thousands. In the mentioned range the Los Órganos Range (mogote-shaped) differ in the strict sense, with its beautiful intra-mountainous valleys and rivers, usually allochthonous, that get across it; and the Alturas de Pizarras del Norte and Alturas de Pizarras del Sur Hills, that as opposed to the calacerous mountainous areas, are made up of heterogeneous terrigenous sediments eith a high tectonism. In the western tip the Pesquero-Guane Plain is found, covering the end of the mountain range.

The region of Sierra del Rosario Range is composed of several sub-regions: Cajálbana, a nickeliferoues-laterite-rich plateau, formed in ultrabasic rocks; the Guajaibón Hills (where the pike with the same name is the highest of the west, with 699 m high, known also as Pan de Guajaibón; the Sierra Azul and the El Rosario Ranges, spreading out from the San Diego or Caiguanabo River (its basin separates the El Rosario and the Los Órganos Ranges), to the neighbouring province of La Habana.

Alturas del Norte de [Heights of the North of] *La Habana-Matanzas.* They are the elevations running parallel to the northern coast, such as the El Arzobispo and Sibanimar Ranges, and others in both Jaruco River banks, and those extending—as the foregoing, in a sublatitudinal way—farther to the south, such as the Escaleras de Jaruco, the Camarones-Pan de Matanzas, and Canasí-Corral Nuevo-Yumurí Ranges.

Alturas del Centro de [Heights of the Center of] *La Habana-Matanzas.* The Bejucal-Madruga-Coliseo, San Miguel de los Baños and Cantel-Camarioca elevations stand out among the hills located in the center of La Habana and Matanzas provinces.

Llanura Cársica Meridional [Southerm Karstic Plain] *La Habana-Matanzas.* This plain is extended from Artemisa in the west to Cienfuegos in the eastern extreme of the macroregion, and is divided into the Artemisa-Colón red Plain with excellent agricultural soils, and both the western and the eastern Zapata swamps that constitute the biggest wetland of the country and house very important natural wealthes. The kamenitzas or ce- notes that are found along the Cochinos Fault are note- worthy. This fault runs parallel to the eastern coast of the homonymous bay, between Playa Larga and Playa Girón.

In the own western macroregion, but rather outside from the territory of the island of Cuba, the following re- gions have been described:

Plataforma Insular Noroccidental [Northwestern Insu- lar Shelf]. This shelf is divided into the Guanahacabibes Gulf, a section of the shelf in the western extreme of Cuba, and Los Colorados, a little group of keys located north of the province of Pinar del Río.

Plataforma Insular Suroccidental [Southwestern Insu- lar Shelf]. This shelf is divided into the subregions La Coloma-Cajío Beach, where groups of keys such as Las Cayamas, Los Guzmanes, and Hambre-Cruz stand out; La Broa Inlet-south of Zapata with another group of small keys; San Felipe-Los Indios, including the groups of keys with the same name; Los Canarreos Archipelago with the keys of this insular group; and the plains and hills of the Isle of Youth. Those plains lie at the south, such as

the Lanier Swamp and the Francés Cape-Punta del Este Plain, and the hills are found in the north of the second important island of the Cuban Archipelago, where the Las Casas and Caballos Ranges, and the Nueva Gerona-Siguanea Plain are located.

CENTRAL [CENTRAL] MACROREGION

Llanura [Plain]*Corralillo-Yaguajay* . This plain is latitudi- nally extended nearby the north coast in the province of Villa Clara, between its borders with Matanzas and Sancti Spíritus.

La Cordillera [The Mountain Range]. This region groups the subregions: Alturas del Noroeste (Hills of the Northwest), Alturas Centrales del Norte (Central Hills of the North), and Alturas del Noreste (Hills of the North- east), where the carbonated rocks from the Mesozoic shap- ing small-height hills and rough physiognomy predominate.

Región de Cubanacán [Cubanacán Region]. In this region, stand out the Manacas and the Real Campiña- Cienfuegos Plains, in which Cretaceous limestone are ex- ploited as ornamental stones; the Santa Clara-Sancti Spíritus-Güines and the Cubanacán Plains.

Región de Guamuhaya [Guamuhaya Region]. This region is the main orographic group of Central Cuba, di- vided into the subregions: Trinidad Mountains, where the San Juan Peak or La Cuca Hill (1072 m) is found; Sancti Spíritus Mountains; and Trinidad-Banao Plains, a zone with a sole microclimate in the country.

Llanuras y Alturas Centrales de [Central Plains and Heights of] *Camagüey.* This plains and hills located in the central part of Camagüey include the subregion of the Florida-Camagüey-Las Tunas Plain, and the mountain- ous one of the Cubitas Range, where the neotectonic move- ments having accelerated uplift caused that the rivers were crossing the region, to leave their courses to empty into the north coast. That is why such rivers turned into completely dry karstic canyons named *pasos,* like the famous Paso de Los Farallones.

Región de Maniabón [Maniabón Region]. This region is formed by the subregions Cupeicillo-La Candelaria; Maniabón—in its strict sense—with typical hills with a strange profile that were sighted from the sea by Admirall Christopher Colombus in his first travel to Cuba; and the Banes-Cacocum Plain.

Región de Camagüey-Maniabón [Camagüey-Maniabón Region]. This region comprises the subregions: Júcaro-Morón Plain extends from south to north crossing the province of Ciego de Ávila; North Camagüey-Maniabón Plain; and South Camagüey Plain, having a marshy character in its southernmost part.

Plataforma Insular Centro-Septentrional [Central-Northerm Insular Shelf]. This region encompasses the Sabana-Camagüey Archipelago with keys (true islands) having an exceptional beauty and a virgin nature, where tourist centers have been recently built. Some of the keys of this archipelago, like Coco, Romano and Sabinal, are larger than some republics of the Lesser Antilles.

Plataforma Insular Centro-Meridional [Central-Southerm Insular Shelf]. This region includes the following subregions: Ana María Gulf, Guacanayabo Gulf and Jardines de la Reina Archipelago,[4] with small muddy, but very picturesque keys.

ORIENTAL [EASTERN] MACROREGION

Llanuras Orientales [Eastern Plains]. The group of regions named Cauto-Guacanayabo is inside this region of eastern plains that includes the subregions: Cauto Plain with considerable thickness of alluvial sediments, coming from

4. The name of this archipelago means "Queen's gardens." *Trans.*

the deposits of this river and its affluents; Guacanayabo Plain and Cabo Cruz Plateau having an eminently karstic character, and where some levels of emerged marine terraces and caves have been described.

Nipe-Báguanos is another group of regions, divided into Báguanos Hills and Nipe Plain.

The Central Valley is one of the groups of regions of the eastern plains, and it comprises the subregions: Palma Soriano-San Luis, Songo-La Maya, and Guantánamo or El Guaso Valley.

Sierra Maestra. It comprises the Western Sierra Maestra, Santiago de Cuba and Eastern Sierra Maestra subregions. In the first one the following sectors are identified: Pilón-Guisa at the west; El Turquino Range in the center, where the Turquino Pike (the highest mountain of the country, 1974 m high), and the Cuba (1810 m high) and Suecia (1734 m) Peaks are found, forming together the Turquino massif; and Tercer Frente-El Cobre-Boniato.

The Santiago de Cuba subregion is made up of the Santiago Basin and the Santiago Plateau, meanwhile the Eastern Sierra Maestra subregion includes the Gran Piedra Range (1250 m high) and the Santa María de Loreto-Sierra Larga Range, a tableau-shaped hill having lesser altitude.

Montañas del Noroeste [Northwest Mountains]. This region is divided into the Mayarí and Sagua-Baracoa subregions. The first one subdivides in the Sagua de Tánamo Plain, the Nipe-Cristal Mountains (1200 m) and the Segundo Frente Hills. The Sagua-Baracoa subregion includes the sectors: Moa-Baracoa Plain; Maisí Plateau, with similar features than the Cabo Cruz Plateau; San Antonio del Sur Plain; Puriales de Caujerí Valley; Guaso Plateau, with an extraordinary karstic development; Moa-Toa Crests, and Baracoa-Purial Range Crests.

The submarine shelf located in this macroregion is just about non-existent; keys which could aggroup in order to make up a relief unit are not found.

KARST AND ITS IMPORTANCE IN CUBA

For Cuba, the predominant existence of carbonated rocks, especially karstified ones in its territory, has a great significance, because this condition determines a dependence of practically all the spheres of life on the karstic environment.

The group of phenomena and processes that—distinguished by the predominance of dissolution and corrosion are carried out under the water action in regions made up mainly of soluble rocks—is denominated karst. This word is the Germanic version of *kars,* a word of Slovenian origin, meaning "field of limestone." It has been applied to define "similar" landscapes to those of the Karst plateau, in the Dinaric Alps region, located between Slovenia and Croatia, the former Yugoslavian republics and, in part, in Trieste, north of the Adriatic Sea in Italy.

Jennings (1971) has defined *karstic landscape* as "... [a landscape] with a distinctive morphology presenting primarily a high and abnormal solubility of the rocks, even in lands where processes such as the mecanic action of the rivers and of the ices, play a significant and dominant role, despite these processes are not exclusive of the karst." Tell (1973, fide Gutiérrez, *et al.*, 1994) adds: "... in the literature, *karst* means a lime territory with fissures, dolines and other depressions, caves and sinks, with a predominance of underground waters; it means, karst is a typical erosive landscape, but where the main action of the erosion has been the corrosive one."

More than 66% of the surface of Cuba is formed by rocks, karstified in greater or lesser degree, presenting a calcareous landscape as it is described above. That is why the Cuban Archipelago may qualify as an eminently karstic territory.

The location of Cuba in the northern border of the tropical rainforest zone—whose latitudinal shift in the geological time has not affected this condition—; the influence of alternating periods of intense rainfall and aridity during the Pleistocene and the very important oscillation of the level of sea waters owing to glacial-eustatic movements registered throughout the territory, which imply an equivalent change in the level of the underground waters and in the base level of erosion; and the corresponding accelerated corrosion of the carbonated rocks in these levels, together with the geological characteristics of the territory, have evidently contributed to the karst building-up. The acidulant action of tropical vegetation, soils and microorganisms have also contributed to the intensity of karstification processes in the Cuban territory.

Approximately 44,000 sq km of the Cuban territory present themselves as naked karst, or covered with thick layers of soils, mainly ferrallitic, in mountainous and flat relief zones.

About 18,000 sq km of karstified rocks are covered with red and brown soils, with greater depths in zones with flat and hilly relief, occupying the bottom of some fertile valleys, and approximately 8700 sq km are buried under thick thickness of soils having diverse origins and features, above all in flat zones.

The karstified rocks are covered with swamps and tidelands in marshy zones, located mainly south of the islands of Cuba and of the Isle of Youth, but also in very particular points at the north coast.

Owing to its shape, Cuba lacks large fluvial streams and, as a matter of fact, many rivers and small streams of the territory cease to flow during the low-water season. However, the underground waters are a more steady supplying source, and they have a considerable potentiality. A great part of these underground aquifers are karstic.

The underground basins of the Cuban territory are calculated in 165, and 151 of them are karstic and fissured-karstic aquifers; stored mainly in organogenic limestone, dolomitic limestone and calcareous marls, with hydrocarbonated-calcic waters on the whole.

Ciudad de La Habana, Matanzas, Artemisa, Güines, Ciego de Ávila, Cárdenas, Colón and other many cities are supplied from karstic aquifers.

The waters for irrigating the biggest and the most important croppings of the country, for industries and other productive centers, come from karstic aquifers.

Very important industries like the thermoelectric plants—Santa Cruz del Norte, Mariel, Matanzas, Nuevitas and Cienfuegos—; the atom-electric plant of Juraguá; sugar cane mills; cement and rum factories; and many other industries should be located in karstified zones. One of the principal present concerns is the pouring of residual materials from those industries, in order to avoid the contamination of a environ so exposed like karst.

It is frequent in Cuba the presence of mineral ores related in some way with the building-up process of karst (and with those that give rise to the so-called *pseudokarst)*, or mineral ores with a secondary character, associated to paleokarstic forms, where the presence of manganese, phosphorite, bauxite, clay, guano bat *(fossil guano)*, and so forth, stand out.

The existence of a deep paleokarst (more than 5000 m north of Pinar del Río, and more than 3000 m in the Sabana-Camagüey Archipelago) in the unit of the continental paleomargin and other structures have affected the presence of hydrocarbons, whose exploration and exploitation is carried out with successful outcomes.

Karst in the Cuban rocks has a great expressiveness and development, because of its tropical condition. Lapiaz—or grikes—is the most common karstic form: *Karren* and *shralten* (in German), *lenar* (in Serbian), *karr* (in Russian), *solcato* (in Italian), *lapiez* (in French) and *diente de perro, seboruco* or *arrecife* (common names used in Cuba). This lapiaz, a common and visible form in the regions of karst either naked or covered with thin soil layers, has angled edges or pinnacles that may be sharp, like true penknives, and its development may attain from few centimeters to some meters.

In the whole national territory dolines, kamenitzas (or cenotes), karstic valleys and other depressions are abundant. Poljes deserve special attention; they are fluvial-karstic valleys of several kilometers of surface area, having fertile soils with a characteristic seasonal behavior that constitute important zones for agricultural production, and require attention in order to guarantee their normal hydrologic operation.

Another surface karstic forms like the tide rock shelters, associated to marine terraces emerged by ascending and descending movements of the sea, are also common. They show in a characteristic form in regions like the north coast of the provinces of Ciudad de La Habana and La Habana, the nearness of Gibara, and very specially in the zones of the Cruz Cape and Maisí, where tens of terraces have been measured in each point.

The cone-shaped, dome-shaped and tower-shaped karstic buttes are typical, the same as in other countries with tropical climates and paleoclimates. "Mogotes" are very interesting; they are hills having vertical or subvertical hillsides and rounded profile summits, but generally, occupied by different-size depressions.

Even though, in practice, in all the natural regions of Cuba there are caves, being the most spectacular karstic forms, the greatest ones are located in the mountainous zones, and above all, in the Guaniguanico Mountain Range.

MAIN KARSTIC REGIONS

Guanahacabibes Peninsula. It lies in the westernmost extreme of the island of Cuba, developed in the tectonic regional unit named *Covering Deposits*. It is a marine origin plain, made up of Pliocene and Pleistocene rocks like limestone and organogenic calcarenites having skeletal or little-thickness soils, concentrated in dolines and cenotes. In the north coast of the peninsula rocks are under swamps, meanwhile the south one is a steep shore with marine terraces and tide rock shelters.

Guaniguanico Mountain Range. It is in the center-north part of Pinar del Río, in the regional tectonic unit named *Southern Continental Blocks.* It has a longitudinal disposition, approximately north-southwest, corresponding with the regional fracturing. The most ancient rocks dated with fossils of Cuba, belonging to the Lower-Middle Jurassic, are found in this region.

Some limestone units from Upper Jurassic and Lower Cretaceous stand out in this place. They are non-porous and notably fractured rocks, with a complex Alpine-typical tectonics, modified by overimposed neotectonic events. The largest cave systems of Cuba have developed in this region: The Palmarito-Pan de Azúcar cave system having some of 50 km long; the large cave of Santo Tomás with 47 km; the Majagua-Cantera cave system with a length over 33 km; and the large Fuentes cave with 23 km. All of these cave systems have been mainly excavated by rivers and small streams that—coming from the elevations made up of silica-clastic rocks which surround the calcareous hills—have crossed them and formed several levels of passages owing to the already mentioned neotectonic and glacial-eustatic movements.

In the Guaniguanico Mountain Range there are the buttes known as *mogotes* in Cuba. They are typical of the tropical karst, with rough walls and rounded or tower-shaped summits. They may be isolated or forming ranges, according to the features of the scaled *nappes* of which they took part.

In this range, there are large fluvial-karstic valleys like poljes, having flat or slightly wavy bottom, and a good-depth fertile soil. Among the calcareous elevations and the slaty hills, other valleys take form and they are named contact or marginal valleys.

Aside from those above mentioned, other depressions with a completely karstic genesis, may be found. They may be collapse, corrosion-collapse dolines, or combinations of dolines and collapses of cavern roof, whose accesses are just through karstic canyons or caves. These are named *hoyos de montaña* or *hoyos de terreno,*[5] according to whether they had reached or not the level of the base of the hills in their development.

Southern Plain of Pinar del Río. It lies south of the Guaniguanico Mountain Range, in the regional tectonic zone named *Covering Rocks.* It is, as its name means, a flat region made up of Paleogene and Miocene rocks, mainly organogenic limestone and marls covered with alluvial-eluvial-deluvial sediments having large thickness coming from the mountain range.

The karstification has been identified in the witnesses coming from the perforations carried out with different purposes, and it is found in zones with smaller-thickness soils, principally in karst-suffosion dolines.

Southern Plain La Habana-Matanzas. It is a region located west of Cuba occupying the regional tectonic zone named *Covering Rocks* and it extends to the south from La Habana to Matanzas, and even part of Cienfuegos, towards the homonymous bay. This region is mainly made up of organogenic limestone, marls and calcareous marls from the Miocene-Quaternary, showing a naked karst, or covered with thin- to medium-thickness soils having great productivity, where the principal zones of vegetable productions are settled.

---

5. They are closed karstic dolines or small valleys. The *hoyos de terreno* have soil in their bottoms, unlike the *hoyos de montaña* that don't have it. The Spanish word *hoyos* means "holes." *Trans.*

In this region, the surface streams are scarce, and if any, they are usually intermittent ones. The water for supplying the population and the crops comes from karstic aquifers, such as those of Cuenca Sur and Ariguanabo. This is a typical zone of corrosion-collapse dolines, lapiaz and caves, with a phreatic and ford genesis on the whole.

There are caves in the plain, like those named El Túnel, Paredones, Torrens and others, which constitute Quaternary vertebrate fossilliferous beds. Those caves have been important sources for the knowledge of the Cuban fauna of that period.

The underground waters arise in the south coast after infiltrating through ferrallitic rocks and soils that form strips of swamps.

Zapata Swamp. This zone is part of the Southern Plain La Habana-Matanzas karstic region, but stand out rather because it is the greatest wetland of the country. It lies in the central-south part of the island of Cuba, where the carbonated rocks from Neogene and Quaternary are total or partially covered with swamps. The reef limestone sequences surrounding the swampy area and the Cochinos Bay (Bay of Pigs) have plenty kamenitzas or cenotes, caves, submerged caves and lapiaz with sharp angle edges, pointing along faults and diaclases named Zapata speleo-lacustrine system. The fresh water and the salt water are stratified in these natural wells (kamenitzas), increasing their aggressive action. Nevertheless, they developed or were excavated in subaerial conditions, and at present they are flooded, because they are speleothems or secondary formations only developed in these environs. These kamenitzas may attain 70 m - 75 m deep; the greatest ones are Ilona, XX Aniversario, Laguna Larga and El Brinco. The largest lake of the Cuban territory is in this region: El Tesoro Lagoon, a karstic depression where the surrounding waters flow into.

Northern Coastal Plain La Habana-Matanzas. This coastal karst strip, made up of reef organogenic limestone, calcarenites, marls and calcareous marls, lies in the plot takes in between Mariel and Cárdenas Bays, in some levels of marine terraces. Some of them are submerged, having an extensive range of surface and underground karstic forms where tide rock shelters and lapiaz stick out.

Neogene and Quaternary carbonated rocks comprise caverns having size just like that of the Bellamar-Gato Jíbaro system, with more than twenty passages and many groups of cavities, like in Boca de Jaruco, where twenty-one caves are known in around 3 sq km.

Caves having marine and karstic origin are also found: The emerged ones like the La Desilusión cave in Punta Jíjira, Santa Cruz del Norte, and the Los Pájaros cave in Puerto Escondido, and the submerged ones like the Cueva Número Uno in Boca de Jaruco.

The caverns of this region housed a relatively numerous population of natives, aside from the Pleistocene fauna remains. Natives' relics, cemeteries, tools and feeding remnants are frequently found, even in the surface of the land.

La Habana-Matanzas Hills. They include two ancient geographical regions: La Habana-Matanzas Hills, comprising the chains of elevations starting from the Tapaste Hills and pointing eastward to the Picadura-Elena Valley, and end in the Pan de Matanzas and El Palenque; and the group of the Bejucal-Madruga-Coliseo Hills, located farther to the south and pointing east-norhteastward, passing through the El Grillo Range in Madruga to the Coliseo Hills in Matanzas.

These relief forms shaped in rocks, ranging since the Paleogene until Neogene, have in common dome-shaped buttes, similar to the mogotes of the Los Órganos Range, but with smaller altitude and relative height.

These rocky massifs with overlying basins have a greater lithologic variety, and because of the insertion of impermeable strata with permeable carbonated layers, they also show a lesser development of the karstic forms in some areas.

As a general rule, the elevations constitute synclinal edges of great expanse structures, and that is why they are examples of the relief inversion (Núñez Jiménez, 1964), a common feature in the Cuban karstic hills (Acevedo, Gutiérrez, et. al., 1976). Their north and south hillsides, in most of the cases, are limited by faults and gravitational movements, like in the case of the Escaleras de Jaruco and the El Grillo Range. This last hill borders to the south with the Cayajabos Valley that is an anticline *horst* valley; it reaffirms the relief inversion (Gutiérrez and Rivero, 1975).

The vertical neotectonic and glacial-eustatic movements have generated abrupt changes in the erosion levels and the break in the development of some karstic forms which remain "hung," such as the hanging valleys in the Escaleras de Jaruco, or like some canyons and underground forms at the El Grillo Range, the Amores Hill, the San Juan de Nepomuceno Hills (Gutiérrez and Rivero, 1975), Tirabeque in Cacahual, and so forth.

There also are karstic valleys without surface streams, where the drainage is carried out through sinks, located in the bottom of dolines or of regular-sized caves, like the El Indio or Los Bichos cave in the Boquete de la Jaula, a karstic canyon that communicates the Tapaste karstic valley with that of Jaruco; the Chaveta gorge in Aguacate; the Havana cave in Cacahual, and others.

Guamuhaya Massif. It is mistakenly known as the Sierra del Escambray Range, and it constitutes the greatest orographic group in the center of the island of Cuba, occupying territories of Villa Clara, Cienfuegos and Sancti Spíritus provinces. It is part of the tectonic zone named *Southern Continental Blocks,* and it is made up of carbonated, carbonated-terrigenous, metamorphic, volcanic and volcano-sedimentary rocks.

Limestone, marbles and calcareous shales, all from the Mesozoic, are intercalated with non-karstified sequences, and they have a karst limited to carbonated packages, with a very peculiar development. The highest levels of karstification are noticed in the Campana cave, at 1110 m of altitude.

The Guamuhaya rock sequences, with a very complex Alpine-typical tectonics, have horizontal caves, but above all, vertical and inclined ones, like the Cuba-Magyar cave —478 m deep—, the deepest of Cuba, Caja de Agua and others.

Some true poljes, like the Jibacoa one, are supplied with surface and underground waters which eventually drain through a cavern—impenetrable up to date—and reappear with other names in surrounding valleys.

Martín Infierno cave—a regular-sized spelunca—is also found in this region. It is famous owing to a stalagmite having 67 m high and 30 m width; undoubtedly, one of the biggest stalagmites of the world.

In this massif, having a great importance and geological complexity because of its natural regions, dolines, varied sorts and shapes of lapiaz, fluvio-karstic canyons, karstic canyons and other forms are abundant.

Hills of the North of Las Villas-Ciego de Ávila. Several chains of hills, made up mainly of limestone, dolomitized limestone and calcarenites, with ages ranging since Cretaceous until Eocene and having a high degree of karstification, are found in the north of the provinces of Villa Clara, Sancti Spíritus and Ciego de Ávila.

From the Mogotes de Jumagua, in the nearness of Sagua La Grande, to the Mabuya Range in Chambas, buttes similar to mogotes—in its strict sense—may be even observed, as well as poljes with a fluvio-karstic origin, diverse sorts of lapiaz, dolines and caverns; most of them having horizontal development and a rich fauna of troglobites and bats.

There are caves like the riverbed of the Jatibonico del Norte River, known as Boquerones cave, and others with an important development. The vertical caves and those with wide openings, where the limestone rocks lie over tuffs and volcanic rocks with a thickness about just tens of meters are abundant at the Chambas zone. They cause wide cavities, many of them stretched because of the collapses of cavern roofs and shoulders, but they deepen only to the impermeable level represented by the non-carbonated layers.

Right in some of the numerous kamenitzas located in the Boquerones zone, the wise man Don Carlos de la Torre, at the beginning of the century, collected remains of the land sloth *Megalocnus rodens,* enough for assembling two complete skeletons that have been preserved at the Museo Nacional de Historia Natural (National Museum of Natural History) in Ciudad de La Habana, and at the American Museum of Natural History in New York, United States of America.

Gypsum Karst. Saliferous domes are found east of the hills at the north of Las Villas and Ciego de Ávila, like those of Punta Alegre and Judas de Cunagua, where, in Jurassic gypsum layers, karstic forms like less-developed lapiaz, dolines, and caves have developed in contact between gypsum and carbonated rocks covering or underlying it.

Although these are not the only places in the archipelago where gypsum karst is found, they are the most representative indeed and those having the largest area. Also low-lying karstified buttes may be observed there.

Júcaro-Morón Plain. This karstified denuded marine plain has practically a north-south position; that is why it occupies a strip from the southern coast to the northern one. It has medium thickness of red soils towards the center of the province of Ciego de Ávila, with small lapiaz fields *(karrenfeld),* many dolines southwards with some karst-suffosion dolines in zones having greater-thickness soils like in Pina, sinks and other karstic forms. These epikarstic displays develop in limestone, marls and calcareous marls from the Neogene and Paleogene, and in Cretaceous rudists reefs.

In the northern coast, the carbonated rocks are covered with marshes and cumulated waters in some karstic depressions—like the known La Leche Lagoon—that constitute extensive aquatories. North of this place lies the Turiguanó Isle, composed of arenaceous limestone and calcareous marls, which has small-sized caves, lapiaz and dolines fields. The karstic aquifer supplies with water Ciego de Ávila city and other towns.

Southern Plain of Camagüey. It is a marine denuded karstic plain, with karst covered with thick-to-medium thickness of brown and black soils having poor drainage because of the plasticity of its clayey components. This plain becomes marshy towards the south coast, and in that zone there are plentiful of surface karstic forms like dolines and sinks.

Cubitas Range. It is a mountainous massif in the center-north part of the province of Camagüey, oriented approximately east-west, made up mainly of Cretaceous limestone in its south side, and reef limestone from the Neogene and Paleogene in its north one. The latter rocks lie over serpentine ophiolites, constituting the regional base level. These calcareous mountainous areas underwent successive elevation processes that generated the break of the hydric operation of fluvial canyons. Today, those canyons constitute the famous *pasos*, allowing the communication between both slopes of the range, like the Paso de Los Paredones, a marvellous fluvial-karstic defile of nearly 100 m high in some places.

Lapiaz fields, dolines and closed karstic valleys have been developed in these hills (like the Bonet doline), and caves and numerous simas, most of them inclined or vertical, constituting a distinctive feature. The Rolando cave (or shaft) is a wonderful example of that, also having a depth of more than 80 m down to the underground aquifer. The fossil bat guano, extracted from some of these caves, exploited as fertilizer.

The Máximo River goes across the mountainous area over marmorized limestone having great hardness, compactness and low permeability, and it has excavated pinturesque pools, known as *cangilones*,[6] a typical phenomenon of a fluvial stream that flows superficially over a calcareous bedrock.

Cubitas Range is the most important exponent of karst in the province of Camagüey, together with the El Chorrillo and Najasa ranges, outstanding karstic areas with many caverns and other karstic forms.

Cabo Cruz Plateau. It is a region with elevated marine terraces, and plateau-like arranged in more than ten levels, located in the southeast of the island of Cuba (Cruz Cape), just in the southwestern utmost tip of the province of Granma. It is made up of Neogene and Quaternary carbonated rocks, ordered in packages of rocks with high homogeneity.

This is a famous region due to its rough topography, almost exclusively made up of lapiaz fields and its impressive shafts, like the Hoyo de Morlote, having about 78 m deep and more than 50 m width.

The cliff shore that is continuously shaked by tectonic movements has large emergent and submerged tide rock shelters, which often collapse during the storms, and become in storm rocks—*huracanolitos.* They are large blocks of strongly-karstified reef limestone that are in the sea, and sometimes are carried away by winds and strong waves over the reef surface of the lowest terrace. Often, clues of the presence of Cuban natives are found in this zone, who used the abundant caves as housing, cemeteries and adoration places.

Guisa-Los Negros Region. This region lies in the north side of the Sierra Maestra, the chief mountain range of the country in the Regional Tectonic Unit of Volcano-plutonic Rocks (Paleogene volcanic arc), but it is developed in recristallyzed and compact limestone from the Eocene Period, liying over vulcanites and other non-carbonated rocks, with an altitude between 400 m and 600 m. In these zones there are manganese deposits, associated to the karst.

This Guisa-Los Negros region has similar features than the Los Órganos Range, for presenting mogote-shaped hills, poljes and a considerable number of karstic forms like different sorts of lapiaz, dolines, karstic canyons, and others, developed under the control of both north-south and east-west faults, giving it a chessboard-like look. The toponymy of the place registers these features, inasmuch as some geographic accidents, like the Mogote River—a tributary of the Contramaestre River—and others, have proper names of karstic zones. Deep fluvial-karstic canyons, true poljes—like those from Las Cruces, Pozo Prieto, Rihíto de Matías and others—, dolines and countless closed karstic valleys and large lapiaz may be observed.

The drainage of these poljes and depressions, on the whole, carries out through large vertical caverns, like the Jíbara cave having 236 m deep, and others not totally explored yet, which carry waters to the impermeable stratum of volcanic rocks.

Maniabón Group. This geologically complex region lies in the north of the province of Holguín, nearby Gibara. It has Cretaceous carbonated banks, like caps, over hills made up of deeply-dissected ophiolitic rocks, presenting as isolated buttes: True mogotes with vertical and concave upper hillsides, rounded summits composed of limestone, and base having inclined slopes made up of vulcanites.

6. It is a natural rocky pool. *Trans.*

These hills do not exceed 300 m high, and they are witnesses of a carbonated covering destroyed by the erosion. They present relatively reduced surfaces, where large dolines and karstic valleys have not developed, as is the case in another regions.

Puerto Padre-Gibara Zone. It is a region with flat karst developed in a marine plain that has underwent recent ascending and descending processes, attributable to the Quaternary glacial-eustatic movements. It is developed in Neogene and Quaternary reef limestone having great homogeneity.

The karstic surface forms—such as lapiaz, dolines, caves and kamenitzas—are abundant, but the region stand out, above all, because of the presence of large flooded caverns—the largest ones in Cuba—like Tanque Azul having 2700 m explored in submerged passages, and Cristalitos de Papaya, true jewels of the Cuban crypto-landscapes. During a span, these caverns were in subaerial conditions, in which all kinds of calcareous concretions (speleothems) were developed, until being flooded or reflooded in the Upper Pleistocene or Holocene Period.

Guaso Plateau. This is a structural plateau that occupies the north of the Guantánamo River basin, in the east of the country. It is mainly made up of Eocene limestone, but also of argillites, marls and other sedimentary rocks having great heterogeneity and complex structure. These hills have some of the most significant karstic irregularities of Cuba, like the canyon-cave of the Cuzco River, a tributary of the Sagua de Tánamo River that is more than 70 m deep in its aerial and underground flow (a high and relatively narrow cavern having a difficult flow because of the number of graviclastic blocks that interrupt the riverbed).

Furthermore, the plateau is important since it is the principal water collector and supplier of the Guantánamo River basin, because part of the rainfall received through some springs drains towards it, which emanates at the foot of its south hillside and feed the aqueduct of the city, and from the Guaso River. This last river, the principal fluviatile stream of the region, has its river head in the beautiful Hondones Valley. After a short distance, it infiltrates into the karstic zone appearing and disappearing until it springs up through the emergence known as the Campanario cave, around 400 m underneath its river head, and having a little more than 900 m of flow. It has a small dam in its mouth that feeds an old hydro-station through a steep pipe.

In 1988, after consecutively forcing three siphons, the speleologists reached the doline known as El Rincón, that is why the length of these passages extends up to about 10 km.

Lapiaz fields are abundant in this region. They have developed, sometimes, in thin lime strata, staying like a stony lacework over superjacent cavities, dolines, poljes, uvalas and numerous caves.

Maisí Plateau. This region, with a similar geography of the Cabo Cruz plateau, occupies the eastern utmost tip of the island of Cuba and the Cuban Archipelago. It is composed of organogenic limestone, calcareous marls and calcarenites, mainly from the Miocene to Quaternary, arranged in many levels of marine terraces, linked to glacial-eustatic and neotectonic movements, both of which have notably influenced in the Cuban relief.

It has an arid climate with small-thickness soils and scanty vegetation, absence of surface rivers, and many surface and underground karstic forms.

Lapiaz fields and dolines, karstic canyons, as well as all-size caverns are frequent, where Cuban natives left evidence of their presence.

Las Casas and Caballos Ranges. These mountainous areas are in the north border of the Isle of Youth, composed of Mesozoic marbles; they are part of the Southern Blocks tectonic zone. Highly fissured marbles present karstic canyons and vertical caverns. In the Caballos and the Las Casas Ranges, the speleologists have entered more than 100 m in gorges opened in marmorized limestone. Surface forms have a limited development because of its hardness, though dolines and *hoyos de montaña* may be found.

Southern Plain of the Isle of Youth. It is an arid region with naked karst in Neogene and Quaternary rocks occupying the whole south of the Isle of Youth. In its flat area, made up of reef limestone, have developed extensive and rough lapiaz fields, dolines, kamenitzas and numerous caves having slight outstanding sizes, but sheltering the most important cave paintings of the whole country.

The Lanier Swamp is a sublatitudinal strip of marshes dividing practically the Isle of Youth down the middle. It is part of the southern plain of the isle, and like the Zapata Swamp, carbonated rocks are under quaking-bogs.

The Sabana-Camagüey (or Jardines del Rey) *Archipelago.*[7] This insular group is made up of 2517 isles and islets, which have a basement of both coralline and arena-

7. The name of this archipelago means "King's Gardens." *Trans.*

ceous limestone, calcarenites, and others. In some of these isles these sediments do not outcrop because they are covered with mangroves, tidelands or marshy zones. In others, however, carbonated layers are arranged in shoals having some meters of altitude above sea level.

The Sabana-Camagüey insular group, located in the north border of the Cuban territory, includes the largest keys of the Cuban Archipelago. A very young and vigorous karst have developed in places like the Guillermo, Coco, Romano and Sabinal keys, and other isles, with plentiful of lapiaz, dissolution dolines and caverns. Some of these caves make evident the presence of natives and their possible cohabitation with specimens of the Cuban vertebrate extinguished fauna.

The denominated *pseudokarst* has also developed in non-soluble rocks in the Cuban Archipelago. Several authors describe examples of karst in serpentines in Moa, in Santa Clara and in San Adrián, Matanzas; karst in troctolites in Camagüey; karst in opal and chalcedony in the El Jacán Hill, Matanzas; karst in conglomerates and sandstones in Río Piedras, Pinar del Río, and in other localities.

CHAPTER III

NATURAL CONDITIONS OF THE CUBAN ARCHIPELAGO

Cuba is a country with a moderate tropical climate. Its large and narrow configuration causes the sea tempers the tropical conditions. The Cuban Archipelago is exposed to prevailing northeast trade winds during winter season, and during the summer they come from east-northeast.

CLIMATE

THERMIC REGIME

Cuban thermic regime is also influenced by the permanent action of two powerful oceanic currents: the north-trade wind and the south-trade wind currents, both of which in turn form the Gulf Stream. The temperature of sea waters in the coasts ranges from 26°C to 27°C in winter, and from 28°C to 29°C in summer.

The climate of the archipelago is also determined by the proximity of the North American subcontinent, by the relatively less rough relief, and by the insularity.

Temperature and winds shift as a result of the changes of both thermic and barometric regime at the northern subcontinent. The relief, rather flat, allows the passing and easy propagation of cold or warm masses of the winds. The insular condition moderates the climatologic extremes because of the nearness of the sea.

Annual average temperature of the air changes only a little, and fluctuates from 21.5°C in January—the coldest month—to 28°C in August—one of the warmest. In contrast, the minimum temperatures have a higher fluctuation, between 7.5°C in January and 20°C in July and September. The variation of the maximum temperatures is much lesser; it is explained by the frequent irruption of cold air masses from the north, meanwhile the equatorial air masses have the same temperature than the air of the place where they are.

Daily temperature changes are lesser in the coastal regions than in the inland, where they increase, and even more when the altitude increases above sea level in the western, central, and eastern mountainous regions of the country. This generalization has inferred from a detailed statistical study shown in the *Régimen térmico del archipiélago cubano* [Thermic Regime of the Cuban Archipelago] written by Luis B. Lecha Estela and Alberto Florido Trujillo, in 1989. In this work, the authors demonstrate that it is possible to obtain the representation of the average values through the data processing of climatic series during fifteen years.

The minimum values of the annual average temperatures are in the high regions, and they oscillate between 17°C and 20°C, according to the height. On the other hand, the maximum values are in the coastal regions, between 25°C and 26°C. July is the typical month of the Cuban summer, when the maximum values of the average air temperatures are recorded, oscillating between 28°C and 29°C, while the minimum ones do not exceed 22°C in the highest regions of the country. The change of weather conditions from summer to winter begins in October.

A typical feature of the Cuban climatic regime consists of that in whatever season of the year, in the warmest zones of the country, daily maximum air temperatures above 30°C may occur, and in uncommon times, these daily maximum values are below 20°C on average.

The minimum values of the minimum average temperature in January occur in the center of the La Habana-Matanzas plain, and in the mountainous regions; they oscillate between 13°C and 14°C.

In spite of the fact that the Cuban thermic system has relatively few variations—either daily, annual and local—, the probability of having extreme differences in temperature for a same place and year, about 34°C, is 5% in the inner plains of the country. In the Indio Hatuey weather station in Matanzas, on May 14th 1971, a maximum value of 36.9°C was recorded, while a few months before, on January 21st, 1.2°C were measured in the same station; it means, 35.7°C lesser. Same extreme differences have been recorded in Jovellanos, Unión de Reyes, Güines, Batabanó and Güira de Melena.

The absolute maximum temperatures are recorded in Cuba between July 15th and August 15th, and the minimum ones between January 15th and February 15th.

The absolute maximum values of daily temperature may be recorded after local noon, during the first afternoon hours, and the minimum ones take place, on average, between four and seven o'clock in the morning.

According to the annual thermic regime, Cuban summer ranges between less than six and more than ten months, depending on the geographical region.

Winter may be absent, as is the case of the southern coastal plain, from Cruz Cape to Maisí Point; or it may have a permanent presence as in the mountainous regions, in a strip between 500 m and 800 m high above sea average level.

The study and processing of large data series about temperature in Cuba have allowed to set during last years, the typological regionalization, based on the extreme daily air temperatures, from where the four thermic regions with the greatest significance have been deduced. These thermic regions are the following:

· Littoral zones with local marked effect from the winds regime. They are the north regions of the eastern half of Cuba, from the northern coast of Camagüey—including keys, islets and isles of the Sabana-Camagüey Archipelago—to the Maisí Point. In these zones the maximum values between 25.1°C and 30.0°C occur more times than in other ones. It means, warm days with small daily oscillations and marked marine influence.

· Littoral zones, where the moderating effect of the winds regime and the plains of Cuba are not significant. These zones include the largest part of the Cuban territory, distinguished themselves by maximum temperatures between 30.1°C and 35°C, and minimum ones between 20.1°C and 25°C. Therefore, these are the typical conditions of the very warm days of the Cuban climate.

· Regions of hills and low-mountains are located in a strip between 400 m and 800 m above sea level, with a warm summer, a subtropical climate in winter, and moderate temperatures between 25.1°C and 30°C, while the minimum ones are in the interval from 15.1°C to 20.2°C.

· Regions of the medium-sized-mountains. They are over 800 m above sea level, although with particular characteristics in each mountainous system, with maximum temperatures between 20.1°C and 25.1°C, and minimum ones oscillating from 15.1°C to 20.2°C.

There are regions with very warm typical thermic regimes, like those isolated zones of the eastern northern coast, south of the mountainous systems of Granma, Santiago de Cuba and Guantánamo provinces, in the inner of the large plains of the country with a strong continental character where remarkable maximum and minimum values are recorded. In the mountainous regions, the vertical distribution introduced by the relief is reflected in different alternatives, according to the locality.

Trade winds influence over Cuba almost the whole year. They come from the periphery of the oceanic subtropical oceanic anticyclon of the Azores-Bermudas. When this is not like that, on most occasions the influence of continental anticyclon systems happens, moving from the North American continent towards oceanic waters, temporarily influencing upon Cuba. Due to these conditions, the predominant direction of the surface winds is from the northeast to the east; so that in the north coast of the island these reinforce the sea breeze, while in the south coast

they oppose it, and reduce the daily marine breeze length. This effect is perceived in more than half of the days in a year. At night, the effect is the opposite with the terral (wind from the land to the sea), which directly causes that the minimum temperatures in the south coast are lower than those of the north one, and the maximum, higher.

The thermic regime in the most elevated zones is very peculiar, like in Topes de Collantes in the Guamuhaya Mountains (Escambray), and in Pinares de Mayarí in the Sierra del Cristal Range and in the Gran Piedra, in the homonymous range, and even different among them. Though, most of the year the low temperature record is remarkable, which determines nice and cool days.

The acceptance of two seasons, the wet and the dry one is something usual in Cuba. Differentiation of seasons owing to temperature changes is seldom accepted, due to the intensity of solar radiation. Although it is not possible to define the four classic seasons, the Cuban thermic regime shows well-defined and differentiated changes in each region of the country. This, of course, is also a consequence of the global changes of seasons produced by the variation of the solar radiation upon the planet.

Two transitional periods, non-similar between them, are noted between summer and winter. As summer turns to winter, there is a decrease in the maximum daily temperatures below 30°C, while the minimum daily ones decrease bellow 20°C. However, the interval between winter and summer characterizes by the increase of maximum daily values over 30°C, while the maximum values have not finally exceeded 20°C. This transitional conditions are not the same in the whole country.

In most of the archipelago, summer lasts six months, from May to October, and it coincides with the wet season, except in the region of Manzanillo (lower basin of the

Yara River), where it extends to November. Winter lasts from three to five months, between December-February and November-March respectively, with the exception of the mountainous zones.

ATMOSPHERIC RAINFALLS

Rains are generous, but not excessive over the Cuban territory. The extreme pluviometric events are caused either by hurricanes or by tropical cyclones and storms.

The irregularity and temporariness of the annual course of rainfalls are due to the general system of winds' circulation, to the topographic contrasts (orographic rains), to the irregularities of global warming, and to coastal waters.

During the winter or dry season, over the western and central regions, cold air masses spread. At the same time, all the territory and the Antilles are under the influence of trade winds, which determines a relatively dry period. In summer, in contrast, the low pressure equatorial zones send wet air masses, which bring about extensive rainfall with storms.

At the beginning of summer, an intense warming of the earth's surface and the atmospheric layers is brought about in the western and central regions, and convectional rains occur, with maximum frequency in May and June. Towards the northeast of the eastern provinces it occurs a little bit later.

The low- and the medium-sized-mountains are involved in the distribution of rainfalls, which are more intense in the windward slopes, specifically throughout the Sagua-Baracoa orographic system and other mountainous groups, particularly when the air currents have an orthogonal direction to the axis of the mountain ranges.

There are less rains in the leeward slopes, which is properly appreciable in the coastal landscape south of the Sierra Maestra and Baracoa mountains. In the basin of the Toa River, the mighty one of the country, developed in the northeast of the eastern region, rainfalls are notably influenced by the vigorous relief, to such an extent that they are outside the chart of the region, and so shape a pluviometric microclimate of orographic rains. There are less rainfalls in the coasts, bays and fluvial valleys.

The distribution of the mean rainfalls during the rainy period are stated bellow.

- In the westernmost territories and in the south and north coasts, they fluctuate between 800 mm and 900 mm a year, and from 1300 mm to 1400 mm in the Guaniguanico Mountain Range. In the eastern part of this orographic group, in El Rosario Range, they may attain 1600 mm.
- In the Guanahacabibes Peninsula the rainfalls fluctuate between 950 mm and 1000 mm.
- In La Habana, Ciudad de La Habana and Matanzas provinces the sum of the annual rains distributes from means of 800 mm to 900 mm in the territories of the north coast, up to attain 1300 mm to 1400 mm in the central zones, and they decrease in the south-littoral territories, down to annual mean sums that oscillate between 1000 mm and 1100 mm a year.
- In the central regions, there is a complex distribution of rainfalls, but as a whole, it increases from 1200 mm in the north coast up to attain 1400 mm - 1600 mm southwards, towards the peaks of the Guamuhaya Mountains, where in some places it may exceed 1700 mm a year. In the south coast it decreases again down to 1200 mm in the section between Cienfuegos and Trinidad cities.
- In the Camagüey-Maniabón region, where the relief is flat with slight undulations, annual mean sums between

600 mm and 800 mm are recorded northwards, from Prácticos Point, north of Nuevitas, to Chaparra Bay, to attain maximum figures between 1400 mm and 1600 mm south of Camagüey city.

· The distribution of the whole sum of annual rainfalls again becomes very irregular in the eastern regions. The value of the isohyet is remarkable in the medium basin of the Cauto River, where it ranges between 800 mm and 900 mm, and attains a minimum value from 600 mm to 800 mm in some years. In the rough territory of the Sierra Maestra Mountain Range, it reaches values up to 2200 mm north to the axis of the highest mountain range of Cuba. Towards the coastal south, minimum values of 800 mm are recorded in the Cruz Cape; and between 900 mm and 1000 mm along the southern coast. Northwards of the east-west axis of the mountain range, the isohyets present values that descend in a gentle way to reach the basin of the Cauto River, with the significant above mentioned low values. In the Nipe-Sagua-Baracoa Mountains, the rainfall increases again, up reach values of 2200 mm and more in some points of the medium basin of the Toa River, where probably more than 3000 mm are noteworthy in the joining of the Jiguaní and Toa Rivers. In contrast, 30 km south-south-eastward of the basin of the Toa River—in the coastal region of Imías—and farther to the east in San Antonio del Sur, considering also the Maisí Point, values fewer than 800 mm are registered, in the most arid landscapes of the country.

There are some regularities that may be observed during rainfalls, such as the following: As a whole, in flat territories, a gradual increase from east to west, and from the coasts landward so much so that in Pinar del Río, La Habana, Ciudad de La Habana and Matanzas provinces, the total sum of the annual rains ranges from 1.3 to 1.5 times more than in the eastern plains. The general trend in the mountains is the increase of the isohyet with the height. In 1965, Davitaya and Trusov succeeded in deducing correlation curves of rainfall *versus* height for some zones and slopes of the chief mountainous systems of Cuba.

Annual distribution of the rainfalls, allows to set up a rainy and a dry periods in the archipelago, together with the regime of the temperatures and the winds. This is particular uniform in the coastal regions of the eastern part of Cuba, from Banes, north of Holguín, to the Maisí Point in the farthest province, Guantánamo. In this respect, the biggest differentiation between both seasons is where the isoline in the dry period is 84 % of the annual mean, and it is registered in the following localities: Central zone of the Zapata Swamp; a small territory east of Cienfuegos Bay (lower basin of the Arimao River and the Gavilanes stream); and from Trinidad to Palizón Point, northeast of Santa Cruz del Sur (lower basins of the Agabama, Zaza and Jatibonico del Sur Rivers, as well as those of many streams draining the mangroves of the southern coast watered by the Ana María Gulf).

The annual sum of rainfalls, its course and space distribution are notably affected by the tropical cyclones, atmospheric phenomena that burst a huge energy when the winds blow with speed up to 300 km/h and the rainfalls reach more than 2000 mm in 3 - 5 days over several zones of the country. These hurricanes are born in the Atlantic Ocean, in the southern part of the trade winds zone in the Caribbean Sea, and also in the Gulf of Mexico. Its passing through the Cuban Archipelago is more likely in September and October, and in a descendent order, in June, July, August and November, seldom in May, December or January.

There are diverse atmospheric phenomena that bring about rain over the Cuban territory; the most part of the grand total of the annual rainfall occur in summer, when summer storms or stormy squalls burst. They begin to form when big clouds named *cumulus* appear, which turn into *cumulus-nimbus* and *nimbus*, then heat increases and even it may be oppressive, wind stop, far off deafly thunders, and soon after a wet and cool wind (rain wind) begins to blow, thunders increase lightning as a consequence, and sometimes one may note the arrival of clouds, running down showers; the atmospheric pressure, which had fallen, goes up again. This change may occur several times in one locality during summer. This phenomenon, as a whole, begins in May, but it delays until June. The stormy squalls may appear at any time in the day, but they are more frequent from three to five o'clock in the afternoon. Later, the sky clears and in some place of the skyline, a rainbow is noted.

Night dew is a watery condensation, looking like a very fine drizzle, nearly unnoticeable, and it may begin at night during summer.

Dew is another sort of watery condensation. It occurs when the surface of the ground turns cold during the night. Small water drops then appear on the surface of vegetation, rocks or soil. It may occur the whole year; during the dry season it helps to keep the soil moisture.

Frost or frozen dew is not frequent, but it occurs in high places of the mountains. Snow is unknown in Cuba.

Hail sometimes goes with the stormy squalls and electrical storms. It may be recorded in the whole island, but it is not so destructive as in other latitudes.

Fog occurs in the Cuban countryside when clouds are low, or in the mountainous hills; then visibility is reduced to less than 1 km, but when it is greater, it is called mist.

Cold fronts (or *nortes)* are responsible, in a good part, for the rainfalls during the winter or dry period. They are cold winds from south and southeast of the United States of America, and in winter it may occur between one and two dozens. The persistence of cold fronts may bring about a "cold wave," accompanied with moderate, intermittent or long rains. It is possible to see when the winter cold fronts appear in the marine skyline of the northern coast of the Island. As a whole, at the beginning, they include the westernmost provinces, up to reach the central ones, and lastly, the eastern provinces where their influence is lower. Immediately, after their passing, the strong breezes from the east-northeast to east-southeast begin to blow. They can strongly lash all the north coast, eventually with sea penetrations in the lower zones of the littoral.

Whirlwinds (tornadoes) often occur over the archipelago and its adjacent seas. When the whirlwinds appear over the sea surface, they may bring about waves of more than 2 m high. When they occur over ground, they usually create large havoc in small areas under their straight course. Tornadoes are compared to an elephant trunk, which falls with oscillating movements from a dark and dense low cloud with hurricane winds. These meteors are less frequent and destructive than those lashing the central valleys of North America.

One of the main features of the climate is the grand total of watery rainfalls during the year and their hyperannual variation. It is considered as a natural resource, but from the agricultural viewpoint, it is not enough for evaluation. The real effectiveness of the rains for the crops depends on the evaporation and the rain wash, variable factors of the hydrologic cycle. Due to lack of direct data about this index, specialists have came to theoretical calculus, taking into account the particularities of this climate, from where they have deduced the value of evaporation from Cuban plains: 900 mm to 950 mm a year. So that for the La Habana-Matanzas karstic plain, where the isohyet is 1400 mm of annual rain and the appraised evaporation, 900 mm, the rain wash would be 500 mm.

HEAT AND HUMIDITY

According to the calculus carried out by the Soviet specialists Davitaya and Trusov (1965), the country is properly supplied with heat and humidity, so in the Cuban Archipelago the drought—with their consequences of desolation and death for plants, animals and population—is unknown. In the most arid zones of Cuba, south of the Sagua-Baracoa Mountains in the Guantánamo province, only the herbaceous vegetation undergoes a little the dry season. Meanwhile trees and bushes with their more-developed and deep root system, are provided with humidity the whole year. On the other hand, the humidity content of the air is high, which noticeably reduces the evaporation from land and watery surfaces.

Cuban climate has prepared an extraordinary variety of soils, vegetation and landscapes. The agricultural crops are favored due to the abundance of humidity and heat, as well as their temporary and space distribution.

Sun radiation is also favorable for nearly all known agricultural crops, and specially for sugar cane, the main economic staple of the country and a generating source of foreign currency, employment, energy (sugar-cane pulp), and sugar-cane by-products, aside from countless raw materials for other sectors of the national economy and exportation. The climate-sugar cane binomial is the biggest and the best distributed natural-cultural resource of the country, because of the prodigality of sun energy over the whole national territory, and the high photosynthetic efficiency of sugar cane—one of the greatest among the cultivated plants—together with the very high exploitation index of the irrigation water and the environmental humidity under normal conditions of nutriments' supply.

The whole of the climatic conditions of Cuba is also propitious for national and foreign tourism, not only for the well-known fact of the plenty of beaches and excellent sea bottoms, but also for the frequent occurrence of sunshine and good weather days. The annual distribution of rainfalls makes the country an everlasting summer, specially in the coastal zones. The intensity of the sun radiation and its space-temporary distribution is favorable not only for agriculture and tourism, but also for a renewable source of thermic and electrical energy.

FLORA

The Cuban Archipelago represents a phytogeographical province of the Antillean Subregion at the Caribbean Region of the Neotropical Kingdom.

Cuban vegetal covering is the result of the microclimatic, edaphic, geological, geomorphological, hydrogeological and landscape varied conditions in the greatest of the Antilles, besides its insularity, from which a marked phytoendemism is derived.

Flora shows affinity with the rest of the Antilles, north of South America, and Central America. It is supposed that the Central American region is a starting point and a migration route; the neighboring island of Hispaniola, a transit zone towards the archipelago. Cuba, in turn, has been way of migrations towards the Bahamas. Several vegetable groups have arrived to Cuba—blown away by winds, cyclones, marine streams—on the epidermis and in the intestinal tract of migratory birds and bats, and land mammals that inhabited the Cuban territory since more than six thousands years ago, and which were originally from Central and South America.

Later, several Indoamerican migrations introduced wild and domesticated species, among them:

· Bitter yucca *(Manihot utilissima)*, probably brought from the savannas of the Orinoco basin, one of their American domestication centers. The *Taínos* from Hispaniola knew, at least, six varieties, according to what chronicler Oviedo stated.

- Tobacco *(Nicotiana tabacus)*, native from South America, which was yet in Cuba when Christopher Colombus arrived.
- Sweet potato *(Ipomoea batata)*, the second crop according to its importance for Cuban pre-Ceramic groups, originally from the low and wet lands east of the Andes.

Another crops with an American origin and a limited or none propagation in Cuba were introduced immediately after the arrival of the European to the Island, among them:

- Corn *(Zea mays)*, not much cultivated and consumed in Cuba because of its recent introduction when the Spaniards arrived.
- Beans, of which more than one species were cultivated in Hispaniola, according to the own observation of the Admiral Colombus and Las Casas.
- Red pepper *(Capsicum frutescens* and *C. Annum)*, used as a seasoning.
- Peanut *(Arachis hypogea)*.
- Pumpkin *(Cucurbita moschata)*.
- Pinneaple *(Ananas comusus)* original from Brazil.
- Cotton, a Malvaceae cultivated and processed in Cuba, according to the testimony of Colombus, although it was also used in its wild state according to another sources.
- Agave *(Agave fourcroydes)*, a textile plant the same as the maguey *(Fourcraea hexapetala* or maybe *F. cubensis)*; calabashtree *(Crescenctia cujete)*, common in the whole Island, pretty used as a pot.
- Annatto *(Bixa orellana)*, processed as food colouring, against mosquitoes and for both ritual and warlike cosmetics in its two varieties, yellow and red.
- Yoke *(Piptadenia peregrina)*, a tree similar to the mimosas, whose seeds, reduced to powder, are a strong ritual hallucinogen.

In Cuba, there were many edible-fruit trees used by the Antillean natives, or propagated from Hispaniola immediately after the conquer and colonization of the Island, among them: guava *(Psidium guajava)*, prickly custard apple *(Annona muricata)*, scaly custard apple *(Annona squamosa)*, mamme apple or mamey *(Mammea americana)*, icaco plum *(Chrysobalamus icaco)*, star-apple *(Chrysophyllum caimito)*, genip *(Genipa americana)*, and yellow mombia *(Spondias mombin)*.

Other plants were introduced by the European and other immigrants from overseas: sugar cane *(Saccharum officinarum)*, coffee tree *(Cofea arabica)*, wheat *(Triticum vulgare)*, as well as others from American lands: cacao *(Teobroma cacao)*, potato *(Solanum tuberosum)* and tomato *(Lycopersicum esculentum)*.

All the latter above mentioned plants obtained the naturalization letter in Cuba about 450 years ago. They spread as cultivated or semi-wild vegetation, and stayed together with the autochthonous and endemic island species in the natural and cultural landscape of the greatest of the Antilles.

The autochthonous flora of Cuba is the richest in the Caribbean-Antillean region, due to its endemic character. It has some 8000 species, and just 44.7% of them are located only in the Cuban Archipelago. That is why Cuba is considered the main speciation center of the region, and nearly has 33 large endemism's areas.

Doctor Ángela Leiva Sánchez, a noteworthy botanist, Director of the Jardín Botánico Nacional [National Botanic Garden] and President of the Sociedad Cubana para la Protección de la Naturaleza (proNATURALEZA)[Cuban Society for Environmental Protection], has stated the Cuban floral wealth in the following table:

Table 2. Floral wealth

Taxonomic Group	Number of Species			
Cormobionte				7540
Phanerogams			6196	
(plants with flowers)				
Angiosperms		6180		
(seeds in the fruit)				
(50% of endemism)				
Monocotyledonous	about 1400			
Dicotyledoneous	about 4780			
Gimnosperms		16		
(lean seeds)				
(87% of endemism)				
Cryptogams			1344	
(plants without flowers)				
Pterydophytes		544		
(ferns, licopods				
and psilotals)				
(8.4% of endemism)		800(?)		
Bryophytes				
(without vascular system,				
moss, hepatics)				
Algae				3000
Fungus				9000
Lichens				1000

The Cormobionte or superior plants with corm or a relatively evolved trunk (stem), including the root and the differentiated shoot with stems and leaves, group also the Pterydophytes and Briophytas (both Cryptogams), and comprise about 7540 species, without taking into accout the algae, fungus and lichens.

Among the Phanerogams and the vascular Cryptogams there are 202 families, none of them endemic. In contrast, 71 endemic genera have been distinguished, all of them, plants with flowers. It is calculated that 14% of wild flora and 27.7% of endemic taxa from the vascular plants, are included in some category of extinction threat. More than 50% of the superior plants are endemic, and only in the Cuban territory are about 3000 species.

In 1983, according to Borhidi and Muñiz there were 994 endangered species, belonging to 381 genera and 105 fami-

lies, included 832 Cuban exclusive species. It meant 86.7% of the species listed by the authors in the *Catálogo de plantas cubanas amenazadas o extinguidas* [Catalog of Cuban Threatened or Extinguished Plants]. Then, the extinction of 13 endemic species from the Cuban Archipelago had already recorded.

Biodiversity of exclusive vascular plant species is six times greater than in California, ten than in Texas, seven than in Spain, twenty-two than in Nigeria and forty-five than in Australia.

Due to the introduction of proved usefulness foreign species, just about all the Cuban plants are known only from the taxonomic viewpoint, while their physiological, biochemical and ecological features that make them useful to national economy are unknown. For instance, the therapeutic potential of the Cuban flora is still unknown, since the exotic species, spread by several great surge of immigrants, have been historically used.

In like manner, the floral and ornamental plants used in Cuban gardens exceed 200 species, most of them, foreign plants. It is necessary to accomplish an effort of artificial selection, supported by modern techniques of genetic engineering and clonation, in order to exploit the native genetic base, looking for the Cuban identity and the ecological harmony in gardening and national urban movement.

Taking into account all the above, the Cuba's flora may be characterized mainly by the three following factors:

· High endemism. It means more than 50% of the native inventory. Within this same item, one must consider the small zones having specific endemism or stenocorous over serpentine and latosol soils. Karstic areas distinguished themselves by typical forms of the hydric dripping, coastal landscapes, relief shapes, and so forth.

· Taxonomic wealth for the high number of known species. Only 6196 species belong to the Magnoliophyta, a subdivision of the Cormobiontes; it means, 0.06 species per square kilometer.

· Micranthia or richness of plants with small flowers. A phenomenon of great ecological importance, inasmuch as it implies special adaptations of pollen-eating animals.

The stenocorous areas identifiy themselves because they shelter endemic species in small territories, with unique and typical ecological conditions. Among more than thirty stenocorous areas, the following species may mention:

· *Microccycas calocoma:* Cork palm, with populations located in dispersed areas in the Guaniguanico Mountain Range and in the southern plain of Pinar del Río.
· *Magnolia cubensis:* Cuban magnolia, known as *marañón de la Maestra* in the mountain range of the same name, or *marañón de mantequero* in the Trinidad Range.
· *Colpothrinax wrightii:* Belly palm, which grows in the Guane flat lands, in the south of Pinar del Río, and in the north of the Isle of Youth.
· *Dracaena cubensis:* Cuban dracena, a species belonging to an European genus that is found only at the northeast of the Guantánamo province.
· *Pinus maestrensis: Pino de la Maestra*, an exclusive pine species of the range of the same name.

Families of Phanerogams or important Antophytes stand out from the phytogenetic viewpoint, among them: Poaceae, Asteraceae and Rubiaceae, having each of the more than four hundreds species; Euphorbiaceae, Leguminaceae, Convolvulaceae, Malvaceae, Piperaceae and Verbenaceae that sum up about one hundred species.

The taxonomic and systematic studies achieved in the last fifty years make easy the use of the phytoresources. During that span, these studies obtained a more systemic and exhaustive character with the work *Flora de Cuba del Hermano León* [Flora of Cuba from Brother León] (Joseph S. Sauget and Barbier), published in Havana in 1946. It was a topmost undertaking of the Cuban botany that was supported by centuries of explorations and studies of the native plants and other efforts. Among the last ones, stand out the edition, in 1928, of the *Diccionario botánico de nombres vulgares cubanos* [Botanic Dictionary of Cuban Common Names], and in 1945 of *Plantas medicinales, aromáticas o venenosas de Cuba* [Medicinal, Aromatic or Poisonous Plants of Cuba], both from Juan Tomás Roig y Mesa, an eminent Cuban wise man. Later, the Instituto de Ecología y Sistemática [Institute of Ecology and Systematics], all the botanical gardens of the Island, and several institutions of the Ministry of Agriculture would have to update, deepen and extend thus far the perfomance of so many famous and hardworking predecessors.

Nowadays, when the genetic engineering and the biotechnology thrive in the planet and in Cuba, the preservation, protection and utilization of the native bio-resources acquire the category of a national security problem and a safeguard of the economic independence; it is so now, and it will be in the future.

In order to better understand the description of the Cuban flora as a whole of species in an ecological balance with the biotic and abiotic factors, its description must be done as vegetable formations, which are divided into the following groups: Arboreous formation (forests), vegetation complexes, shrubby formation (underbrushes), herbaceous formation, and secondary vegetation.

National and foreign botanists in the last twenty years have studied the Cuban forests, such as O. Muñiz, E. del Risco, R. Capote, A. Leiva, J. Bisse, V. Samek, A. Borhidi and others. They finally set up certain consensus in order to classify the vegetable formations and the forests of the archipelago.

ARBOREOUS FORMATIONS (FORESTS)

Forest is the cohabitation place (biotope) of plants and animals in a two-univocal and dynamic relationship with the abiotic factors (soil, water, climate). Arboreous species, with more than 3 m high, predominate in this vegetable formation, and they cover more than 50% of the area. Several floors or strata often coexist, like: the herbaceous stratum (gramineae, cyperaceae, herbaceous, up to 1 m - 2 m high), the shrub stratum (shrubs with more than one trunk or woody stem, up to 3 m - 5 m high), and the arboreous stratum (trees and small trees having woody consistency). In the Cuban forest may be other plants forming no strata, like lianas, climbers, epiphytes (such as orchids, bromeliads, ferns, mosses, lichens), parasites and epiphyllous (on the leaves).

It has already been established during the study of the evolution of the Cuban forest that before the arrival of the man to the insular territory, it was covered entirely with diverse types of forests (between 93% and 96%); the rest of the country was occupied by savannas with several kinds of vegetation, typical of rocky coasts, sandy beaches, or low gramineae vegetation, with palms, pines, latifoliaceous and disperse shrubs. At the turn of the 16th century, before the Spanish conquest, the human groups with a development of the productive forces corresponding to different stages of the Neolitic, had introduced the culture of yucca, sweet potato and something of corn. The burning of forests to convert them to croplands, for feeding a population of nearly one hundred thousa Amerindians —spread rather to the central and eastern regions—then remained between 88% and 92% of forest cover, according to calculus. Soon, the wood of these trees made up the timberwork of the Navy of Florida. The West Indian mahogany (*Swietenia mahagoni*), the cedar (*Cedrela odorata*) and the Cuban sabicu (*Lysilona sabicu*) were transported towards the Iberian Peninsula for the magnificent constructions of the Spanish clergy and crown, the San Lorenzo del Escorial monastery, among these ones.

According to calculus, around 1774, forests still covered 83% of the archipelago. At the ends of the 18th century, about 6710 ha a year were cleared for firewood collection. But with the development of sugar industry, a mortal enemy of the forest, this figure grew up to 13,420 ha a year around 1819. Between 1828 and 1900, were cleared 2,959,939 ha of forest. In 1900 still remained 4,547,875 ha of Cuban forest. It means, 41% of the territory. From now on, the vigorous expansion of the sugar cane industry, because of the introduction of North American capital, delivered shattering blows to the remaining forest cover. Between 1926 and 1946, forests were cleared at an average annual rate of 75,048 ha. In 1958 it remained 1,817,234 ha, that is, 16% of the national territory, distributed as following: Disperse forests in the Guanacahabibes and Zapata Peninsulas, south to the former Isle of Pines, south to Ciego de Ávila and Camagüey provinces, and in mountainous areas. But this forest mass had lost its original quality owing to the forest clearance that select to cut the best trees and the most valuable woods. The reforestation plans started in the first years of the 1960s, would finally achieve a positive balance, because the forest area was slightly increased, reaching 21.1%—according to data up to 1999— of forestland, but having a less ecological and wood value.

Nowadays, and from 1990 onwards, the country undergoes an energetic crisis that threat to reduce to ashes the huge efforts of the Revolutionary Government.

State authorities carry out bold attempts to put wood cutting in order, doing an adequate forest management for firewood collection. Also, they give priority to the reforestation in the most degraded and important hydrographic basins, legislating and putting into effect juridical regulations, and organizing the protection of forests, their flora, fauna and soils, with a special vigilance body.

According to doctor Enrique del Risco Rodríguez, from the Instituto de Investigaciones Forestales [Institute of Forest Researches]of the Ministry of Agriculture, in Cuba the following zonal wooded formations may be noted:

Semideciduous Forests. From 40% to 65% of the emerging trees of these forests, and those from their upper arboreous stratum lose their leaves along the dry season. This forest displays a lower evergreen stratum and an upper one containing trees and palms with 25 m high or more; it has shrub and herbaceous strata with lianas and abundant epiphytes. They were the most abundant forests of Cuba at the beginning, arranged over red or brown soils with a limy origin, and they were spread out in the flat and wavy areas of the western and center of the Island, where there were between 1250 mm to 1600 mm of annual rain, and average temperatures between 24°C and 25°C. Considerable areas remain at present in the karstic Zapata, Carapachibey (south of the Isle of Youth) and Guana- hacabibes Peninsulas, over red, rendzina, and brown-with-carbonates soils. In past years , these forests were the richest, considering their fancywoods; nowadays, the most representative species are: kapok tree *(Ceiba pentandra),* West Indian birch *(Bursera simaruba),* royal palm *(Roystonea regia),* partridge wood *(Andira inermes),* dagame *(Callycophyllum candidissimum),* cedar *(Cedrela odorata),* geiger tree *(Cordia gerascanthus),* Cuban sabicu *(Lysiloma sabicu),* West Indies mahogany *(Swietenia mahagoni),* Jamaica oak *(Catalpa punctata),* "guara hembra" and "guara macho" *(Capania americana* and *C. glabra),* "jibá" *(Erythroxylum havanense),* and "guaguasí" *(Zuelania guidonia).*

Subperennifolious Forests. These forests, also denominated evergreen forests, present deciduous trees, in contrast with the true evergreen forests.

This type of woodland has two arboreous substrata, and some emerging trees with fewer than 30% of deciduous trees. The evergreen trees constitute the most of the proportion, inasmuch as they are located in zones having one to two months of drought, annual rains between 1600 mm and 2000 mm, and temperatures between 24°C and 25°C.

In the first substratum, the trees attain between 20 m and 25 m high, and in the second one, between 15 m and 18 m. This forest has no much dense shrub and herbaceous strata; it is found, as a whole, over brown soils (with and without carbonates), in plains with edaphic humidity in heights of 400 m. Nowadays, this forest is found in small zones of the Zapata and the Guanahacabibes Peninsulas, and in the very-small-mountains of all the orographic groups in just about all the country, although they are notably degraded. The most representative species are: Kapok tree *(Ceiba pentandra)*, "aguacatillo" *(Alchornea latifolia)*, West Indian cherry *(Prunus occidentalis)*, "cuajaní hembra" *(Prunus myrtifolia)*, and "caguairán" or "quiebra hacha" *(Guibourtia hymenaefolia)*.

When these types of forests develop over acid yellow and even yellow-reddish soils, they appear lower, have some acidophile species and the calciphile ones disappear; the floristic composition and their physiognomy change, and the tree leaves are more coriaceous (hard). This type of subperennifolious forests has been cleared, and these lands occupied by crops; scarcely remain some very-small-mountain areas with these forests in Pinar del Río. A very different type of forest than that of the plains appears in the zones of very-small- and low-mountains, in the center and eastern part of the Island, between 400 m and 800 m, over mountainous brown-reddish, yellow and red soils. A great part of these have disappeared, and their areas are croplands for coffee and cacao.

Coastal and Subcoastal Semideciduous Forests. They are low forests with two arboreous substrata, one of them having 10 m to 12 m high, and from 5 m to 10 m the other

one; more than 40% of the trees of the first substratum are deciduous. It has between 1000 mm and 1200 mm of annual rain. This forest has microphyle species, small palms, thorny shrubs, and both column and arborescent cactaceae; it grows over coastal limestone containing red and scanty deep black soils (rendzinas). These forests are distributed in the high places of the center-western and western zones, and in the south coast of the Isle of Youth and the Guanahacabibes Peninsula. Many of these forests have been affected by the wood cutting of their hardwoods in order to cultivate henequen and to construct roads, towns and neighborhoods, as it was done in sections between Vía Blanca Road and Ciudad de La Habana.

Dry Thorny Shrubby Forests. They are low forests or dense underbrushes composed by trees and thorny shrubs, sclerophyllous and microphyllous. They settle in strips having 750 mm to 800 mm of annual rain. In them, the deciduous species are not plentiful; they have a low arboreous stratum of between 2 m to 4 m, with some small trees and emerging palms, and non-dominant column and arboreous cactus as well. They settle over the naked rock of limy terraces and karren coasts. These forests appear in some areas between Maisí and the Cruz Cape, Maisí and Nibujón, Banes and Nuevitas Bay, in the Sabana-Camagüey Archipelago, and from the south coast of Cienfuegos to the eastern part of the Zapata Peninsula. These forests, also named coastal secondary woody vegetation, have been destroyed in order to build roads between Cienfuegos and Trinidad, and in the coastal region of the Sierra Maestra Mountain Range.

Semiarid Shrubby Forests. These constitute a shrubby or open underbrush woodland, having 4 m to 5 m high, made up of trees and small shrubs, thorny on the whole, with abundance of dominant cactaceae over the shrub stratum. They settle in arid strips with fewer than 500 mm of annual rain. These bushes grow between Imías and the

Guantánamo Bay, over rocky and sandy soils. The still existing shrub forests are affected by cattle and goats grazing.

Plain Rainforests. These are the evergreen, true rainforests (of low altitude), where the annual rains are of 3500 mm or more. They have a vigorous vegetation, where the highest trees of Cuba grow (up to 40 m high and 1 m width), having an arboreous stratum with three substrata of 30 m, from 20 m to 30 m, and between 10 m and 20 m. The arboreous ferns growing up to 10 m, broad and long lianas, epiphytes (bromeliads and orchids), and epiphyllous (algae, lichens and hepatics) appear. They occupy brown soils over siliceous rocks, in regions having up to 400 m high, between Baracoa and Moa, in the basins of the Toa and Duaba rivers. The crabwood *(Carapa guianensis),* bulletwood *(Manilkara albescens),* date plum *(Diospyros caribaea),* and others are plentiful there. Among the lianas or vines there is the climbing entada *(Entada phaseoloides).* These forests have been notably degraded because of the growing timber demand, and their areas have been converted to croplands for coffee, cacao and coconut.

Submountain Rainforests. They are evergreen rainforests located in low mountains, with lower temperatures (between 23°C and 24°C), rains between 2000 mm and 3000 mm a year, and the average height of their trees is a little lower. In these forests the epiphytes are not so abundant, and the epiphyllous and lianas grow. They occupy red soils in the Sierra del Cristal and Nipe Ranges, in the Moa, Toa and Baracoa Crests, between heights of 400 m and 800 m. Another sort of this forest is located in the highlands of the Moa Crests, in a locale with deficient drainage, where the Cuban bonetia *(Bonnetia cubensis),* an endemic species of this zone grows.

Mountain Rainforests. They are evergreen or mountain forests, located in a higher height than the foregoing; they have a cool climate, temperatures between 20°C and 23°C, and annual rainfalls between 1600 mm and 2000 mm or more. The trees have from 23 m to 25 m high, and they have two strata of epiphytes, epiphyllous and arborescent ferns. These forests occupy mountain red soils, between 600 m - 800 m and 1200 m - 1600 m in the Sierra Maestra, El Purial, Imías and Guamuhaya Ranges.

Cloudy Forests. They are evergreen forests conditioned by the mountain tropical climate, without dry season, with an annual average temperature from 12°C to 15°C, and 2000 mm of annual rain. In these regions the clouds are at the same height of the mountains, and it increases humidity. There are two arboreous substrata: From 10 m to 15 m, and from 6 m to 10 m high, and a dense shrubby stratum with ferns and mosses, which cover the trunks up to 3 m high. The soil is covered with sphagnum mosses *(Sphagnum)* and selaginellas *(Selaginella).* The trunks of these trees are twisted by the strong winds; the soils are yellow, and they are generally situated between 1200 m and 1600 m high, or in lesser heights, according to the localities. They are found in the El Purial, Sierra Maestra, Imías and Trinidad Ranges, and in the Pan de Guajaibón.

Subparamos. They are low stunted forests, known as cool woodland, located between the cloudy forests and the bleak plateaus. (There are no bleak plateaus in Cuba owing to lack of height.) It doesn't snow there, as is the case in the bleak plateaus; there are magueys and a tree with aciculate leaves: the Turquino red-cedar *(Juniperus saxicola).* They grow from 1800 m high, in a mountain tropical wet and cold climate, with annual rains of 1200 mm and temperatures fewer than 12°C. They have a dense arboreous stratum of 3 m to 4 m and emerging small trees of 5 m to 7 m with microphyle leaves and xeromorphous features. They are only in the Turquino elevations and their surroundings, and are better preserved than the other ones.

Some forest formations answer to edaphic factors in extreme conditions: poor in nutriments, dry, with a high contents of toxic elements, very scanty deep, rocky or with high contents of sodium, silicon dioxide, aluminum, and magnesium (the two latter derived from the serpentine), naked rocky of mogotes or sandy of coastal dunes. They are: pine groves, *cuabales* and *charrascales*.

Pine Groves. They are evergreen forests having aciculate leaves (needle-shaped leaves), with an arboreous stratum dominated by one pine species (mono-odominant), and seldom, twice. They present a more or less developed shrubby stratum, mainly made up of gramineae, ciparaceae and ferns.

The following pine groves are developed in the Island: those from the Sierra Maestra Mountain Range where the "pino de la Maestra" *(Pinus maestrensis)* is the builder; the "pino hembra" groves, with only one arboreous stratum made up of "pino hembra" *(Pinus tropicalis)* and belly palm *(Colpothrinax wrightii)*, both endemic species of the western part of the country; the pine groves made up of "pino hembra"[8] *(Pinus tropicalis)* and slash pine *(Pinus caribaea* ssp. *caribaea)* that are forests with only one arboreous stratum having both mentioned pine species, typical of the slaty hills of Pinar del Río and the northeast of the Isle of Youth; the Mayarí pine groves, inhabited with *Pinus cubensis*, an endemic species from the northeastern zone of Cuba, where it forms large wooded massifs over red latosol soils derived from serpentine; and the pine groves of slash pines *(Pinus caribaea* ssp. *caribaea)*, and endemic subspecies from Pinar del Río and the Isle of Youth, which grow in the highland of Cajálbana and its surroundings, where form a compact massif between 10 m and 464 m high, over red latosol soils, also derived from serpentine.

It is possible to see pine groves in some elevated places of the country; they have been planted as soil-protecting for-ests or accordingly sequence reforestation, or even with industrial purposes. Among such places one may mention: Alturas de Pizarra del Sur in the Guaniguanico Mountain Range, and Topes de Collantes in the Guamuhaya Mountains.

The Cuabales. They are low xerophytic, sclerotic, thorny and subperennifolious (a great number of evergreen species with some deciduous ones) forests, over skeletal soils, having annual rains between 1000 mm and 1800 mm. They occupy plains and low-mountains along the serpentine axis from Pinar del Río to Holguín. The isolation and the extreme edaphic conditions have caused the development of numerous endemic species, among them: anón de cuabal[9] *(Annona bullata)*, pigeon berry *(Bourrera divaricata)*, black ebony *(Diospyros crassinervis)*, and also several palm species of the *Coccothrinax* and *Copernicia* genera. There are secondary savannas in places where some of these forests existed, because of their intentional burning, to convert them to pastures.

The Charrascales. They are low sclerophyllous, xerophytic and evergreen forests that grow in the hillsides over skeletal or very scanty deep soils, developed over ultrabasic rocks, mainly serpentine. They are less xerophytic than the *cuabales*, because these zones receive up to 2000 mm or more of annual rain. The species are sclerophyllous, but they have no many thorns. This type of woodland is found only in the northeastern mountains, between Peladero de Jauco zone in Maisí, and in the Nipe highland. Its flora is very rich in local endemic species (steno-endemic), and that is why the florula changes in each locality. Among the most representative and the best distributed species there are the following: The "jaragua" *(Acrosynanthus taquiphyllum)*, some box from *Buxus* genus, the "cuaba amarilla" *(Leucocroton cordifolius)*. In the region of Moa, mining has affected some of their ar-

8. This Cuban common name means "female pine," meanwhile the Cuban common name of the slash pine means "male pine," due to their sex features. *Trans.*

9. It means "sugar apple of this kind of forest." *Trans.*

eas, but as a whole, the *charrascales* are well preserved, because the soils are unsuited to agriculture.

Mogotes Vegetation. They are shrubby forests found in highly karstified limestone hills, with poorly developed soil, where the vegetation grows among the rocks. The typical mogotes (a tropical cone-karst display) are found in the Los Órganos Range in Pinar del Río. There are mogote-shaped hills in the Escaleras de Jaruco, in La Habana province; in the Isle of Youth; in the Trinidad Range; in Baracoa and Moa, and in Baire, north of the Sierra Maestra Mountain Range. In these limy hills, six different vegetable formations may be found, that is why it is denominated complex of mogotes vegetation. Among these formations, there are three types of forests: The subperennifolious forest of dolines or *hoyos de montaña* [wetter]; the semideciduous forest that lies in the rocky basis; and the forest of mogotes in the conic summits. The most representative species depend on the locality, but the most typical mogotes are in Pinar del Río, and they are very rich in endemic species, among them: "ceibón" *(Bambacopsis cubensis),* "palma de sierra"[10] *(Gaussia princeps),* and cork palm *(Microcycas calocoma).*

Sea Grape Groves. They are evergreen forests, dominated by the sea grape *(Coccoloba uvifera),* sometimes with some deciduous species, at which they form a narrow strip, growing over the dunes in the sandy or rocky coasts. They perform an important protective function against the winds and sea splashing. These forests have been partly destroyed by the construction of coastal roads. There are other species in these forests: west Indian birch *(Bursera simaruba),* buttonwood *(Conocarpus erecta),* icaco plum *(Chrysobalanus icacus),* among others.

Finally, several forest formations are conditioned by the humidity of the substratum. They distinguish them-selves by the excess of humidity in the rainy season, or in the whole year, or by the occurrence of semideciduous forests with fluctuating humidity and the swamp forests, and others with salt or fresh water all the time.

Semideciduous Forests with Fluctuating Humidity. Their species must be resistant to sudden humidity changes. They have only one arboreous stratum about 15 m high, and poor shrubby and herbaceous strata. These forests grow over the hydromorphic soils of the Cauto Plain and the coastal plains of Holguín, north and south of Camagüey and Ciego de Ávila, and in other localities of the rest of the Island. These forests were notably exploited because of their fancywoods, like the "majagua de Cuba" *(Atkinsia cubensis),* the West Indian mahogany *(Swietenia mahagoni)* and others.

Swamp Forests. These forests grow in swampy zones, with permanent floods, or a more or less large period of flooding, having fresh or salt water over peaty soils. They have trees whose trunks are thickened towards their basis with a protective suberous tissue. They have two arboreous substrata: The upper stratum, from 10 m to 15 m, mostly with evergreen trees, and the lower, from 5 m to 8 m. These forests have a well-developed shrubby stratum, and epiphytes, lianas, and even some mangroves and palms may appear. Some of their species are: whitewood *(Tabebuia angustata),* black olive trees from the *Bucida* genus, and blue mahoe *(Hibiscus elatus).* They grow in the coastal zones of the Remates, Lanier, Zapata, Majaguillar, Morón, Birama Swamps, and in many other littoral strips, where they are moderately well preserved.

Mangrove Trees. They are evergreen forests, notably specialized because of the great salinity conditions and the excess of humidity; that is why the trees have roots with special adaptations (long-legged) and pneumatophores (roots with negative geotropism in order to supply oxygen to the roots.) This is the only land vegetation that has direct contact with the sea. Among their roots, the

10. It means "mountain range palm." *Trans.*

larvae stages of various crustaceans develop, like shrimps, lobsters, and also fishes from the shelf. The arboreous stratum is dominated by four mangrove species: red mangrove *(Rhyzophora mangle)*, black mangrove *(Avicennia germinans)*, white mangrove *(Laguncularia racemosa)*, and buttonwood *(Conocarpus erecta)*. The mangrove trees have been notably affected because of the coal production and the extraction of the bark of the red mangrove searching for tannin; besides, some hydrotechnical works and roads (stone-roads) over shallow seas have block the free flow of sea water, so that, many species have died and others are threatened, thereby, the whole coastal ecosystem has been affected.

SHRUBBY FORMATIONS (UNDERBRUSHES)

In these formations predominate the shrubs, and the emerging trees may be present or not. In Cuba there are the following:

Coastal and Subcoastal Xeromorphous Underbrush (Coastal Secondary Woody Vegetation). It is a bush with stunted shrubs and trees, chiefly sclerophyllous, microphyllous, nanophyllous and thorny deciduous elements, often with an appearance of a shrubby forest with succulent plants, palms, herbaceous and lianas.

Thorny Xeromorphous Underbrush over Serpentine (Cuabal). It is a bush with a dense shrubby stratum, from 2 m to 4 m, with emerging trees, herbaceous, palms, epiphytes and lianas. It is found in plains and low hills over serpentine soils.

Sub-thorny Xeromorphous Underbrush over Serpentine (Charrascal). It has a dense shrubby stratum, from 4 m to 6 m with emerging trees from 7 m to 10 m, and disperse herbaceous, lianas and epiphytes. It grows in plains, hilly and mountainous zones, over serpentine soils of eastern Cuba.

Sub-Alpine Underbrush (Cool Woodland, Cold Woodland). It is a bush with stunted shrubs of about 3 m high, with succulent plants, epiphytes and climbing petrophyles. It is found only in the Turquino massif above 1600 m.

HERBACEOUS FORMATIONS

In this vegetal formation the herbaceous species predominate; there are the following:

Fresh-water Aquatic Communities, Having Freely-floating and Rooting Species. Among the first ones, there are the water hyacinth *(Eicchornia* sp.), the duckweed *(Lemna minima),* and the bladderwort *(Utricularia* sp.), and among the latter, the water-milfoil *(Myriophyllum* sp.), the waterlily *(Nymphacea* sp.), *Najas* sp. and many others.

Halophytic Communities (Saline). They are made up, on the whole, of herbaceous and succulent plants that allow high salinity levels; some species are *Batis maritima* and *Helitropium,* and also those like the herbaceous undergrowth from swamp and from banks of rivers and streams.

VEGETATION COMPLEXES

They include groups of similar vegetable communities that are specifically distributed in each territory, to which they give particular features. In Cuba there are the following: mogotes vegetation, rocky coast vegetation and sandy coast vegetation.

The mogotes vegetation has been also qualified as a vegetation complex with discontinuous arboreous stratum, palms and deciduous trees, succulent plants, epiphytes and plentiful of lianas.

The rocky coast vegetation is an open community, with both large and small succulent plants, small shrubs, sometimes stunted, and herbaceous plants.

The sandy coast vegetation includes herbaceous and disperse subfructicose plants, and among them may appear arboreous species.

SECONDARY VEGETATION

It is a community that arises as a consequence the degradation of the natural vegetation. This concept may be expanded towards the degraded forests, where trees and other "opportunist" species appear, like the royal palm *(Roystonea regia)* and the kapok tree *(Ceiba pentandra).*

ECONOMIC-POTENTIAL VALUE OF SOME GROUPS OF CUBAN PLANTS

A summary of the economic potential of some of the Angiosperms' families—the most known—that are present in the described vegetation types, will allow to obtain an approximate idea about the importance of the Cuban natural genetic base.

Among the monocotyledonous the Poacea family (gramineae) stand out; they are plants with a broad ecological spectrum, sometimes turned into invading grasses for the crops, and others in cosmopolitan crops that constitute the basis of human and animal feeding, such as the cases of species from the *Paspalum* genus. Species of natural fodders and the cereals naturalized in Cuba belong to that mentioned genus: corn *(Zea mays)*, rice *(Oryzea sativa)* and wheat *(Triticum vulgar).* The last one is waiting for more attention for its better spreading in Cuba.

Fourteen indigenous species from the *Agave* genus, Agavaceae family, grow in Cuba, but only the henequen *(Agave furcoydes),* an exotic species, is cultivated. Cuban specialists have found some substances in the Cuban agaves, useful both of them to the phamaceutical industry and to the production of fibers and surface-active agents.

Among the outstanding families whose species characterize the Cuban landscape, the woodland and the gardens, one must mention: the Arecaceae family. This monocotyledonous plant belongs to the Arecales order, Nymphaeopsida class; we refer to the palms. Fifteen genera grow in the Cuban Archipelago, from which fourteen are endemic ones including seventy-three species described, among others, by Johannes Bisse in 1981. To them it may be added about twenty-five subspecies and a few not described yet. In all, it would exceed the hundred of species and subspecies of Cuban autochthonous palms.

Among the palmaceae there is the royal palm *(R. regia)*, the more abundant, useful and beautiful. It belongs to the *Roystonea* genus that include other three native species. This palm grows in the whole country; it is typical from the semideciduous forests and deep soils with good drainage, and is very frequent in the secondary vegetation. The peasants use the outer tissue of its trunk to make resistant planks, and its fruit, the royal palm nut (bunches of small nut-like seeds) for animal feeding. The oil of this palm has different uses in the industry. Another palmaceae are the following: the prickly palm *(Gastrococos crispa),* an endemic and monotypical genus that grows in rocky and calcareous lands of the whole Cuba; the belly palm *(Colpothrinax wrightii),* an endemic species of the sandy savannas of Pinar del Río and the Isle of Youth; the "palma de sierra" *(Gaussia princeps),* an endemic species of the mogotes of Pinar del Río; species from the *Calyptrogyne* genus (known in Cuba as "manacas"), with five species, two of them endemic from the central and eastern forests; the "palma pajúa" *(Bactris cubensis),* an endemic species from the western forests; and the *Copernicia* genus, with twenty-five species, twenty of them endemic ones, divided into three ecological groups: Big species *(yareyones)*, medium species *(yareyes)* and medium species with short or non-existent petiole *(jatas),* all of them with appropriate fibers for knitting hats, mats and other very useful objects.

Among the dicotyledoneous plants, whose endemic species exceed two thousands, one must mention those that are phytogenetic resources, like the *Piper* genus of the Piperaceae family, represented by thirty native species, some of them having high concentrations of insecticide substances and others, recognized as seasoning and therapeutic substances.

The Moraceae family includes *Trophis racemosa* and *Brosimum alicastrum,* having great potential to forage and shade for livestock.

The "guaniquique" or "bejuco de canasta"[11] *(Trichostigma octandrum)* stand out within the Fitolocaceae family; it is useful for furniture, baskets and other craft objects.

The Fabales order (legumes) includes several families, ranging from trees, shrubs to grasses. Among them, several species are useful due to their wood, for forage or coloring, and there are other useful species: the melliferous, medicinal, nutritional, ornamental ones, and others.

The Myrtaceae family comprises about 300 species, and has a great potential because of their high and varied contents of essential oils, eatable fruits and hardwoods with thin grain.

From the Annonpsida class, Opuntiales order, three subfamilies grow in Cuba, distributed in fifteen genera, two of them endemic and monotypical: *Rhodocactus* and *Dendrocereus.* The botanists have studied and classified in the Island until 1980, thirty-one species of Cuban cactus, at least, twenty-one endemic.

The Euphorbiaceae family is well represented in Cuba. The scholars consider that the *Chamaesyce, Croton, Jatrofa* and *Phyllanthus* genera have a great pharmacological potential. In like manner, the *Plumeria, Rauwolfia* and *Tabernaemontana* genera, from the Apocynaceae family are rich in indole alkaloids, useful for the pharmaceutical industry.

The *Datura* and *Solanum* genera, from the family of the autochthonous Solanaceae, Rubiales order, reveal also therapeutic potentials.

11. It means "reed for basket." *Trans.*

Because of their textile properties, the *Gossypium, Hibiscus* and *Urena* genera, among others, belonging to the Malvaceae, are waiting to be exploited.

The Gimnosperms deserve an aside paragraph, specially those from the *Pinus* genus with its four autochthonous species, and the southern red-cedar *(Juniperus lucayana),* from the Uprossaceae family a well-distributed species in the Cuban Archipelago.

Among the vascular Cryptogamous (Pteridophytes), the Filicophytina subdivision of the Macrophylophyta division includes the ferns. The wealth of ferns is such that in the Tope de Collantes sector, the high basin of the Caburní River in the Trinidad Range, in an area of around 10 sq km, seven species of arborescent ferns, and more than seventy herbaceous ones have been classified. Twenty three species of ferns are recognized as species used in popular medicine.

The family of the orchids is rich in species. The tireless botanist Dr. Marta Aleida Díaz Dumas has achieved to summarize her work and that of several researchers, and has calculated in more than three hundreds the orchid species growing in the country.

The aquatic plants are a group having a great ecological interest. Among them one must mention some species belonging to the *Nymphaea* genus, so-called "ovas" in Cuba; the most common species is *N. ampla.* From the *Nuphar* genus, the yellow pond-lilly *(N. luteum* ssp. *Macrophylum)* is abundant in rivers and lagoonsin the western region. The water hyacinth *(Eichohornia crassipes),* typical from the tropical regions, is an invader of both natural and dammed aquatic surfaces, and indicates the high contamination degree of some of these aquatories.

This marvelous floral world of the Cuban Archipelago has an ecological support in the surviving forest formations described above; from their protection and development depend the animal kingdom, the soils, the hydrologic balance, and the conservation of the natural genetic base for agriculture, industry and, specially, for biotechnology.

FAUNA

The Cuban Archipelago, according to the *Nuevo Atlas Nacional de Cuba* [New National Atlas of Cuba], is part of the zoogeographic subprovince of Cuba-Western Bahamas, of the Greater Antilles province[12] in the Antillean region, which bounds to the west with the Central American region, to the south and to the east with the Orinoco one, and to the north with the Neartic.

The Cuban territory is inhabited by a fauna of land and wild vertebrates; some of them have been evolved since before the Pleistocene. Nevertheless, most of the Cuban current land fauna is very young, not more ancient than the Pleistocene, or at utmost, than the Pliocene.

The origin of the Cuban fauna is still polemic, because according to several zoologists and paleontologists, the fauna relations between this Antillean territory and the neighboring areas are closer with the rest of the Greater Antilles than with South and Central America, and still less than with south North America.

Cuban fauna is the result of the accumulation and interaction of immigrants that arrived by different ways at diverse times, and probably, from several American regions.

According to several hypothesis, the immigrant land fauna could have arrived to Cuba in "natural balsas," as a result of landslides and floating vegetation from isles or continental regions and generated by floods, earthquakes or hurricanes. Other authors, like M. Iturralde-Vinent, point out the Aves Rise as a migration way to the Antilles, when

this ridge—submerged today—put the current Antillean territory in touch with north South America as a peninsula during the Eocene, forty million years ago. In accordance with this theory the geological processes that took place in the Miocene caused the sinking of the ridge and gave rise to the current configuration of the Greater Antilles Archipelago, and to the isolation of the islands among themselves. This is why the fauna evolved in each one of the islands in an independent way.

General features of the Cuban fauna depend on the insular condition of the country in the different stages of its geological evolution, which has lent to it the pronounced characteristic of being center of evolution and endemism, and having wealth of species and subspecies, abundance of invertebrates, relative poverty of vertebrates, absence of big mammals, survival of archaic groups, relative poverty and high endemism of fresh-aquicolous fauna, great number of ichthyofauna marine species—typical from the American Mediterranean Basin—and pollinators or pollen-eating animals with morphologic adaptations owing to the mycranthia of many Phanerogamous (plants with flowers).

Some carnivorous were probably introduced with the arrival of the Amerindian to Cuba, like the canids (dumb dogs), which together with the man dealed the final blows to the fauna that survived despite the climatic and geographical unsteadiness brought about by Pleistocene glaciations and rainfall periods. Likewise, the majority of the vertebrates became extinct, among them: All the sloth species, seven of bats, sixteen of rodents, five of insectivorous, three of sirenids, all the species of canids and primates, and one of pinnipeds among the mammals, and twelve species of birds.

Later, when the European man arrived at the end of the 15th century, but more markedly in the 16th, with the

---

12. The word "province" is used as a hierarchical category of the physical geographical regionalization, and not as part of a republic.

consequent introduction of carnivores (canids and felids), rodents, artiodactyls, lagomorphs, perissodactyls, and others, and with the destruction or modification of forests and other natural ecosytems, the Cuban fauna underwent irreparable losses with regard to population and biodiversity.

At present, the Cuban fauna biodiversity, is approximately, the following:

Table 3. Cuban Fauna Biodiversity

Taxonomic Groups	Number of species and subspecies	
Mollusks		2947
Insects		7493
Arachnids		1300
Other groups of invertebrates		3380
Fishes		900
Reptiles		121
Amphibious		46
Birds		350
Mammais		40
Bats	27	
Rodents	8	
Insectivorous	1	
Sirenians	1	
Cetaceous (Delphinidae)	3	
Total		16,577

The total number of species and subspecies of the Cuban fauna is noteworthy, but its most outstanding feature is the endemism, which may be proved through the following figures:

From the 40 species of mammals, 23 are endemic; from the 350 species of birds, 70; from the reptiles, 70 species belong to the Sauria suborder that includes 50 taxa of the Iguanids family (chameleons, anoles lizards, lizards and ground lizards), and the overwhelming majority are exclusive of the Cuban Archipelago.

Among the amphibious, about 90% are endemic; among the arachnids, the Cuban scorpions sum up 25 species, 20 of them exclusive of Cuba—80% of endemism—; among the land mollusks, the pulmonate species of the Gastropoda class include 6 species of the *Polymita* genus, a Cuban endemic one. It has been calculated that 80% of the invertebrates, specially, the land mollusks, with more than 1000 species, are endemic. Fresh water fishes have several exclusive species of Cuba, among them, at least, 2 of blind fishes (anophthalmic), belonging to the *Lucifuga* genus.

Until 1974 it has been calculated a total of 142 endemic species of land vertebrates (36 amphibious, 70 reptiles, 22 birds and 14 mammals), grouped in 12 endemic genera: 1 of amphibious, 2 of reptiles, and 9 of birds. Nowadays, a lot more endemic species are known.

In 1979, 5 species and 9 subspecies of endemic bats were described, from the 26 taxa discovered until then, which represent 54% of exclusivity.

Gilberto Silva Taboada, a biospeleologist, in 185 caverns from the thousands that exist in Cuba, has reported 228 species of vertebrates and invertebrates, from which 36 are endemic of these speluncas. This figure includes 8 arachnids and 16 crustaceans, 8 insects, 2 fishes 1 diplopod.

The areas of greater endemism of the vertebrates are, in a descending order: the Isle of Youth; the south coast of the eastern mountains; the mountains of the northeast of the eastern region, specially, in the basin of the Toa River; the Los Órganos Range and in Rangel and Soroa, at the El Rosario Range; the coastal strip between Puerto

Padre and Banes; the Sierra Maestra Mountain Range; the Zapata Swamp and the western part of the Guanahacabibes Peninsula. The fauna of the insular groups made up of small isles or keys has a high degree of endemism.

Some characteristic examples of the extreme endemism and the localization of many species or animal forms are:

1. Several species of hutias inhabit in a sole isle or key.

2. Many mollusks are only found in a specific mogote, even with differences of races, depending on the hillside they occupy.

3. Some lizards are found in a sole hill or in one range.

4. Three genera of the avifauna have dispersion areas that hardly exceed tens of square kilometers.

LAND FAUNA COMMUNITIES

In accordance with the ecological conditions, mainly with the presence of water and humidity and the vegetation types, the Cuban land fauna communities have been divided into hydrophylous, hygrophylous, xerophyle and anthropic faunas.

The fauna of the mangrove trees is considered the hydrophylous one. The mangrove trees are forest formations that are distributed in the major part of the Cuban coasts, which are one of the richest and most important ecosystems, not only for the land fauna, but also for the marine species of the shelf, as well as the species inhabiting lagoons, swamps and dams.

The hygrophylous fauna is associated to three types of forest vegetable formation:

1. Semideciduous and mesophytic forests, spread out in the southern part of the Guanahacabibes Peninsula at the El Rosario Range; in the eastern part of the Zapata Swamp; south of the Isle of Youth, in the medium-sized mountains of the Trinidad Range; in the north hillside of the Sierra Maestra Mountain Range; and in the major part of the Nipe-Sagua-Baracoa Mountains.

2. Mountainous forests located in the hills of the Trinidad Range and in the northeastern part of the Sierra Maestra Mountain Range, and in the most elevated parts of the mentioned Nipe-Sagua-Baracoa group.

3. Mountains with pine groves, linked to the Alturas de Pizarras in the region of the Los Órganos Range, the parts to the northwest and south of the Isle of Youth, and small areas of the Sierra Maestra Mountain Range and the Nipe-Sagua-Baracoa Mountains.

The xerophyle fauna is related to coastal forests and vegetable formations, ranging from rocky coasts to sandy beaches; it is also associated to *cuabales* and *charrascales* areas, in a close link with xerophytic and thorny vegetation over skeletal soils covering serpentinized ultrabasic rocks, from La Habana to Holguín the first ones, while the second ones are found in the hills of the eastern northeast.

The anthropic fauna is notably related with the presence of man and crops that dominate great part of the national territory, with the exception of the above mentioned regions.

The autochthonous wild fauna of Cuba was affected during a long time, because of the destruction and occupation of the natural ecosystems, the degradation of forests, the indiscriminate capture and hunting, and the introduction of exotic species, specially, carnivorous mammals. The following list, excluding the domestic animals, point out the naturalized species that were, intentional or accidentally, introduced in Cuba in historic times.

· Artiodactyls. Two peccary species belonging to the *Tayassu* genus were introduced in 1930 from Mexico towards western Cuba and the Sierra Cristal, and also dromedaries from the *Camelus* genus in 1832 from the Canary Islands towards the eastern provinces, which quickly died, infected by chigoes. Later in 1856, from South America towards La Habana, came the llama *(Lama glama)*, another species belonging to the Camelidae family. Pigs *(Sus scrofa)*, introduced as farmyard animals, have occasionally adopted wild life. Also in the last times, wild boars have been imported with hunting purposes. The white-tailed deer *(Odocoileus virginianus)* was introduced in 1850; it quickly adapted itself and spread out by the most wild places of the country, specially, in the mountainous zones and swamps.

· Perissodactyls. The horse *(Eqqus caballus)* was transported since the very beginning of the conquest by the Spaniards. Some of them, got away from ranches or survived from the shipwreck of a packet boat in the coasts of the Sabana-Camagüey Archipelago and settled true pairs in the fairly uninhabited lands of the Guajaba and Romano keys.

· Lagomorphs. They were introduced in 1880, from Canary Islands towards inland of the province of La Habana. Such is the case of the wild rabbit *(Oryctolagus cuniculus)*, but its successful adaptation and dissemination has not been possible.

· Rodents. The agouti *(Dasyprocta mexicana)* was introduced from Mexico in 1930 in the Los Órganos Range in Pinar del Río, and the Sierra Cristal in Holguín. It is known by the peasants as "jutía mocha" or "jutía de casquitos." In the same year, and from the same place, also moved to Cuba a subspecies *(Dasyprocta punctata yucatanica)*, and the paca *(Agouti paca nelsoni)*, extinguished now. Rats *(Rattus norvegicus, R. rattus alexandrinus* and *R. rattus rattus)* and mice *(Mus musculus)* were accidentally introduced since the arrival of the first conquers' ships.

· Carnivores. They were introduced in Cuba and have been a pest for the autochthonous fauna of the country. Among them, one must mention in the first place dogs *(Canis familiaris)* that have been a big predator of the endemic species, such as the "almiquí" *(Solenodon cubanus)* and the hutias; and in second place cats *(Felix catus)* that attack small reptiles, the "almiquí" and, probably noticeably decreased the population—maybe still existing—of the small insectivorous *Nesophontes*, with a look similar to a rat.

Among the carnivores, the most harmful animal from those introduced in Cuba—for its adaptability and rapacity—is mongoose *(Herpestes auropunctatus auropunctatus)*, badly denominated ferret in Cuba, brought by the Spaniards from Jamaica in 1886, in order to fight the rats and mice that destroyed the fields of the former Toledo sugar mill. These animals are a true whip for the small and large ophidians, the amphibious, the birds that nest in the ground and the poultry, and also their eggs or the eggs of any other species. After a century of its introduction, mongooses have been observed and captured in localities so distant and diverse, like the Los Órganos Range, Topes de Collantes in the mountainous group of Guamuhaya, plains and agricultural zones of the provinces of La Habana, Matanzas, Cienfuegos and Manzanillo in the Granma province, towards Guantánamo. This small wild beast is also very harmful for both animals and men, because it is a rabies virus carrier.

Furthermore, in the two last decades, controlled imports of antelopes, bisons, buffalos, primates, and other animals with cynegetic and experimental purposes have been carried out.

Wild Fauna. Cuban wild fauna has noteworthy specimens in each zoological group, from the ecological, zoogeographical, morphologic, etologic, aesthetic, historical and other viewpoints.

According to the systematic order, the "polimitas" stand out. They are pulmonate land mollusks, gasteropods that are one of the most spectacular cases of located endemism. This varied-colouring genus *(Polymita)* has six species, distributed in the northern coastal regions from Camagüey to Holguín, and in the northeast of Baracoa and the terraces of Maisí.

Among the insects, Cuban butterflies deserve special mention; among them the *Parides gundlachianus* stands out, with a remarkably reduced distribution in the high basin of the Cuyaguateje River in the Los Órganos Range, and in the Sierra Maestra, and the *Anetia cubana*, spread out in the eastern mountainous groups.

Cuban scorpioids, among the group of the arachnids, have seventeen endemic species. Among them, *Heteronebo bermudezi* is one of the most singular; it has a wide distribution in the country, from the Guanahacabibes Peninsula, to the south of Cienfuegos.

Scorpioids in Cuba are not a danger because of their bites (Fide Armas, 1985). Only the bite of the black scorpion *(Centuroides gracilis)* and of the red scorpion *(Rhopalurus* junceus*)* may be uncommonly fatal. Bücher, from the Butantan Institute (Brasil), includes the sinanthropic species—*Centuroides gracilis*—as highly harmful, well distributed in Cuba and in the Caribbean region.

Species belonging to the three groups of anurous amphibious live in Cuba: the land, the arboreal and the petricolous amphibious. Among the first ones, Cuban small frog *(Sminthillus limbatus)* stands out, one of the smallest of the world that is spread out in the provinces of Pinar del Río, La Habana, Cienfuegos and Guantánamo, and also giant toad *(Peltophryne fustiger)* that is the maximum expression in size of the Antillean family, because it attains between 16 cm and 18 cm long.

Sauria suborder including lizards, is well represented in Cuba; in first place, because of the Gekkonidae family, to which the geckos belong; the Cuban gecko *(Tarentola americana)* is the biggest, living in palm-leaves roofs and in the inner of caverns.

The known *Chamaeleolis* genus, from the Iguanidae family, is the most outstanding. Its species may reach up to 32 cm long. The *Chamaeleolis barbatus* is one of the two species of the anoles lizard known in Cuba as "chipojo bobo" or "chipojo blanco,"[13] and it always lives far off from inhabited places.

Anolis is another interesting genus, which includes the most interesting members of this family. With regard to number, it is the most numerous and varied regarding their shapes, colours and habits. One of the biggest is the "chipojo verde"[14] *(Anolis equestris).*

The Iguana *(Cyclura nubila)* is the largest lizard of Cuba; its size, although averaging from 100 cm to 150 cm, may attain up to 185 cm. It is strictly a coastal species, even though there are populations in the Los Órganos Range.

Among the lizards, the *Leiocephalus* genus comprises five species. The biggest of the genus is the lion lizard *(Leiocephalus carinatus),* whose scientific name alludes to have always the thick tail raised and rolled. From the same genus, one must mention the ground lizard *(L. macropus),* inhabitant of earthy soils.

Among the genera of Cuban ophidians there are not poisonous species. The Cuban boa *(Epicrates angulifer),* as its name indicates, belongs to the family of the boas, and may attain more than 4 m long. Among the serpents there are the snakes, represented in Cuba by five genera; two of them are the water snake *(Natrix sipedon)* and the *Alsofis angulifer* that may reach 1.6 m long.

Turtles *(Chelonia* genus) are represented by diverse species ranging from the sea giants like the leatherback

---

13. It means "stupid" or "white anoles lizard." *Trans.*
14. It means "green anoles lizard." *Trans.*

sea turtle that reaches a weight up to 750 kg, the hawksbill sea turtle *(Eretmochelys imbricata)* and the loggerhead sea turtle *(Caretta caretta)* that attains 266 kg and 1.50 m long, to the ground turtle *(Pseudodemys decussata)*, the only representative of land turtles in Cuba.

From the Loricata order, there is a genus with two species, the denominated alligator *(Crocodylus acutus)*, known in the whole Caribbean basin and in the Gulf of Mexico, which may measure up to 4 m long, and the Cuban crocodile *(Crocodylus rhombifer)*, an endemic species of Cuba, very similar to the alligator, but with a shorter and less sharp-pointed snout, and a more elevated head. The female is fierce, above all when taking care of its nest.

Cuban avifauna is very abundant and varied since the recent geological past, and has very noteworthy species owing to their sizes. At present, this is the vertebrate class with a major number of endemic taxa: twenty-four subspecies and twenty-two species, included all in twenty-six families and thirteen orders. Among the migrant hunting birds belonging to the Anatidae family the following species are known: one swan, three geese, four whistling ducks and ninteen ducks. Also sea birds are abundant: one frigatebird species, one pelican and ten species of gulls and terns.

The tiny bee hummingbird *(Mellisuga helenae)*, having no more than 63 mm long; and the ivory-billed woodpecker *(Campephilus principalis bairdii)*, the largest of the living woodpecker species, which is considered remarkably threatened with extinction and lives in the rainforests of the basin of the Toa River, stand out. These woodpeckers probably fly over the mountains of the Sierra Maestra Mountain Range, where they have been observed and listened by several people, according to the recent reference of the ornithologist Arturo Kirkconnell.

Cuban parrot *(Amazona leucocephala)* is one of the most picturesque birds of Cuba. It was threatened with extinction times ago, but its populations have been recovered. At present, it is found in the Isle of Youth, the Zapata Swamp, and the Trinidad Range.

Cuban trogon *(Priotelus temnurus)* is the national bird of Cuba, which displays the colors of the national flag in its feathers. It inhabits in the arboreous woodlands, far off from villages.

Zapata wren *(Ferminia cerverai)* is, possibly, the bird having the most restricted habitat in the world; it only lives in the north of Santo Tomás, a location in the Zapata Swamp, where the Zapata rail *(Cyanolimnas cerverai)* also inhabits under the same conditions.

Many migrant birds cross Cuban skies; some of them nest in the country in order to continue their travel later.

Among the endemic species and subspecies threatened with extinction are considered the following: sandhill crane *(Grus canadensis nesiotes)*, Cuban hook-billed kite *(Chondohierax wilsonii)*, Zapata rail *(Cyanolimnas cerverai)*, Zapata wren *(Ferminia* cerverai), Zapata sparrow *(Torreornis inexpectata)*, ivory-billed woodpecker *(Campephilus principalis bairdii)*, and West Indian woodpecker *(Melanerpes superciliaris)*, among others.

The country has a poor mammal fauna, although the order of the chiropters is notably represented, with 27 species that inhabit in caverns and Cuban woodlands, occupying a very important place in the pollination and the control of agricultural pests.

The butterfly bat *(Natalus lepidus)* is the smaller of the world, with a span from 186 mm to 213 mm from one tip to tip of its wings, and a weight of 2 g - 3 g. It is possible to find the fishing bat *(Noctilio leporinus)* in the north coast of the central region, although it is not an endemic species.

The "almiquí" *(Solenodon cubanus)* is an archaic representative from the Pleistocene fauna; it is an insectivorous that was considered extinct, but today it inhabits in caves and tunnels that it digs among the roots of the trees or underneath the rocks, and is singularly a giant within its family. Nowadays, it has been captured in the dense mountains of the northeast of Holguín and the north of Guantánamo. In the Quisqueya Island (Hispaniola) there is another species of "almiquí" *(Solenodon paradoxus)*.

Among the rodents, the Capromidae family (hutias) is the most typical of Cuba,. There are eight living species, belonging to five subgenera; the "jutía conga" *(Capromys pilorides)* is the most noteworthy because of its great size and appreciated meat.

The hutias have a large adaptability, they are distributed in all the natural regions of the Cuban Archipelago, from the most isolated cays, to the most dense mountains. They are hunted down both by the men and wild dogs, though they are protected by the law. The "jutía enana"[15] *(Capromys nanus)*, the "jutía garridoi" *(Capromys garridoi)*, and the "jutiíta de la tierra"[16] *(Capromys sanfelipensis)* are, by diverse causes, threatened with extinction.

When Columbus navigated through Cuban waters and believed to see a human shape having a fish tail nursing its breed, and leaned on a rock, he thought that he had seen proven the ancient Greek legend about mermaids. He, in fact, had seen the manatee or sea cow *(Trichechus manatus manatus)*, one of the most singular representatives of the vertebrate fauna of Cuba, belonging to the group of the sirenians. The members of this order are exclusively aquatic and phytophagous; they inhabit rivers, tidelands, lagoons, and even coastal shallow waters. Two decades ago, they were considered at the border of extinction, but strict regulations have allowed the recovering of the populations.

The Cetacea order is represented in Cuba by the Delphinidae family. The dolphin *(Tursiops truncatus)* is

15. It means "dwarf hutia." *Trans.*
16. It means "ground small hutia." *Trans.*

the most common species in the coastal waters, to which it comes close, and even goes in the bays. It is possible to domesticate this species, and that is why it is looked for and captured for the aquariums. In this respect, according to international regulations, Cuba has exported specimens to diverse aquariums of the world.

Among the fishes, the Cuban alligator gar *(Atractosteus tristoechus)* stands out. It lives in fresh water, because it is a true historic-geological relic that inhabit rivers and swamps of the south coast of Cuba and the Isle of Youth.

Because of its insular feature, Cuba has a great variety of sea fishes, and among them are the Nassau grouper *(Epinephelus striatus)*, the cero *(Scomberomorus regalis)*, the yellowtail snapper *(Ocyurus chrysurus)* and many others. Moreover, among the sharks there are more than thirty-five species. The white shark *(Carcharodon carcharias)*, a species that do not inhabit these seas, and the huge whale shark *(Rhyneodon typus)* that weighed more than 4 tons have been captured in Cuban waters.

SOILS

Coinciding with that which has been stated in the *Nuevo Atlas Nacional de Cuba* [New National Atlas of Cuba], the study of the soils of the Cuban Archipelago have had a great development starting at the very beginning of the century. Pedologic studies have been carried out with many-sided purposes that at present allow to have a good information about the features of the soils with regard to genesis; physical, chemical, and agroproductive conditions; and their relationships with the relief, weathering, and other factors. These studies have made feasible soil classification in several ways.

The research started at the threshold of the 20th century aimed to know the agroproductive features of the soils in order to offer directions to the consortiums that wanted to invest in the country about the places with better options. As a result of the course of action, the most advantageous places were occupied by sugar cane, and its agriculture was developed very fast. The interests in the research stood after that, but encouraged this time by the needs of the banks to know which were the most productive lands in order to grant credits.

Bennett and Allison's works in 1928 allow to make the first classification of Cuban soils, which was used until 1975, according to what has denoted in the *Nuevo Atlas Nacional de Cuba* [New National Atlas of Cuba]. Later, it was replaced by a second genetic classification of Cuban soils.

From 1979, thanks to the sustained work of both scientific and educational institutions created by the Revolutionary Government, the establishment of a qualitatively superior version of the mentioned classification was possible. It sets up divisions in its upper unities, such as groupings, types and subtypes.

Groupings comprise the types of soils having in common the main process of the soil formation and its degree of evolution, according to the existing interrelation among the factors of their formation.

Types are the basic units of the classification; they include those soils that evolved in similar formation conditions, and have a common main formation process, aside from other genetic processes, such as the migration and transformation of substances, and the character of the hydric regime.

Subtypes reflect the qualitative forms of the main and secondary formation processes of the soils, within the limits of the type in the diverse conditions of the environ; they are intermediate stages among the types.

The classification of these units has ten groupings and twenty-nine types, which, together with what noted above regarding the geological features of the territory, give an idea about the complexity of the layer that covers the subsoil.

The chief features of the groupings are the following:

· Ferritic soils. These soils show an intense alteration of primary minerals, and a high content (over 30%) of iron sesquioxide; they have variable amounts of concretions of that mineral, forming armors sometimes. These soils evolve from basic and ultrabasic rocks. They may have secondary minerals like hematite, goethite and kaolinite.

· Ferrallitic soils. The ferrallitization process in these soils is characterizad by an intense alteration of the primary minerals, the elimination of the major part of both alkaline and alkaline-earth bases and a part of silica with the formation of clayey minerals—iron and aluminum oxides- and hydroxides-type—like the montmorrillonite. These evolve from hard carbonated rocks and shales, and in a lesser degree they may make up from igneous rocks. Due to the high presence of carbonated rocks in the geological composition of Cuba, these soils are vastly expanded. They are divided into the following types: red ferrallitic, leached red ferrallitic, yellowish ferrallitic, yellow quarzitic ferrallitic, and leached yellow quarzitic ferrallitic soils.

· Fersiallitic soils. These soils evolve from eluviums of silica sandstones, some hard limestone, serpentines and redeposit materials. Secondary clayey minerals and iron oxides are formed during the siallitization process that carries out together with the ferrugination one. They include four types: red brownish ferromagnesian fersiallitic, brown reddish fersiallitic, yellowish fersiallitic, and red fersiallitic soils.

· Brown soils. These soils are characterized by a relatively young siallitic evolution. The differentiation among the different types is based on the siallitization process that is developed in them (accumulation of free irons, less than in the fersiallitic soils), either in a calcium carbonate-rich environ, or because of the evolution from the eluviums of igneous rocks, and in a lesser degree, metamorphic ones.

- Calcimorphic humic soils. The accumulation process of humus predominate in these soils, favored by the presence of high content of active calcium and montmorillonite-type clays. They evolve from eluviums of calcareous rocks, with a high percentage of clayey material inherited from them. The content of organic material is about 3% to 9%, and that is why they are generally dark. They comprise the types: red rendzina, black rendzina, and carbonate humic soils.

- Vertisol. They are soils having siallitic composition, where in many cases, the magnesium oxide content is higher than the calcium one, among the components of the soil mass and clay. The latter is characterized by mainly having, a high content of montmorillonite. They evolve, as a whole, from clayey and loam-clayey sediments, both in inner plains and in those having marine origin. Because of their composition and during the alternate stages of humidity and drought, they show contraction and dilatation phenomena bringing about fractures and a microrelief sort. They are divided into: dark plastic gleyed, dark plastic gleyed-like[17] and dark plastic non-gleyed soils.

- Hydromorphic soils. These soils abound in low plains, where the oscillations of the layer of underground waters, having sometimes a clayey layer in the bottom, predominate. This excess of moisture conditions the gleyzation process, with the formation of gleyed horizons gone with the accumulation of row material in the upper part of the profile. They may be salinized, depending on the degree of mineralization of the underground layer. They evolve from clayey sediments, very rich in minerals, and from alluviums and deluviums of shale. They are divided into: humic gley, ferrallitic gley, quarzitic yellowish gley, marl humic and swampy soils types.

- Hallomorphic soils. They have an accumulation of soluble salts higher than 1 % in all their profile, or in anyone of their horizons. They may also have a certain sodium content, but with a lesser accumulation of soluble salts in the soil mass. Spots and whitish crusts, named *calvas salinas*[18] may be observed when salts cumulate in the surface. They include the types: solonchak, mangrove solonchak, and solonetzic soils.

- Alluvial soils. Their distinctive feature consists of a non-defined developmental process. Not only the existing soils in the frequently flooded fluvial valleys are included in them, but also those which are currently not subject to floods, but still have no differential features in the profile, because of the development of new edapho-genetic processes. Absence of well-differentiated genetic horizons is typical in these soils. The physical and chemical properties of these soils depend on the original material, which may be highly varied. The sole type is the alluvial soil.

- Few evolved soils. They are soils that have an incipient chemical and biological alteration; however, the fragmentation and redistribution of the mechanic composition of the material are greater. The limited alteration of the materials is due to the elimination of the thin part of the soil because of the strong erosion or the fortuitous contributions of minerals. They include the types: quarzitic sandy, calcareous sandy and skeletal soils.

17. It means they have had a softer gleyzation process. *Trans.*

18. This circular spots are formed generally over saline soils where do not grow any vegetation. Those words mean "saline bald patch." *Trans.*

The relationship established between the relief and the combination of soils is greatly interesting. In the Bennet and Allison's work is pointed out that in the plains having advanced hydromorphic processes also show, plastogenesis, laterization, organic accumulation and salinization processes. Meanwhile, in the plains having predominant denuded or scrubbing processes under a climate like the Cuban one (common and tropical climate with alternate humidity), combinations of automorphic soils with predominant siallitization and fersiallitization processes carry out. The ferrallitization process develops in the most ancient plains.

Denuding processes are dominant in the highlands, and correspond with the combination of the siallitization and fersiallitizacion processes, without the ferrallitization one. In the mountains, on the contrary, with a rainy tropical climate, there are ferritic and ferrallitic soils, made up over ancient weathering crusts. Also combinations of fersiallitic and brown soils are carried out in these places.

The agricultural productivity gives a general view about the quality of soils; it is based on the limiting factors of the different types of soils. Among them, one must mention: negative physic and chemical features, hydro- morphism, salinity, soil concretion in depth, erosion, slope, and rocky character, which directly affect the efficiency of the chief crops. It allows to give a view of which are the most productive edaphologic zones, those having an intermediate and lower value, and to set up relationships with aspects of the local and national economy linked with agriculture. In this way it has been stated that the provinces with more productive soils are La Habana and Ciego de Ávila; those having less productive ones are Granma, Pinar del Río, Holguín, Santiago de Cuba and Guantánamo; and Camagüey, Las Tunas, Sancti Spíritus, Cienfuegos, Matanzas and Villa Clara occupy an intermediate position. This evaluation includes the whole surface area of the territories. Therefore in Matanzas, for instance, the Zapata Swamp is being considered; in Guantánamo, the arid strip in the southern coast; and in other provinces, the mountainous regions.

HYDRIC RESOURCES

The narrow and elongated shape of the island of Cuba (within the Cuban Archipelago, it is the territory where the fluvial currents concentrate, except for the Isle of Youth, because in the smaller islands and keys there are not defined riverbeds of rivers or streams, permanent or intermittent ones) as well as the position of the hills, in general, longitudinal to the axis of the archipelago; and their summits that also as a whole, behave as a water-parting or a dividing line of the waters, determine the fluvial currents to have a short flow: From the center towards the north coast and from the center towards the south coast.

Furthermore, the volume is small, except in rainy seasons and during the tropical cyclones. In the first case, many riverbeds that remain dries during the rest of the year, turn into activity. In the second case, those meteors affect the hydric regime and then, the spates may be truly fabulous, at such extent that many rivers and streams move their riverbeds, and even change the direction of the rivers' current before the impossibility to go through natural barriers. This was seen, in past times, in the Cuyaguateje riverbed. There, during the Alberto cyclone (in the 1960s), the Clara and the Resolladero caves, both of which allow the Cuyaguateje River to run across the Sumidero Range, were completely flooded, and it brought about the inversion of the current. This fact was officially recorded in the gages station of Sumidero.

From west to east, the most important rivers in the province of Pinar del Río are: the Cuyaguateje—the biggest of the west—that begins to flow in the Alturas de Pizarras del Sur and goes across the Los Órganos Range emptying into the Cortés Inlet in the south coast of the province, with a basin of 737 sq km and a main basin having 99 km long; Mantua, one of the few that approximately runs in the direction of the Island axis and empties into the Guadiana Inlet, after a flow of 66 km in a basin of 293 sq km; La Palma, having 76 km long and 878 sq km of basin. Furthermore, there are rivers that after beginning to flow in the El Rosario Range, empty into the southern coast of the province, like the San Diego, whose basin divides the Guaniguanico Mountain Range into two mountainous groups mentioned yet, with a basin of 442 sq km and a length of 88 km; the Río Hondo, with a basin of 578 sq km and a basin spanning 106 km long, and the Bacunagua, having a basin of 153 sq km and 40 km of flow.

In the provinces of La Habana and Ciudad de La Habana stand out the following rivers: Mayabeque, with 652 sq km of basin and 53 km of flow; Jaruco, having a basin of 31 km and 160 sq km of surface in its basin; and Almendares, that goes across Ciudad de La Habana in its 50 km long and 402 sq km of surface.

In the province of Matanzas stand out the rivers: Hatiguanico, draining the Zapata swamp and flowing into the La Broa Inlet; Hanábana that separates the provinces of Matanzas and Cienfuegos, with a basin of 1050 sq km and a length of 111 km; and La Palma that empties into the northern coast of the province. The Sagua la Grande and Sagua la Chica Rivers, with hydrographic basins of 2188 and 1055 sq km, and lengths of 144 and 91 km respectively, as well as the Agabama River with 1713 sq km of catchment area and 118 km of flow—shared with the province of Sancti Spíritus—are the most remarkable rivers in the Villa Clara province. The Hanabanilla River, meanwhile, located in the mountainous local territory (the Trinidad Range), is important because it has been retained in an homonymous dam, which was one of the first finished after 1959; it is a wonderful tourist and sport place

for fishing the "trout,"[19] and it has the world record in a captured specimen.

The Cienfuegos province is proud of rivers like the Damují, having 62 km in length and 1167 sq km of impounding area; the Arimao with 979 sq km of basin and 86 km of flow; the Caonao, the Salado and others.

Sancti Spíritus is a privileged province in its hydrographic features; in its territory there are rivers like the Zaza that takes in the biggest dam of the country, and has a basin of 2394 sq km and a length of 145 km. Also the already mentioned Agabama flows through the lands of this province, and likewise, the Jatibonico del Norte and Jatibonico del Sur Rivers stand out, with 835 and 252 sq km of basins, and 117 and 70 km long, respectively.

In Ciego de Ávila stand out the Chambas River, retained in the homonymous dam, and the Caonao River with 1235 sq km of basin and 132 km long, among others of less significance.

Among the main hydric resources of Camagüey there are the Saramaguacán, with 1241 sq km of catchment area and 91 km of flow; Máximo, shaping in a section of its riverbed the beautiful natural pools known as *cangilones*, being 60 km long and with a 653 sq km basin; Las Yeguas, in whose banks General Serafin Sánchez died in combat, with 562 sq km of basin and 78 km of flow; and Najasa, San Pedro and Sevilla, spanning basins of 895, 893 and 743 sq km, and 104, 116 and 92 km long in their riverbeds, respectively.

The territory of La Tunas includes the Jobabo River, former provincial boundary, with a length of 77 km and a basin of 682 sq km. This province has numerous not important watercourses. It may also be mentioned the Manatí River, with 70 sq km of catchment area and only 28 km of flow.

The Cauto River—the largest of Cuba—has the peculiarity for running along the Cauto-Guacanayabo plain—

19. Although in Cuba this fish is known with this name due to its similarities with the real trout, in fact, the authors refer to the black bass, *Micropterus salmoides. Trans.*

one of the few that is oriented from east to west. Through its flow of 343 km long, it goes along the provinces of Granma, Santiago de Cuba and Holguín. Hence, its basin, the biggest of the archipelago, occupies a surface of 8964 sq km.

In the province of Granma also stand out the rivers: Salado, with a basin of 2285 sq km and a length of 120 km; Bayamo, with a flow of 88 km and a basin of 747 sq km; Buey, being 90 km long and an impounding area of 531 sq km; and Gua, with 906 sq km of basin and a length of 76 km.

Contramaestre and Guaninicum Rivers are the most important fluvial currents of Santiago de Cuba, having 958 and 640 sq km of hydrographic basin and 92 and 56 km long, respectively. The first one is retained in the Carlos Manuel de Céspedes dam.

Holguín is a territory of numerous fluvial currents, like the Sagua de Tánamo, Mayarí and Cacoyugüín Rivers that have, respectively, 1174, 1231 and 240 sq km of basins, and 89, 107 and 46 km long. The last one is important because it is partly used for water supply to the aqueduct of Holguín city.

Guantánamo has one of the mightiest rivers, the Toa, with a basin of 1053 sq km among mountains, and a flow of 118 km, having an elevated rain regime. In this province also stands out the Guantánamo River, spanning 1221 sq km of basin and 98 km long, and the Yateras River, 667 sq km and 76 km long.

The Isle of Youth has, among its most important fluvial currents, the Las Casas River, through which most of the naval traffic is carried out, with 65 sq km of basin and a lenght of 17 km, and the Medio-Las Nuevas River, being 31 km long and with a basin of 226 sq km.

The waterfalls or big cascades are not abundant in Cuba. The existing ones are associated with young rivers in mountainous zones, like the waterfalls of the Caburní and Vega Grande Rivers in the Trinidad Range, and that of Soroa in the Manantiales River in the El Rosario Range. In the mountains of the Sagua-Baracoa group that have a great rainfall, waterfalls and medium-sized and small cascades are found. The highest waterfalls of the eastern region are in the basin of the Toa River.

UNDERGROUND WATERS

Underground waters, whereby are hydric resources for the national economy, are, most of all, in fissured carbonated rocks, which are distributed for the whole country, both in coastal and inner plains, and in the hills and mountains. The chief karstic aquifers in calcareous rocks are in the western regions of the country, and they supply the population with high-grade waters, crops and industries. The displays of mining-medicinal, thermal and also drinking waters, broadly distributed in the whole Island, are linked to the underground karstic aquifers. As a general rule, they are bicarbonated-calcic-type waters, with a mineral concentration between 0.4 mg/l and 0.7 mg/l, and volumes fluctuating between 1.5 l/s and 2 l/s (fide Fagundo et al., 1996).

NATURAL LAKES

In the Cuban territory there are not large lakes as it is the case in other countries of the geographical area. Therefore, as a whole, the natural dams are denominated lagoons.

Between the Cortés and the Guadiana Inlets in Pinar del Río, there are more than one hundred of these lagoons, and that is why this is the most representative lacustrine region of the country. The biggest lagoon of this zone is Pesquero, with 12 sq km of water surface and 4 m deep. The lagoon of the San Juan Valley is another important lagoon in the region, located in the threshold of the Guanahacabibes Peninsula; it has 25 m deep and 110 m width.

The Ariguanabo Lagoon (partly disappeared now), in the La Habana province, was the biggest natural lake before 1961, epoch when an extensive drought affected it. The lagoon spanned 8 km in length from east to west, and 2.5 km in its widest part. Some small lagoons are found in a lineal succession in the San José zone.

In Matanzas, the El Tesoro Lagoon in the Zapata Swamp is one of the biggest lakes of the territory; it has an approximately circular shape, a length measured from north to south about 4 km, and a maximum width from east to west of 1200 m. The Facundo Lagoon, with 100 m width and 47 m deep also stands out.

The La Leche[20] Lagoon is in the province of Ciego de Ávila; it is, in fact, a coastal pool, because it has direct contact with the sea. This aquatory owes its name to the marly character of the bottom, since when it is stirred up adopts a milky shade. The Redonda Lagoon, very close to the preceding one, has the same features.

ARTIFICIAL LAKES (DAMS)

The project and the construction of dams were, after the Revolutionary victory in 1959, a main measure for the agriculture development, aside from preventing the floods caused by the frequent tropical cyclones and extreme rainfall events. The floods provoked by the torrential rains of the Flora cyclone in 1963, speed up the necessity of organizing the denominated "hydraulic will." It means a process of assimilation of knowledge, techniques and financing to build dams, irrigation channels and other works that impel and warrant the economic plans. All of that caused

20. It means "milk." *Trans.*

that the pond water volume was multiplied by 145. Thus, hydraulic works were constructed in order to dam seven billions cubic meters.

Before 1959, there were only thirty thousand cubic meters of pond water to supply to cities like Santa Clara, Camagüey, Holguín and Santiago de Cuba, because the Hanabanilla dam that was one of the biggest, was not finished until 1962.

Nowadays, the main hydraulic facilities are: Pedroso-Mampostón-San Juan, between La Habana and Matanzas; Alacranes in Villa Clara; Zaza in Sancti Spíritus, and Carlos Manuel de Céspedes in Granma-Santiago.

The artificial lakes have also been useful to aquiculture, as a way to warrant animal protein in the diet of the population, and the breeding of fishes for promoting tourism, and for practicing water sports.

SWAMPS

The swamps cover about 8.26% of the surface of the island of Cuba and the Isle of Youth. They are close to the coast, like the Zapata Swamp—the largest of the country—, that of Morón in the north of Ciego de Ávila, and others. In non-coastal territory there is the Lanier Swamp in the Isle of Youth. Others, like the Buey and the Birama Swamps, are associated with fluvial mouths.

These swampy zones have, as a whole, a rich biodiversity, which determines their preservation and protection before the possibilities of an irrational or sudden use. Although the possibility of using turf—many times present in the swamps—as an energetic resource is feasible from the technical viewpoint, it would harm the environment by highly altering the existing hydric regime in these zones.

CHAPTER IV

CUBAN COASTS AND SEAS

The island of Cuba displays a sinuous and irregular littoral spanning 5745 km long. The insular territory is tilted—an accepted fact, as a whole—, and it is usually more elevated in the north coast and depressed in the south one. This condition does not keep in the rest of the smaller isles and keys that may have elevated or emerging coasts, and depressed or submersing coasts without distinction.

The marine transgression movements, it means, the invasion of the lands by sea waters, and those of regression or withdrawal of the sea from the lands are denominated *eustatic* movements. Throughout its geologic history, Cuba has had its share of these types of movements along with tectonic ones. But, mainly during the Quaternary, in the Earth there were periods when the temperatures were extremely low, such at that extent that brought about a general cooling in the globe and a movement of the polar caps towards lower latitudes, and of the snow line of the mountains towards lower altitudes.

The stages during which the ices moved forward comprising tens of thousands of years are named *glacial periods* or *glaciations*. These periods were intercalated with others named *interglacial periods*, in which the ices came back towards the polar zones and the high places. The glacial and interglacial periods are named according to the place where they have been studied for the first time, or thoroughly. In America the first ones are named *Nebraska, Kansas, Illinois* and *Wisconsin,* and the second ones, *Afton, Yamouth, Sangamon* and *Flandriana.*

Sea waters froze and caused a regression during the glaciations, which exposed lands that were submerged until that moment, to the action of weathering agents. On the contrary, during the interglacial periods, the waters rose again their level, although they did not reach the level of the previous stage. The recorded fluctuations have attained values up to 120 m - 150 m.

The oscillation movements of sea level owing to the glaciations are denominated *glacial-eustatic* movements, and they have led to the mentioned emerging and submerging coasts, as well as to the establishment of erosion levels on different heights (because sea level is the "0"—zero—erosion plane, which the subaerial levels tend to). They have brought about, for inarstance, the excavation of caves and passages' systems having big caverns on different heights in the same mountainous massifs, and the formation of marine terraces, also on several altitudes.

The neutral and compound coasts are other types of coasts described for Cuba. The neutral coasts do not owe their presence to emerging or submerging processes, but to other events, such as the formation of deltas, the coral growing, and the occurrence of tectonic movements. The delta coasts are as a whole low coasts, because they are shaped from the growing of bars and small islands in the mouth of rivers that drag all-kind materials along their riverbeds and deposit them in their mouths. There are some examples of this type of coasts in the Cuban Archipelago, like those of the Guacanayabo Gulf in the western part of the eastern province of Granma, where the Cauto River—the largest of the country—flows into; or in the north part of Villa Clara province, in Isabela de Sagua, where the Sagua la Grande River, among others, has cumulated the dragged sediments.

Fault coasts may be found in the south of Granma and Santiago de Cuba provinces, in the eastern region, caused by the large tectonic movement generator of the Oriente fault and the known Bartlett Trench. These are as a whole elevated-type coasts, and tectonism evidences may be observed in them, more or less masked by the sea abrasive action.

The most common coasts in Cuba are those shaped by coral growing, and they are distributed throughout the archipelago.

In Cuba there are many compound coasts, because the simultaneous action of diverse-type processes is a common fact in nature.

COASTAL SECTORS

Several geographers have described the coasts of the Island of Cuba and divided them in sectors having distinctive features (Núñez Jiménez, 1965). It have been pointed out the following sectors from west to east:

· San Antonio Cape-La Gobernadora Point, a sector in which a low and marshy coast is found often covered with mangroves, where many rivers of the north slope of the island flow into forming deltas, like the Mani Mani, San Juan, Santa Lucía, and others. The Los Colorados Archipelago is located north of this sector, and farther to the north there is a coral reef barrier with a significant extension.

· La Gobernadora Point-Hicacos Peninsula, a complex coastal sector. Between the La Gobernadora Point and the La Habana Bay there is a low submerging coast, where the sea has invaded the lower valleys of the rivers forming bottle bays with narrow entrances and broad insides, like Bahía Honda, Cabañas, Mariel and La Habana Bays. The section between Bahía Honda and Cabañas includes a marshy zone partly covered by mangroves; between the last one and the La Habana Bay there is above all a rocky coast with tide rock shelters and caves having marine origin. It proves that a submerging process happened, as the bottle bays indicate, and another of emerging, as the abrasive-karstic forms do.

Between the La Habana and Matanzas Bays there are low-cliff shores towards the Guanabo zone, and in the rest of the section, high-cliff ones, like those of Rincón de Guanabo, Boca de Jaruco and Jíjira Point.

Many rivers flow into among these bays, which havemade canyons in the calcareous hills that skirt the coastal zone, like the Cojímar—forming a deep incised meander—, Bacuranao, Tarará, Guanabo, Jaruco and Puerto Escondido Rivers. Some of these streams have deposited sandy bars in their mouths, sometimes inside the estuary as is the case in the mouth of the Jaruco River.

In the low levels of the marine terraces, present in the whole section, are found residual witnesses of the backwards movement of the cliffs, like the Del Fraile and De la Monja walls of rock, in the zone of Jibacoa.

Some of the most beautiful and crowded beaches of the archipelago are found in this sector, like the Playas del Este beaches in the province of Ciudad de La Habana, and the famous Varadero Beach in the Hicacos Peninsula, Matanzas. The Matanzas Bay, unlike the generality of this sector, is not a bottle bay, because it is opened along a fault or a zone of faults and the extreme of a large folded and faulted structure.

· Hicacos Peninsula - Nuevitas Bay, a sector in which is expanded a long portion of low and marshy coast as a whole, where one may observe deltas like those of the Sagua la Grande and Sagua la Chica Rivers. The marshy zone attains 30 km wide in the Morón region in Ciego de Ávila, surrounding the "isle" of Turiguanó to the south, and is spread out towards the province of Camagüey. In the first one, a saline dome of singular importance surrounds part of the Judas de Cunagua Hill.

In Caguanes, Sancti Spíritus, there is a well-developed littoral swamp, which surrounds the homonymous natural reserve, turning it virtually into a key.

The Sabana-Camagüey Archipelago is spread out offshore, facing this coastal section, at a distance between 10 km and 20 km, which we will be mentioned later. Between the mentioned archipelago and the coast, a whole of "bays" is formed: The Cárdenas, Santa Clara, Buena Vista, Los Perros Bays, and others. These represent an inner sea having a great fauna wealth.

A coral reef barrier is spread out north of the group of keys that owing to scope, it has cataloged as the second in the world, after the Great Australian Barrier.

The Nuevitas Bay is a remarkable example of a well-protected bottle bay; its entrance and exit channel is 14 km long. It is a well-known bay because of its depth and the strong current that is established during the tidal changes.

· Nuevitas Bay - Maisí Point, a sector that has many bottle bays caused by the marine transgression that flooded the low valleys of the rivers, as did in Banes, Gibara, Nipe—one of the biggest of Cuba—, Cabonico, and others. As a whole, this sector has low coasts, even though in its inner sectors they are crowned by low-altitude hills.

· Maisí Point - Cruz Cape, a coastal sector that includes the south coast of the provinces of Guantánamo, Santiago de Cuba and Granma, in this order from east to west. It has an eminently fault littoral, in which the largest unevenness of the territory—about 9000 m —is found; it is observed between the Oriente Trough (7243 m deep) and the Turquino Pike (1974 m high). The most developed terrace marine levels of the country are found both in the Maisí Point and in the Cruz Cape; they were carved in Neogene and Quaternary rocks during the glacial-eustatic oscillations. The stepped terraces have numerous karstic forms: Tide rock shelters, dolines and caves having phreatic origin drained by the elevation of the mentioned terraces.

The rest of this coastal sector is shaped by cliff shores and headlands made up of igneous rocks, which have been deposited as pebbles, large in diameter and very unstable in composition. Some of this thousands or millions of large rocks that have formed *in situ* because of the action of marine waters over the granitoids and other rocks with a characteristic exfoliation are found in some sectors of the narrow coastal plain or directly in the coastline.

The whole currents flowing into this sector came from the hills, because of its nearness to the Sierra Maestra Mountain Range, and almost all of them deposit bars of pebbles and sand in their mouths that even may close them.

· Cruz Cape - Trinidad, a sector where the deposition processes predominate over those of erosion. The most extensive littoral swamp of the archipelago is included here, begining in Birama in the Guacanayabo Gulf, Granma. It is spread out by the south of Camagüey, Ciego de Ávila, towards Sancti Spíritus, in the delta of the Agabama or Manatí River that takes land from the sea.

In this sector there are not bays, only the Guacanayabo and Ana María Gulfs. The Jardines de la Reina Archipelago is south of the coastline.

· Trinidad - Cochinos Bay (Bay of Pigs), a sector in which the erosion processes predominate. It has a cliff high shore caused by the presence of a fault that lifted up the littoral and brought about the sinking of the submarine shelf. This zone is included in the provinces of Sancti Spíritus, Cienfuegos and Matanzas. The excellent bottle bay of Cienfuegos is found in this section, where some rivers flow into forming deltas. The Zapata eastern swamp is part of this region; it is a littoral swamp delimited by a belt of calcareous rocks that impedes its direct contact with the sea, and the largest wetland of the country.

· Cochinos Bay - Francés Cape, a sector that has a low and marshy littoral; it includes the rest of the Zapata swamp in its western part. There is the Cochinos Bay that is an open bay along a zone of faults and depressed structures.

The Hatiguanico River, forming a broad and marshy delta, flows into the La Broa Inlet, which is found between the territory of Matanzas and La Habana.

Between the Cochinos Bay and Francés Cape there is none important bay or shelter; therefore, there are neither important towns. The Los Canarreos Archipelago is found south of this sector.

· Francés Cape - San Antonio Cape, a sector that is found entirely in the province of Pinar del Río; it corresponds with the southern coast of the Guanahacabibes Peninsula, where in contrast with other regions of the country, there is a cliff shore in the south. Calcareous headlands are found here, separated by excellent beaches that are named Los Balcones, and where sea caverns, tide rock shelters and numerous karstic forms may be observed. The Corrientes Inlet is between the Corrientes Cape and the San Antonio Cape, in whose eastern part the María la Gorda Beach is located, having excellent sand and wonderful marine bottoms.

ARCHIPELAGOS OR INSULAR GROUPS

As it has already noted, Cuba is made up of the island of Cuba and 4194 isles and keys. Almost all of them are grouped in four smaller archipelagos or insular groups; the rest are isolated or inside the bays. These archipelagos are Los Colorados, Sabana-Camagüey (or Jardines del Rey), Jardines de la Reina, and Los Canarreos.

LOS COLORADOS ARCHIPELAGO

It is in the coastal sector between the San Antonio Cape and the La Gobernadora Point, comprises 160 keys with a latitudinal arrangement along 225 km. It mainly settles over the submarine shelf. On the whole, these keys have a sandy section in their north coast, and in the south, a muddy one; generally they are covered with mangrove and are uninhabited.

This archipelago is divided into five groups of keys that are from west to east: La Leña Keys, muddy and covered with mangrove trees; Buenavista Keys including the homonymous key spanning, and Levisa Keys. The latter stand out owing to their good marine bottom and a welcoming sandy beach, to which tourist trips are carried out.

SABANA-CAMAGÜEY (OR JARDINES DEL REY) ARCHIPELAGO

This is one of the insular groups that includes the isles having the largest sizes of the country after Cuba and the Isle of Youth. It is spread out between the Hicacos Peninsula and the Nuevitas Bay, covering a distance of 465 km; it is made up of 2517 isles and keys.

In general this archipelago may be divided into four groups of keys, having varied features and sizes. To the west, and coinciding with the territory of Matanzas, there is the small group of the Mono, Monito and Piedras del Norte Keys, having a muddy composition, and covered with mangrove trees.

East to the Hicacos Peninsula, which includes the famous Varadero beach, is a group of keys named Cruz del Padre-Fragoso comprising the northern utmost point of the Cuban territory located in the first of its islets. This group of keys are spread out along the north coast of Matanzas and Villa Clara comprising 961 keys. The typical feature of this group is the presence of beaches having fine sand in the north coasts of its keys, while the southern ones are covered with mangrove trees resting on muddy soils.

The length of the Fragoso Key is 40 km, almost totally filled by mangrove trees, and the group known as De Las Cinco Leguas Keys stand out in the far east of this group. East of these ones, there is the group named Santa Maria Keys that takes its name from the biggest of their islets; it has 567 keys located north of Villa Clara and Sancti Spíritus, which are spread out towards Ciego de Ávila. These keys are made up of covering rocks, in this case, Quaternary calcarenites and Neogene organogenic limestone, with wonderful beaches in their northern coasts, and marshes and mangrove trees in the south ones. These islets come fair near to the littoral in the zones of the Judas and Caguanes Points. As a matter of fact, this two points surrounded by marshes and bogs, are practically, keys on mainland.

These keys have a basement that is part of the geological structure named Bahamas Shelf. They have a geological history, where the cyclical ascending and descending processes have alternated. This has allowed that systems of caves have developed there, many of which have drinking water by outcropping the phreatic mantle in them.

Presence of water in these places allowed the existence of a numerous land vertebrate fauna, whose remains have been found in the caves. These two factors made possible the settlement of native groups, whose remains may be found in this place.

The far east of the Sabana-Camagüey Archipelago is made up of true isles, named Coco, Romano, Guajaba and Sabinal keys. They have a huge area, even bigger than some Antillean republics, although they are depopulated, with the exception of the Coco cay because of the influx of tourists. These isles are arranged in the above mentioned succession, from the Buenavista Bay to the Nuevitas one, along 193 km parallel to the littoral of Ciego de Ávila and Camagüey provinces, separated among them by narrow channels determining the existence of true "inner seas" named Los Perros, Jigüey and La Gloria Bays. These isles constitute extensive plains, sometimes interrupted by small hills, and they are also made up of carbonated rocks with evidences of an accelerated karstification like the saddle-shaped hill of Romano key, having 58 m above sea level. Outcrops from the phreatic mantle are found in these plains, although there are not hydric currents.

JARDINES DE LA REINA ARCHIPELAGO

It is made up of 661 keys, and spreads out along 360 km, from the Cruz Cape in the extreme of the Guacanayabo Gulf in the province of Granma, towards the María Aguilar Point near the Casilda Bay in Sancti Spíritus, facing the southern coast of the island of Cuba.

The group of keys of the Guacanayabo Gulf may be identified in this archipelago, with 187 muddy keys and small keys, in whose genesis have decisively taken part the sediments that the Cauto River abundantly and continuously gives to the gulf coast. Some of them are surrounded by coral barriers giving a determined perimeter to these small bogs.

Westwards there are the keys in the Ana María Gulf, similar to those above mentioned; both sum up 418 keys.

A small insular group located in the southeast of the littoral of Sancti Spíritus is called the San Pedro and Sabanalamar Inlets; they are fewer towards the Casilda Bay.

The most important insular group of this southern archipelago is the Laberinto de las Doce Leguas,[21] located in the far south of the insular shelf, near to the submarine slope. This group is spread out from Cabeza del Este Point in the east direction to Cachibocas key to the west, along 135 km, with a similar orientation to the axis of the island of Cuba, that is, northwest-southeast.

21. Its name [Labyrinth having twelve leagues] is due to its shape and length, although that is not the exact length. *Trans.*

Among these 243 keys stand out the following: Cabeza del Este, Caguamas, Caballones, Grande, Alcatraz, Cinco Balas and others, because they are the largest ones. As a whole, they are small and made up of organogenic calcarenites and sand in their southern coasts, and of bogs covered with mangrove trees in the northern ones. They are arranged as a true barrier, and they are a real labyrinth, in which navigation is hard and danger for ships with usual draught, not only due to the keys and small keys, but also for the presence of numerous reefs that only allow circulation by navigable channels or small and narrow passages.

A quite generalized feature is the presence of beautiful beaches and an admirable sea floor, having very little depth (only 3 m) between the Island of Cuba and the insular group, but up to 2500 m in the south part of it.

By the end of the first semester of 1998, the influx of tourists towards the facilities in this small archipelago began.

LOS CANARREOS ARCHIPELAGO

It is spread out 268 km, from the Francés Cape to the Cochinos Bay, south of Pinar del Río, La Habana and Matanzas, made up of 672 keys and small keys, and one isle: the Isle of Youth.

This group may be divided into several groups of keys and small keys that are named, from east to west: Jardines y Jardinillos, 111 small keys similar to the Laberinto de las Doce Leguas extending along 148 km; Sur de Zapata, with 338 keys where bogs and mangrove trees abound, though beautiful sand beaches may be found in some small keys made up of calcarenites, like República Democrática Alemana in the Ernest Thëlman key; Las Cayamas, south of Guanímar; Los Guzmanes, in the north and west of the Isle of Youth; and Los Indios and San Felipe, that are in the seas west of the Isle.

The groups of keys named Las Cayamas, Los Guzmanes, Boquerones and Buena Vista are different from the rest of this archipelago, regarding their alignment, because they are aligned from north to south.

Cayo Largo del Sur, being 23 km long and having beautiful beaches in its south littoral, stands out in the Jardines y Jardinillos; it is broadly fitted out for tourism. Thirty two muddy keys covered with mangroves are east of the Isle of Youth. The groups of keys named Los Indios and the San Felipe are made up of marshes and mangrove trees, although some of the latter may be rocky and may have modest sandy beaches. The average depth of the shelf in this archipelago is 4 m, while in the south it may be attained 2500 m.

The Isle of Youth that is part of the Los Canarreos Archipelago has a surface area of 2199 sq km and 70,000 inhabitants. It is a territory with a varied geology, made up of a metamorphic complex to the north and center of the isle, and a karstified plain to the south.

Cuban insular groups have a total of 4010 isles, keys and small keys. Furthermore, in bays and estuaries there are 75 keys in the north coast of the island of Cuba that joined to the 93 keys that are in the same situation in the south coast, sum up 168. Facing the north coast, outside of the limits of the insular groups, there are 11 keys in the region of Moa; in the south one there are 5 keys. All of them sum up 4194 keys.

SEAS SURROUNDING CUBA.
SEA CURRENTS

The seas surrounding Cuba are part of the world-wide ocean (Scholkalsky, 1917, *fide* Núñez Jiménez, 1982); only the inner seas such as the Caspian Sea and the Black Sea do not make it up. They are the latitude filled by the water portions of the world; the sea currents moving—as rivers—within the large oceanic volumes, and other factors; the ones giving different features to the diverse parts of this world-wide ocean.

Cuba is surrounded by three differentiated units of the world-wide ocean: The Caribbean Sea by the south, the Gulf of Mexico by the west, and the Atlantic Ocean by the north. All of these ocean portions occupy contiguous spaces without any land separating them; therefore, it is very difficult to define their accurate borders.

It is considered that the Caribbean Sea is comprised between the continental coasts of South America, Central America and the Yucatan Peninsula—a frontier between this central part and the northern one in the American continent—, and the arc of the Antillean islands, that is, the arc of the Lesser Antilles by the east, and that of the Greater Antilles by the north.

The largest distance in this sea is 2800 km, from southeast to northwest, between the isle of Trinidad—the closest to South America to the east—and the San Antonio Cape in Cuba, the last emergent land to the west. The largest width is 1500 km, from north to south, between the Los Mosquitos Gulf in Panama and the Batabanó Gulf in Cuba.

The Gulf of Mexico occupies the northwestern extreme of the Caribbean-Antillean region with an area of 1,944,570 sq km. This gulf has an almost-circular shape, and it is practically closed by the Florida and Yucatan Peninsulas and by the Island of Cuba. The Yucatan Channel and the Straits of Florida are between both peninsulas and Cuba. The largest length of the gulf is 1700 km, from east to west, between the Coat Coalcos in the Campeche Gulf and Tallahassee in Florida. Its largest width is between Corpus Christi in Texas, the United States of America, and the San Antonio Cape in Cuba.

Some authors have denominated American Mediterranean the large aquatory constituted by the Caribbean

Sea and the Gulf of Mexico. Nevertheless the similarities between both, there are other features that allow to separately identify them, such as the circulation of waters, the differentiated temperatures because of the presence or not of the submarine shelf, and the content of sulfates and dissolved oxygen.

The north coast of Cuba is bathed by the waters of the western sector of the Atlantic Ocean, which also do it to the Bahamas and Bermudas Archipelagos and the eastern coast of the United States of America.

The temperature of the seas' surfaces surrounding Cuba is determined as a whole by the warm streams that go into the Caribbean Sea through the Lesser Antilles, but very specifically among these and the north coast of South America, as well as by sunshine, specially in summer, and the atmospheric cooling caused by polar cold fronts in winter.

The waters of the Atlantic Ocean, the Gulf of Mexico and the Caribbean Sea in summer keep in a similar average temperature that fluctuates between 28°C and 30°C, even though it is slightly higher in the gulf, specially in the Straits of Florida. During winter, the waters around Cuba are colder, and there is a larger stability in the surrounding aquatories.

Salinity is also higher in the western sector of the Gulf of Mexico, because there is less interchange and more evaporation. Rainfalls exceed evaporation in the rainy season, hence, salinity decreases. The average concentration of oxygen in the waters diminishes in the harshest months of winter, just like the concentration of phosphates, although both parameters are higher in the waters of the Straits of Florida.

The sea currents are very active in the region and change their speeds in the "narrow" passages that they must run across in several sectors; above all, between the isles of Barbados and Trinidad in the southern extreme of the Lesser Antilles, and in the Straits of Florida.

Broadly speaking, there is a northwestwards waters' movement in the region, although there are currents and countercurrents taking different directions. Gulf Stream stands out among all of these currents. Its origin is in the Southern Current of the Equator that flows through the Atlantic Ocean towards the continental projection of Brazil, where it is divided into two currents flowing in different directions. The northern branch flows northwestwards along the Brazilian, Guyanese and Venezuelan coasts, going into the Caribbean Sea through the Lesser Antilles; in that sector, it is denominated *Caribbean Stream.*

The current behaves like a river with some secondary riverbeds and it has its main flow along the south of Jamaica, turns to the west in the Cayman Trough, and later to the north to flow through the Strait of Yucatan, where it divides in three branches. The first branch cross the Gulf of Campeche; the second one goes in the Gulf of Mexico and ramifies in turn looping over itself; the third branch turns above the northwestern region of Cuba to go into the Straits of Florida and to follow the east coast of the United States of America. (Guitart, 1978, *fide* Núñez Jiménez, 1983).

When the current passes facing the north coast of the Guanahacabibes Peninsula it reaches a considerable strength, and raises up to 15 mm above the general sea level. There, it gets a speed between 1.3 km/h and 1.5 km/h (the highest speed has been calculated between 38 cm/s and 43 cm/s), in an 80 km average width and a depth between 600 m and 1000 m. That is why it is estimated that the current moves 30,000,000 m^3/s (Fairbridge, 1986).

Then, the current goes to the north throughout the eastern coast of the United States of America, reaching that of Canada.

SUBMARINE SHELF

The insular shelf, the submerged natural link of all the components of the Cuban Archipelago, has a surface of 67,831 sq km. It is a wavy shelf, sometimes hilly, with channels and submerged fluvial riverbeds, that is, with a well-defined relief—sometimes shaped in subaerial conditions. Its width changes from a few hundreds of meters south of the Sierra Maestra Mountain Range up to about 140 km south of La Habana and Matanzas. Its borders are in the edge of the insular slope, where the depth of the sea increases quickly.

The Cuban insular shelf is divided into four regions associated to the large basins of the Batabanó, Ana María-Guacanayabo and Guanahacabibes Gulfs, and also to the Sabana-Camagüey Archipelago. These regions are denominated southwestern, southeastern, northwestern, and northeastern shelves, and they are separated among them by narrow and scanty deep sea areas that are not part of them. This insular shelf has depths between 6 m and 7 m in its broadest sector—the southwestern one—in the Batabanó Gulf, 20 m - 25 m in the southeastern; and 50 m - 70 m in isolated areas.

The outer edge of the shelf is limited, as a general rule, by a vertical relief of the insular slope. In that edge the shelf has a reef elevation (*Nuevo Atlas Nacional de Cuba* [New National Atlas of Cuba], 1985), which is useful, in its inner edge, as a retaining wall to the contribution of the rivers and currents that flow from the coast, made up of muddy and sandy sediments.

The presence of bays and gulfs far in mainland, as well as the presence of deltas in many rivers, make the coastline be sinuous and irregular, features already noted before.

The broad shelf littorals are related to biogenic cumulative coasts (mangrove trees) and to those formed by river deltas, as it may be observed in the shelf of the north coast of the central provinces, the south coast of La Habana and Matanzas, and the southeastern zone, between Casilda and Cruz Cape.

The open littoral sectors with narrow shelves, like the north coast of La Habana-Matanzas and the Maisí Point, show a typical morphology with terraced surfaces and ancient leveled bars, both of which owe their origin to abrasive and abrasive-cumulative processes.

The lythological composition of the deposits of the shelf is linked with the whole of abiotic factors, typical of tropical environments. The morphologic particularities of its geological formation, the features of the supply sources of sedimentary material, the transport conditions of terrigenous material, the influence of the oceanic water masses in the sedimentation, the climate, the hydrodynamic processes, are some of such abiotic factors. In the general composition of sediments, the carbonated ones predominate. The process of carbonization is owing to the deposition of biogenic material coming from the calcareous algae, corals and mollusks, as well as from the accumulation by decantation of carbonated chemical or chemical-biologic substances dissolved in water.

The Cuban Archipelago together with its shelf, attaining between both a surface area of 178,753 sq km, is located in the Caribbean-Antillean geomorphologic region. Submerged reliefs that have undergone transformations during the geological time are identified in this zone, outside from the emergent areas. Thus, elevated mountain ranges, plateaus, and among them, defiles, deep canyons —riverbeds of ancient rivers—, valleys, and bottomless ocean troughs are found beneath the waters of the American Mediterranean and the Atlantic Ocean.

The Yucatan Basin is found towards the south of the Cuban Archipelago, beyond the border of the insular shelf, between the San Antonio Cape and the province of Ciego de Ávila. This trough, being 290 km width and about 1000 km long, has depths up to 3395 m. There are mountain ranges and plateaus in this large depression, running from southeast to northwest, and the Paz, Silver Town, Bucanero and Jagua shoals are included. The first two ones form a mountain range being 48 km long and 7 km average width. These shoals attain depths of 21 m below sea level in their tops.

The northeastern extreme includes the Bucanero shoal, a 10 sq km plateau, whose leveled summit is 30 m deep, after it has risen from –2025 m. Far to the west, the trough attains its maximum depth, over 3300 m and again it rises just up to 3 m underneath the surface in the Jagua shoal having a somewhat circular shape.

The Cayman Trough is eastwards; it has a lengthened shape toward the Central American continental territory. Between it and that of Yucatan the Cayman Ridge is found; this submerged positive structure is directed from southwest to northeast, and comes closer to the Cuban submarine shelf at the same latitude than the Cruz Cape, as a continuation of the Sierra Maestra mountains. The ridge elevates up westwards to outcrop and to constitute the Cayman Islands.

The Cayman—or Bartlett—Trough is a large depression, also south of Cuba and close to it—above all, near the southern littoral of the eastern provinces of Granma, Santiago de Cuba and Guantánamo—where the shelf has a reduced width. This trough is spread out from the Honduras Gulf to the Windward Passage, with a maximum width of 125 km, and has an east-northeast direction in its western extreme, and east-west in its central and eastern parts.

The Cayman Trough takes in two of the largest troughs of the area and of the world—considering as such the biggest depth point or areas—, the Bartlett Trench (–7680 m) that is located directly south of the zone of Trinidad and the Cayman Islands, and that of Oriente (–7239 m), located 21 km south of the Turquino Pike, at which brings about in that zone an unevenness over 9000 m, one of the largest of the world.

The Nicaragua Ridge broads its base towards the Nicaraguan territory and others of the Central American isthmus, and it narrows towards the eastern extreme of Cuba and the west of Hispaniola. It is very important for the theories that try to explain the origin of the land vertebrate fauna of Cuba. In the west, the Colombia and Venezuela Troughs, divided by the Beata Ridge, are important depressions that in turn have mountain ranges in their bottoms with a transversal direction to the general direction of the troughs.

The extreme of the region closes with the Aves Rise, the Granada Trough and the arc of the Lesser Antilles—it is a ridge, whose highest points are small islands—, limited in the east by the Tobago Trough.

The Cuban Archipelago is bounded at the north by the Straits of Florida, a channel of 165 km width, with a depth of about 1700 m (it attains 792 m between Bahía Honda and the Tortugas shoal); the shoal of the Sal cay, a submarine plateau over which the Sal, the Double Headed Shot cays and the Anguila isle are found. The latter spreads out along 115 km, breaking this gap and dividing it into two parts. Between this shoal and the cays of Florida, the channel is narrower than between the first one and the north coast of Cuba, where it is named Nicholas Channel, and has a maximum depth of 963 m.

MAIN BAYS OF CUBA

Cuba is characterized by the irregularity of its coasts, and in the northern ones the bottle bays predominate—with narrow mouths and broad interiors.

From the viewpoint of economic activity, the Havana Bay is the most important port of the Cuban Archipelago. Following it (not in a hierarchical order) there are the

Santiago de Cuba and Cienfuegos Bays in the south coast, and Mariel, Nuevitas, Manatí and Nipe—the largest one—bays in the northern littoral; all of them are bottle bays. Also in the north, there are the Matanzas and the Cárdenas Bays that are open-type ones. In the southern littoral there is the Guantánamo bottle bay—partially and illegally occupied by a naval base of the Government of the United States of America.

The Bahía Honda and the Cabañas Bays in the northern littoral of Pinar del Río have excellent natural conditions, as well as Banes, Felton, Nicaro and Sagua de Tánamo, in the north coast of the eastern region, and also Isabela de Sagua, Caibarién, and Punta Gorda in the central region. In the south coast, the bays or ports of Niquero, Campechuela, Manzanillo in the Guacanayabo Gulf, as well as Santa Cruz del Sur, Júcaro, Batabanó, Casilda and La Coloma, are also important places for Cuban trade, because of their natural conditions.

In the Isle of Youth, only along the Las Casas River, there is an appropriate depth for ships having small and medium draught; it may reach the latitude of Nueva Gerona, capital of the special municipality.

Throughout the extensive string of keys, sheltered harbors with adequate depths are non-existent. Although the effects of currents, tides, and winds are less amid the string of keys, shallow waters limit their use by big ships.

The tides in the Cuban coasts and bays do not accomplish, generally, spectacular changes in waters' level, which is 70.5 cm above the zero geodetic level on average; nevertheless these values are higher in the north coast (between Isabela de Sagua and Nuevitas), while in the south one the most outstanding values are 22 cm in the Guacanayabo Gulf.

In the bottle bays, these little differences may generate strong currents in the entrance channels, like in the Nuevitas bay, where tidal currents about 125 cm/s have recorded.

CHAPTER V

NATURAL REGIONS OF CUBA

A natural region is a landscape unit defined by geographical accidents, in which the boundaries may be not perfectly defined if they do not coincide with well-delimited shapes, but it must be distinguished because of their territorial community and the relative genetic homogeneity.

The analysis of landscapes as typologic systems makes possible to set up objective basis to accomplish the physical-geographical regionalization of a territory. The genetic focus [within it, mainly the geological structure] and the analysis of the zonal and azonal peculiarities play the most important role in the analysis..

The Cuban geographers, since their first research, attempted to study Cuban Nature through an integral view. Thanks to this integral concept diverse versions of the natural physical-geographical regionalization of the country have been achieved.

The first scheme was worked on by doctor Salvador Massip in 1925. Afterwards, other schemes have been published, worked on by the same author and his wife Sara Ysalgué, and by doctors Pedro Cañas Abril and Antonio Núñez Jiménez.

According to the criterion stated in the *Nuevo Atlas Nacional de Cuba* [New National Atlas of Cuba] (1988) about the physical-geographical regionalization, Cuba lies on the part of the American continent named *Center America*. This part includes Central America, the Antilles, and the Bahamas, and it is characterized for being a young region with a complex origin and a predominant mountainous relief, a marked influence of wet tropical air masses, and a strong insular and peninsular character. The Antilles defined as a regional unit stand out by their insular character and their significant geographical diversity, conditioned by a relief where mountains alternate with plains, a complicated geological basis, and a variety of types of climate ranging from the dry tropical one to the very wet.

PHYSICAL-GEOGRAPHICAL REGIONALIZATION

Cuba is a physical-geographical province belonging to the Center America subcontinent. Cuban landscapes, unlike the rest of the Greater Antilles, are characterized by a great predominance of plains, and the ones developed over carbonated rocks, and by the preponderance of the wet low-mountains, while medium-sized-mountains only occupy 1% of the territory. The differentiation of landscapes on the basis of the latitudes is just about non-existent, due to the lengthened shape in the latitudinal way of the Cuban Archipelago; however, in accordance with the bioclimatic regime, there are two well-defined categories: The landscapes of dry and moderately dry plains, and those of moderately wet plains.

Geochemical methods and a complex physical-geographical focus were applied in the research of the landscapes properties defined as integral systems, and particularly, the determination of the dynamics in the energy and substance interchange.

Heat and the humidity of the landscapes of the territory that condition a fast growing of the vegetation and a high annual production of living substance, determine a similar intensity of the biological circulation in that period. The hydric circulation is strong and in the first place the main hydric migrants are calcium and silica; in the second place, potassium, aluminum, magnesium and iron; and in the third place, manganese, sulfur and boron.

Relief differences and the nearness to the surface of the water table cause an important change in the migration conditions of chemical elements arisen by variations in the oxidation-reduction potential of the soils.

According to the physical-geographic differences and the history of the development of the Cuban territory, it splits up in four subprovinces, two of them in the emergent territory, and the rest in the submerged part which is the insular shelf.

The emergent regions are the *Cuba Occidental y Central* [Western and Central Cuba], and the *Cuba Oriental* [Eastern Cuba] subprovinces. The submerged regions are the *Islas y Llanuras Sumergidas de la Plataforma Septentrional de Cuba* [Isles and Submerged Plains of the North Shelf of Cuba], and the *Islas y Llanuras Sumergidas e Islas de la Plataforma Meridional de Cuba* [Isles and Submerged Plains of the South Shelf of Cuba] subprovinces.

CUBA OCCIDENTAL Y CENTRAL [WESTERN AND CENTRAL CUBA] SUBPROVINCE

It encompasses the Pinar del Río District, divided into Llanuras de Pinar del Río [Pinar del Río Plains] and Montañas de la Cordillera de Guaniguanico [Mountains of the Guaniguanico Range]; La Habana-Matanzas District, with the Llanuras del Sur y Este de La Habana-Matanzas [Plains of the South and East of La Habana-Matanzas] and the Alturas del Norte de La Habana-Matanzas [Heights of the North of La Habana-Matanzas]; the Centro [Center] District, divided into Llanura del Norte [North Plain], Llanuras y Alturas de Cubanacán [Cubanacán Plains and Heights] and Montañas de Guamuhaya [Guamuhaya Mountains]; and the Camagüey-Maniabón District, divided into Llanuras de Camagüey-Maniabón [Camagüey-Maniabón Plains], and Llanuras y Alturas del Centro de Camagüey-Maniabón [Plains and Heights of the Center of Camagüey-Maniabón].

Pinar del Río District. It is the westernmost district of the physical-geographic units of the Cuban territory, and in it, the regions and subregions have different features. It includes the Llanuras de Pinar del Río and the Montañas de la Cordillera de Guaniguanico regions.

Llanuras de Pinar del Río Region. It comprises the Llanura de Guanahacabibes [Guanahacabibes Plain], the Llanura Norte de Pinar del Río [North Plain of Pinar del

Río] and the Llanura Sur de Pinar del Río [South Plain of Pinar del Río] subregions.

• Llanura de Guanahacabibes. This plain occupies the homonymous peninsula in the western extreme of Cuba. It is considered a moderately wet and karstic plain, formed over very young sedimentary rocks—on the whole, organic limestone, reef limestone and calcarenites—containing ferrallitic- or red rendzina-type soils [in some sections skeletal soils may either be found or are nonexistent], where a semideciduous forest grows. The plain is slight wavy, but it has some dune towards the southern part coinciding with a positive tilting zone. The plain has a bigger thickness of soils northwards, but it is swampy. In its eastern extreme this plain is named Guane-Mantua, with a northeast-southeast direction, and it is characterized by having cumulative processes in its genesis that generate bigger thickness of sandy and calcareous soils.

• Llanura Norte de Pinar del Río. This north plain is a complex physical-geographic unit, where flat territories have diverse origins, ranging from cumulative plains made up over carbonated and terrigenous-carbonated sedimentary rocks, kaolinitic and quarzitic weathering crusts, and sandy deposits with quarzitic ferrallitic soils and also leached yellow ferrallitic and sandy-quarzitic soils, to denuded plains formed in volcanic, volcanic-sedimentary and metamorphic rocks.

This subregion is arranged in a latitudinal way along the northern coast of Pinar del Río and receives the contributions of the currents descending from the Guaniguanico Mountain Range. That is why it is covered with non-worthless thickness of sediments. It is a zone notably modified by man, and for this reason, crops—sugar cane among them—, forests and pastures may be observed in it above all.

• Llanura Sur de Pinar del Río. It is an alluvial southern plain, located between San Luis and Artemisa, made up over carbonated rocks of the Paleogene and Neogene covering and covered by eluviums and alluviums coming from the rivers of the south slope of the Guaniguanico Mountain Range hills.

It has marshy features towards the southern extreme. For this reason, it is an appropriate plain for growing rice. It is covered with sandy-clayey soils with an extremely anthropic vegetation, where belly palms and palmettos stand out. The Río Hondo, Los Palacios, Santa Cruz, San Cristóbal Rivers and other fluvial currents go across the plain flowing into the south coast, or disappearing in the swampy terrains.

Montañas de la Cordillera de Guaniguanico Region. It includes the Montañas de la Sierra de los Órganos [Sierra de los Órganos Mountains] and the Montañas de la Sierra del Rosario [Sierra del Rosario Mountains] subregions.

• Montañas de la Sierra de los Órganos. This subregion comprises the Los Órganos Range, made up of mogote-shaped hills, which attain heights higher than 500 m, that are spread out from Guane to San Diego de los Baños. In this subregion are included the calcareous mountainous areas, isolated at times or like chains of mountains having vertical, subvertical, and sometimes concave hillsides, and rounded, or tower-like, or ruined castle-like summits; also large fluvial-karstic valleys named poljes; closed valleys having diverse bottoms that are named *hoyos de montaña* and *hoyos de terreno*, according to whether they reach or not the level of the surrounding plains; numerous caverns cutting the mogotes at different altitudes; varied lapiaz forms or *diente de perro*—the name after which they are known in Cuba—and many others.

This subregion encompasses also hills made up of highly tectonized non-carbonated rocks such as slates, sandstones, silicites, and quarzites; they are known as Alturas de Pizarras Range, which surround the mogotes by the north and the south. There are low-grade soils in the slaty hills; hence, they are unsuitable for cultivation, since only the pine groves abound there.

Both the Los Órganos and the Alturas de Pizarras Ranges have a complex tectonics, in which overthrusts and characteristic *nappes* structures may be observed, and where the most ancient rocks of Cuba are found.

· Montañas de la Sierra del Rosario. This subregion forms the eastern part of the Guaniguanico Mountain Range, separated from the Los Órganos Range by the valley of the San Diego or Caiguanabo River. Even though the karstic morphology of these hills has also a remarkable development, they have not really a mogote-like profile, but crests, *mesas*[22] and hills because of the alternation of carbonated, volcano-sedimentary, silica-clastic and other rocks that give a heterogeneous character to the sequences.

The presence of numerous fluvial-karstic canyons excavated by the rivers and small streams having cut the rocks because of the fast elevation of the hills, in order to shape true defiles, is a singular feature of these mountains.

Presence of diverse hydrogeological levels causes the existence of caverns having stepped profiles, whose riverbeds are suddenly flooded owing to the complex hydrogeological relations of their passages. The Los Perdidos cavern system—one of the biggest of the country—is a reliable example of this feature, because it receives contributions of several underground basins, and even in drought season, it may flood without previous warning.

22. A flat, table-like upland, which falls away steeply on all sides; this word in Spanish means "table." *Trans.*

Pan de Guajaibón [699 m] is in the western extreme of the El Rosario Range and it is the highest hill of the western of Cuba. Cajálbana Plateau is just north of the Pan de Guajaibón; it is made up of ultrabasic rocks and serpentines having iron and nickel deposits, similar to the Moa and Nicaro mineral ores in the east of the country.

La Habana-Matanzas District. This territory, mainly flat, includes three provinces of the Cuban Archipelago: La Habana, Ciudad de la Habana and Matanzas. An important part of the population of the country is concentrated in this district, and its agricultural production is one of the biggest of the nation. It encompasses several physical-geographic units, Llanuras del Sur y el Este de La Habana-Matanzas, and Alturas del Norte de La Habana-Matanzas.

Llanuras del Sur y el Este de La Habana-Matanzas Region. This physical-geographical region, that are plains located south and east of both provinces, is the geomorphological unit known as Llanura Cársica Meridional [Southern Karstic Plain] that spreads out from Artemisa to Zapata, west of the Cienfuegos Bay. It groups the Llanura de Artemisa [Artemisa Plain], the Llanura de Colón [Colón Plain] and the Llanura de Zapata [Zapata Plain] subregions.

· Llanura de Artemisa. This subregion includes the karstic plain sub-latitudinal spread out and located between Artemisa in the southwestern extreme of La Habana, and the zone of Alacranes, Bolondrón and Pedro Betancourt in the southwest of the Matanzas province.

The plain has a predominant underground drainage between Artemisa and Batanabó. There are scarce fluvial riverbeds that go across it, like the Capellanía and San Antonio Rivers, and small streams, which as a whole, submerge in caverns or infiltrate into the Neogene limestone where the plain has been formed. Only the Mayabeque River, which springs up to the northwest of

Güines town, runs across the karstic plain to reach the southern littoral swamp. Cenotes, dolines, blind valleys, sinks and caves abound in the plain, and many of them are access ways to the underground aquifer. Some of these caverns, like those of Astón in Las Cañas, near to Artemisa, and those of Juanelo and Luis Piedra in Güira de Melena, are partly subaquatic, and display totally or partially flooded halls and passages with cristalline waters, submerged paradises for speleologic diving, where blind fishes and anophthalmic shrimps [without eyes] may be observed.

There are sugar cane, vegetables [the biggest potato production], citrus fruit and other fruit crops in the medium and scanty thickness soils covering the limestone and marls that predominate in this subregion.

Llanura de Colón. This plain spreads out in a latitudinal way from the northwestern coast of Matanzas to the north boundary of the physical-geographical unit named Llanura de Zapata. It is a denuded and karstic plain with an almost absolutely underground drainage. Limestone, marls, and in a lesser degree, dolomitized limestone from the Miocene predominate among the rocks where it is made up. Also sand and clay lens among the limestone are found in the plain. This substratum is covered with fertile red ferralitic soils, where sugar cane, vegetables and all kind of fruits are cultivated.

There are numerous caves, caves with outcrops of the underground aquifer, and flooded passages, some of them of considerable size, where blind fishes [anophthalmic] inhabit in the zone of Jagüey Grande, Torriente, and in the southern area as a whole. Northwards, the plain spreads out towards Cárdenas, where the thickness of the soils is fewer by sectors. In this zone there are also submerged caves, but above all, caverns stand out for preserving remains of the native cultures that should abound in pre-Colombian times. In the coast of the Cárdenas Bay, a regular-sized littoral swamp is developed.

Llanura de Zapata. This plain, partially flooded by marshes, is the largest wetland of the country. It has a very young origin, because it is made up of limestone, calcarenites and other carbonated rocks from the Pleistocene. The plain shows a strip of rocks that surrounds its southern extreme in contact with the Caribbean Sea and in the margins of the Cochinos Bay, as well as in some inland places; the rest of its territory is covered by peat-rich marshes.

The plain is located between the La Broa Inlet and the western margin of the Cienfuegos Bay; the Cochinos Bay divides it into two halves. The plain and swamp of Zapata is one of the most interesting places of the Cuban territory for the study of the typical and own fauna and vegetation of the archipelago. The Hatiguanico River crosses its most swampy part from east to west, twisting through the quaking-bogs, emptying into the La Broa Inlet.

All kinds of karstic forms are developed in the rocky strips, mainly lapiaz, karren or *diente de perro*—local name for this surface shape, a sort of inland reef—, dolines and caverns as well. Above all, the kamenitzas and cenotes stand out, formed along the tectonic lines at the expense of totally or partially weighing down caves, throughout the littoral of the Cochinos Bay. Some of these kamenitzas, very similar to the cenotes from Yucatan, have depths of almost 70 m, and horizontal and subhorizontal passages comprising hundreds of meters long.

Alturas del Norte de La Habana-Matanzas Region. It encompasses the following three subregions: Llanuras y Alturas del Norte de La Habana-Matanzas [Plains and Heights of the North of La Habana-Matanzas], Llanuras Ariguanabo-Almendares-San Juan [Ariguanabo-Almendares-

San Juan Plains], and Alturas Bejucal-Madruga-Coliseo [Bejucal-Madruga-Coliseo Heights].

- Llanuras y Alturas del Norte de La Habana-Matanzas. This subregion includes the littoral karstic plains of the north coast of both territories that spread out uninterruptedly, from the Mariel Bay to that of Matanzas, above all, between La Habana and Matanzas Bays. The beautiful Playas del Este beaches of the capital and those of Jibacoa and Arroyo Bermejo in the province of La Habana follow one another with the plains. This sector is characterized not only by the *diente de perro* or coastal lapiaz, but also by the emerged and submerged marine terraces, aside from tide rock shelters.

This subregion also includes the hills that spread out in a longitudinal way to the coast, south of the littoral plain, like those west to the La Habana Bay, the Mariel Hills and the Mesa de Anafe Plateau [also named the Loma del Esperón Hill], where there are many caves and deep karstic canyons, longitudinal to the axis of the limey hill, in which it may be found remnants of animals that lived in the most recent geological past. In this subregion, east of the mentioned bay are included the Morro, Cojímar and Bacuranao Hills, the Sibarimar and Jibacoa Ranges, up to the Loma de la Cumbre Hill in Matanzas—all of them very near to the coast—and farther to the south, the Escaleras de Jaruco Range, the Canasí-Lomas de Picadura Range, the El Palenque Hill and the Pan de Matanzas. All of these hills are made up of carbonated rocks that range from marls, calcareous marls and silicified marls from the Early to Upper Eocene that outcrop in the inner sides, even to those from the Miocene and Pliocene that may be found in the outer side of them. There is a valley between both groups of hills with a wavy or leveled-by-sections bottom that is the result of the erosion of positive tectonic structures (named *anticline blocks-horst),* a process that has left in the open

terrigenous-carbonated sediments from the Upper Cretaceous until the Eocene, as well as ophiolites in the surroundings of Guanabacoa and Canasí, and gypsum in San Adrián in Matanzas.

The Escaleras de Jaruco Range, the El Palenque Hill, Pan de Matanzas, Sibarimar Range, other elevations, and the northern plains have numerous surface and underground karstic forms. Among the most remarkable forms there are: De los Sacrificios and De la Virgen caves in Ciudad de La Habana, where remains of the natives that inhabited Cuba and evidences of their culture, like tools, petroglyphs and pictographies have been found; the caves of Boca de Jaruco and Jíjira Point in La Habana, just to mention two examples where a large amount of remains of natives and vertebrate fossils from the Quaternary are concentrated. The Bellamar-Gato Jíbaro cavern system, located in Matanzas, is one of the largest of this part of Cuba.

The rivers that go across this subregion, usually from the center towards the north coast, cut the mentioned groups of hills forming canyons, because of the fast neotectonic uplift or the glacial-eustatic movements. Some examples of these canyons are those formed by the Bacuranao, Guanabo, Jaruco, Jibacoa, Santa Cruz, Puerto Escondido, Bacunayagua Rivers, and even the Yumurí River that shapes, maybe, the most famous canyon.

- Llanuras Ariguanabo-Almendares-San Juan. This flat subregion lies in a longitudinal way to the axis of the island of Cuba, approximately to the center of the provinces of La Habana and Matanzas, similar to a slight uneven depression relative to the surrounding terrain.

Part of the area corresponding to Ariguanabo was occupied, long time ago, by the lagoon with the same name, whose dam volume diminished because of water infiltration, the decrease or suspension of external contributions and high evaporation. This subregion, owing to the carbonated composition of the rocks where it lies, also houses very important karstic aquifers for the water supply of part of the capital and Matanzas city (Ariguanabo basin, El Gato aqueduct, and San Juan basin, respectively). The aquifers are found in limestone and clayey limestone from the Miocene.

The sink of the San Antonio River, which is in San Antonio de los Baños town, is a very outstanding geographical accident in this zone. This plain has red and brown-reddish soils; they are suitable for vegetables and sugar cane growing, as well as for cattle raising. Many hydraulic works have been built in this depressed plain with the purpose to transfer water from the basins of Matanzas, which are exploited less than those of La Habana province with much bigger exploitation.

· Alturas Bejucal-Madruga-Coliseo. This orographic group is arranged in a west-east sublatitudinal way, with a slight inclination in its far east to the east-northeast. The hills begin east of the Ariguanabo depressed plain with gentle slopes cut by the waters of the Govea and San Antonio Rivers, and in the east of the subregion they have its topmost point in the El Cacahual Hill that is southwest to Bejucal town. This plateau, made up of limestone, clayey limestone, calcareous marls and marls, mainly from the Miocene, has a complex geomorphologic evolution, because the karstic forms, which are abundant in it, like sinks, abysses, dolines and lapiaz, alternate with generations of other forms that have remained "hung" half-way along the hillside, like little caves, blind valleys and others.

This subregion continues with little hills—karstified as a whole—and raises in the nearness of Madruga in the Sierra del Grillo Range (321 m) with a similar morphology to the mogotes, with numerous canyons or dry karstic canyons and several erosion levels, where the lapiaz,

dolines and small caverns abound. This range borders at the north with La Gloria Hill, made up of serpentinites and ultrabasic rocks, and at the south, after the anticline Cajayabos Valley, with the San Juan de Nepomuceno and Pipián Hills, both of which form a southern branch of the subregion that spreads out southeastward as far as the nearness of Cabezas in Matanzas province.

The easternmost group of hills of the subregion spreads out east of the Sierra del Grillo Range. It includes the hills of Coliseo, Limonar and San Miguel de los Baños that have a calcareous composition, and the El Jacán Hill, made up of serpentinites. In the latter, karstic forms in opal and chalcedony have been recorded (Acevedo and Gutiérrez, 1978).

Centro District. This district located in the center of the Island encompasses the Llanura del Norte, the Llanuras y Alturas de Cubanacán and the Montañas de Guamuhaya regions.

Llanura del Norte Region. This northern plain comprises the Llanura Corralillo-Yaguajay [Corralillo Yaguajay Plain] subregion.

· Llanura Corralillo-Yaguajay. This subregion is a littoral plain of an abrasive-denuded and abrasive-cumulative character, made up of very young calcareous sediments of marine origin, interrupted by fluvial sediments contributed by the big number of rivers flowing into the north coast. Due to this reason, the plain becomes a fluvial-marine one in its highest part (100 m - 120 m) because of the accumulation of deltaic sediments, and at times, it turns into marshy zones, like the Majaguillar swamp. Sometimes, these swampy areas isolate segments of mainland and they look like keys or isles. Such is the case of Cayo[23] Caguanes, where moreover, in a package

23. It means "key." *Trans.*

of organogenic limestone from the Neogene and Quaternary, a huge net of passages of phreatic cavities, known as Caguanes cave system have developed.

This subregion spreads out along the north coast of Villa Clara, Sancti Spíritus and part of Ciego de Ávila, to the zone of Punta Alegre, where the corrosion of a saline dome allows the observation of karstic forms in gypsum, like little caves and dolines.

- Llanuras y Alturas de Cubanacán Region. It includes the subregions: Llanura de Manacas [Manacas Plain], Llanura Corralillo-Yaguajay [Corralillo-Yaguajay Plain], Llanura Real Campiña-Cienfuegos [Real Campiña-Cienfuegos Plain], Llanura Santa Clara-Sancti Spíritus [Santa Clara-Sancti Spíritus Plain], Alturas de la Cordillera Septentrional [Northern Mountain Range and Heights], and Alturas y Montañas de Cubanacán [Cubanacán Heights and Mountains].

Llanura de Manacas. It is a denuded plain located in the central zone of the island of Cuba, west to Santa Clara. It separates two different geological structures and it is used as a border to the La Habana-Matanzas and the Centro districts. Due to that reason, this subregion was considered, without distinction, part of one or another physic-geographical unit.

This subregion spreads out nearly from coast to coast, from its north border with the Llanura Corralillo-Yaguajay subregion, to the south coast, between the Zapata Swamp and the Cienfuegos Bay. It borders to the west with the Llanura de Colón.

This plain is made up, mainly, of carbonated and terrigenous-carbonated sediments from the Paleogene, as well as serpentinites. It has brown and clayey soils, where the palmettos abound.

- Llanura Real-Campiña-Cienfuegos. It is an abrasive-cumulative plain, flat to wavy in its southern part having a marine origin, and combines with cumulative and erosive-cumulative plains, developed over carbonated and volcanic-carbonated rocks from the volcanic arc. It has a considerable area, and spreads out from the hills bordering the northern littoral plain to the Cienfuegos Bay. It is possible to find remains of rudist reefs in the carbonated parts, among which many microforaminifera are found.

- Llanura Santa Clara-Sancti Spíritus. This plain lies east to the Real Campiña-Cienfuegos Plains, but in an approximately longitudinal way to the axis of the island of Cuba. The plain is complex in this zone; it is hilly, denuded-erosive, and in some places where the fluvial currents have a considerable magnitude, it is cumulative and erosive-cumulative. North and west to Santa Clara, the plain is made up over serpentinites, tuffs and volcanic rocks, covered with brown and siallitic brown soils. This subregion has monoclinous buttes (*nselbergs*) of up to 150 m high, associated with intrusions, which exceed the average level of the plains (100 m).

- Alturas de la Cordillera Septentrional. The name of this region makes allusion to the hills of the northern mountain range; it includes the units known as Lomas del Noroeste [Northwest Hills] that occupies a strip in the north of Villa Clara [Sierra Morena Range, Mogotes de Jumagua Range and Lomas de Mogote Hills], bordering with Matanzas—part of which also this subregion occupies—, and the Lomas del Noreste [Northeast Hills] [Meneses, Matahambre, Bamburanao, El Purio, Mabuya Ranges and others]. This subregion lies in a lengthened zone north of Sancti Spíritus and in the western part of Ciego de Ávila; it consists of hills and denuded-karstic hills, which height do not exceed 400 *m*. It is made up of sedimentary rocks, mainly Cretaceous carbonated rocks, where remains of ammonites, *aptychus* and other fossils abound; terrigenous-carbonated, and terrigenous rocks that dip mainly at the north, and have numerous karstic forms, both surface one like valleys, dolines, lapiaz, canyons, and caverns, sinks, and so forth.

The Boquerones (or Boquerón del Jatibonico) cave, the speluncas of the Mogotes de Jumagua Range, those of the Chambas Hills and many others are found in this zone.

Alturas y Montañas de Cubanacán. This subregion is essentially made up of dissected and slightly dissected, *horst* and blocks, mountains- and erosive-tectonic submountains- type hills, smaller than 400 m altitude; buttes and chains of monoclinous buttes and in intrusive lens, as well as denuded-erosive and erosive, and fluvial erosive-cumulative plains.

The Sierra Alta de Agabama Range that do not exceed 300 m high, the true Sierra del Escambray Range, and the María Rodríguez Range are found in this zone. The most known hills belonging to these ranges are Cerro Calvo (320 m, a butte), and Pelo Malo and Capiro Hills, all of them very close to Santa Clara city, made up of intrusive rocks, serpentinites and also some sedimentary rocks, such as intercalated limestone. Some rivers and streams, like the Agabama, Arimao, Yabú Rivers and others, set out from this subregion towards all the directions, like a domo.

Hilly plains develop among the hills, made up in serpentinites, tuffs and other rocks, with brown and siallitic soils, and two levels of fluvial terraces between 100 m and 120 m high with elevated residues *(inselbergs)* of up to 150 m, associated with intrusions.

Montañas de Guamuhaya Region. The name of this region refers to the Guamuhaya Mountains, and includes the Llanura de Trinidad-Banao [Trinidad-Banao Plain], the Montañas de Trinidad [Trinidad Mountain] and the Montañas de Sancti Spíritus [Sancti Spíritus Mountains] subregions.

· Llanura de Trinidad-Banao. This flat subregion skirts the hills of the Guamuhaya mountains, and spreads out to the southern coast of Sancti Spíritus, bathed by the Caribbean Sea. In this zone there are combined the abrasive-erosive, abrasive and erosive-cumulative, slightly wavy plains having a marine origin, with fluvial cumulative and erosive-cumulative, and low and flat cumulative plains, where a great number of rivers that spring in the mountains empty into. The flows of these rivers may be short, but because of their gradients, they depose heap of sediments in the alluvial planes of the plain, and contribute with a varied mineral richness to the soil.

Since Banao is located south of the mountainous massif, it has singular conditions, owing to which and to the circulation of winds and other factors, there is a specific microclimate very favorable to several crops, like high-grade strawberries and onions, very difficult to obtain in other places.

· Montañas de Trinidad. It occupies the western sector of the Guamuhaya orographic group, bounded to the east by the Agabama River, including the highest hills of the region. This subregion has a very complex geology; it has had its share of overthrust tectonic movements along with a great variety of every kind of rocks. Among them, calcareous slates and metamorphized limestone from the Upper Jurassic stand out.

From the geomorphologic viewpoint, the elevations classify in tectonic-erosive, tectonic-lithological and tectonic-structural low- and small-mountains. These are traversed by the valleys of the Hondo, Guanayara, Negro, Hanabanilla—flooded nowadays for the lake of the homonymous dam name that caused the disappearance of the very beautiful cascades that were in its flow,—Boquerones Rivers and others. Sometimes, the mentioned rivers have partially underground courses, like the Boquerones one that empties into the Jibacoa polje through a cavern. It is common to find zones of great karstification in the metamorphosed limestone and calcareous slates, where every kind of surface and underground forms abound.

The sink of the Ay River is in the Jibacoa polje; it is a narrow ponor that easily obstructs itself by the foliage and sediments that the river carries away. This fact have caused the full flood of the valley in times of hurricanes and strong rains.

The San Juan, La Cuevita and Potrerillo Peaks, 1140 m, 1072 m, and 931 m high respectively—the highest hills of the center of the Cuban Archipelago—are found in this subregion.

Some speleologists have discovered a cave in the La Campana Hill, at more than 900 m high; it is probably the highest spelunca of Cuba, and maybe the most ancient one. A paleontologic bed also have been found in this cave; it may give out new information about the age of the land vertebrate fauna in this region.

The Martín Infierno and the Cuba-Magyar caves are also in this subregion. The first one has one of the biggest stalagmite of the world, and the second one, the great depth of the Cuban Archipelago with more than 400 m between its mouth and its bottom.

· Montañas de Sancti Spíritus. The mountains of this subregion on average have fewer altitude than those of Trinidad (the highest hill is 842 m), and from the geomorphologic viewpoint they are tectonic-lithologic low- and small-mountains, shielded, dissected and karstified, and shaping chains or not.

It has valleys with fertile lands, where coffee is raised. Those valley are bathed by the waters of the Caracusey, Unimazi (tributaries of the Agabama River), Hondo, Higuanajo, Manacas, Tuyabacoa, Banao Rivers and others, flowing into the Caribbean Sea.

The Caja de Agua cave is found in the hills of this subregion; it is one of the most interesting vertical caves, but at the same time, one of the most dangerous of Cuba.

Camagüey-Maniabón District. It includes the Llanuras de Camagüey-Maniabón, and the Llanuras y Alturas del Centro de Camagüey-Maniabón regions.

Llanuras de Camagüey-Maniabón Region. It comprises of the following subregions: Llanura de Júcaro-Morón [Júcaro-Morón Plain], Llanura del Norte de Camagüey-Maniabón [Plain of the North of Camagüey-Maniabón], and Llanura del Sur de Camagüey [Plain of the South of Camagüey].

· Llanura de Júcaro-Morón. It is also named La Trocha[24] Plain, because in that same position there was a troche or fortified line whereupon the Spanish colonizers attempted to impede the movements of the Liberating Army. Unlike many of the Cuban natural physical-geographical divisions that, to a great extent, follow the directional development of the axis of the island of Cuba and the whole archipelago, this subregion lies in a transversal way to this imaginary line. All this subregion is approximately in the territory of Ciego de Ávila, and generally includes marine abrasive, abrasive-cumulative, and flat abrasive-cumulative plains, and swampy in part; and lacustrine and flat boggy cumulative plains, swampy and swampy in part in the northern coast; as well as fluvial-marine, deltaic, flat, and partially swampy plains in the southern coast. These plains do not have altitudes higher than 50 m.

All of these plains, made up of limestone and other carbonated and carbonated-terrigenous sediments, are very young (from the Miocene and Quaternary). It is an eminently karstic subregion, covered with slight deep red ferralitic soils, where karren, dolines and other karstic forms abound.

Northwards there are three saline domes, where caves and other karstic displays in gyspum rocks are found, like Turiguanó, Punta Alegre and Judas de Cunagua.

· Llanura del Norte de Camagüey-Maniabón. This plain spreads out from the banks of the Caonao River, a natural

24. It means troche. *Trans.*

boundary in the northern coast between the provinces of Ciego de Ávila and Camagüey, to the nearness of Gibara in Holguín. It is also composed of abrasive, erosive-abrasive and abrasive-cumulative plains of marine origin, made up of Miocene and Quaternary rocks; these plains are traversed by rivers like Máximo, Manatí, Chaparra, Saramaguacán and so on.

Some authors divide this subregion in three zones according to their elevation above sea level. In this way, they identify a level between 0 m and 5 m having soils of turf and marshes with mangrove; another level from 5 m to 10 m, having gray gleyed and humic soils, and savannah and grassy vegetation; and another between 10 m and 40 m, not notably spread, with red soils and crops— among them, sugar cane as the most important one. It is a territory that has undergone great anthropic transformations, and has is a highly industrialized, mainly by the present sugar mills.

The coast of this subregion is shaped by some bays, either inner or closed by the keys of the Sabana-Camagüey Archipelago, such as the Jigüey and La Gloria Bays, Sabinol Inlet and Nuevitas Bay, and other non-limited bays by islets, like those of Manatí, Malagueta, Chaparra and Puerto Padre.

Tanque Azul and Cristalitos de Papaya, the biggest flooded caves of the Cuban territory are found west of Gibara, where there is a cliff shore and, by any reckoning, it has undergone a fast flood process after a period of terrace formation.

· Llanura del Sur de Camagüey. This plain, located in the south of Camagüey, spreads out from the borders of the Itabo River that separate it from the Trocha plain in the south of Ciego de Ávila, to the nearness of the mouth of the Sevilla and Tana Rivers, a territory of former Camagüey, belonging now to Las Tunas.

This subregion is composed by abrasive and abrasive-cumulative plains of marine origin, swampy in part, and slightly wavy and flat, made up in rocks and terrigenous sediments from the Miocene and Quaternary. It has humic soils in anthropic savannas with gramineae [sugar cane] and pastures. The closer to the coast, the more marshy the lands; therefore, their productivity diminishes.

Llanuras y Alturas del Centro de Camagüey-Maniabón Region. It includes the subregions: Llanura del Centro-Norte de Camagüey [Plain of the Center-North of Camagüey], Llanura del Centro-Sur de Camagüey [Plain of the Center-South of Camagüey], Alturas de la Sierra de Cubitas [Sierra de Cubitas Heights], Llanuras y Alturas de Maniabón [Maniabón Plains and Heights] and Llanuras y Alturas de Banes-Cacocum [Banes-Cacocum Plains and Heights].

· Llanura del Centro-Norte de Camagüey. This plain, located in the central-northern part of Camagüey, is mainly composed, by the geomorphologic types of denuded and footing denuded-erosive and slightly wavy plains, made up over rocks from the ophiolitic association predominantly: serpentinites, peridotites and serpentinized dunites; gabbros, diabases, troctolites and gabbro-troctolites, lava and semi-basic tuffs, andesites and basalts. Also the plain may cut granitoids. This territory shapes the denominated Florida-Camagüey-Las Tunas peniplane.

The plain has an altitude between 100 m - 120 m, and there are small residual buttes over it that resisted the flattening. Ferritic soils over serpentinites and the typical vegetation of them abound.

The soils are siallitic brown over another rocks, and they are used, above all, for sugar cane growing and cattle breeding.

· Llanura del Centro-Sur de Camagüey. From the morphologic viewpoint, it bears a resemblance with the center-north plain; it is a center-south plain. It is chiefly made up of slightly wavy denuded plains, shaped over

Neogene carbonated rocks. The San Pedro, Najasa and Altamira Rivers cross it and facilitate its drainage.

Tectonic-structural, dome-shaped block, monoclinous and karstfied hills are found in this subregion that constitute the Najasa Range, which has its topmost hill in the denominated El Chorrillo Range being 321 m high. All of these hills are made up of karstified limestone, where numerous surface and underground karstic forms have developed. In spite of the degradation of the vegetation and the intense anthropic activity in the surrounding plains, the environment of this El Chorrillo Range is sufficiently well preserved.

· Alturas de la Sierra de Cubitas. This is a territory made up of hills that are *horst* hills, massive and levelled, and *horst* and blocks hills, stepped and karstified, from the geomorphologic viewpoint. They are made up of Cretaceous recrystallized limestone, with remains of abundant rudists that constituted shoals as reefs in that time, subject to an accelerated neotectonic movement associated with an intense karstification process, which has led to the development of numerous karstic forms, including vertical caves and deep canyons—known as *pasos*. These canyons cross in a transversal way the mountainous area, and are ancient fluvial riverbeds drainned by neotectonic uplifts. Some of these *pasos* are about 100 m deep.

The Cubitas Range has also typical closed depressions [dolines] at different altitudes, just like the cavern systems. Many of these speluncas have remains of the Amerindians, their tools and cultural expressions, and probably, the only graphic evidence of the Spanish conqueror seen by a native, in the Los Generales cave.

The karstic mountainous areas that in some places have cupola-shaped profiles, like in Los Órganos Range, are covered with a degraded semideciduous vegetation with a high xerophytism degree.

· Llanuras y Alturas de Maniabón. It is a very complex physical-geographical unit, where the volcanic, pyroclastic and carbonated rocks, above all from the Cretaceous, are combined. Three sorts of landscapes and geomorphologic units stand out in a close interrelation. On the one hand, there are two types of hills in an orographic group known with the common name of Maniabón: the Cupeicillo-La Candelaria Hills to the north, and the Maniabón buttes; and on the other hand, there are plains having diverse genesis around these buttes.

The Cupeicillo-La Candelaria Hills, bordered to the east by the Cacoyugüín River, are hills (242 m) made up of Cretaceous limestone, of the geomorphologic type known as tectonic-structural *horst* and block hills, in anaclynal chains, and folded, stepped and karstified, that shape true mogotes with caves at different levels. Karstification reaches the level of the underground waters of the zone.

The Maniabón buttes are isolated mogotes having cupola-shaped and cone-shaped karst. They are calcareous caps that lay over a basement of tuffs and serpentinites. This geological feature gives a particular hallmark to their morphology; these buttes present a base with a gentle- to moderately-steep slope, over which abrupt vertical walls rest that end in cone- or cupola-like summits. The surface and underground karstic forms are common in these hills, but they are unique in that fluvial currents surround rather than run through them as it occurs in other karstic regions.

From the geomorphologic viewpoint these are tectonic-structural *horst*, and *horst* and block hills, and dissected tectonic-erosive *horst* and block hills.

Although the hills do not exceed 400 m high because of their nearness to the coast, and for being surrounded by plains, they may be seen from the sea, as it was testified by Admiral Christopher Colombus in his first trip to Cuba. Even though the buttes may be counted by hundreds, some of the most known are the Silla de Gibara Hill, a mogote which shape remembers a saddle, and

Cerro Colorado Hill, like a semicircular cupola having steep walls.

The plains in the region are chiefly abrasive-erosive, abrasive and abrasive-cumulative, and in a lesser extent, abrasive-cumulative partially marshy, of marine origin.

Llanuras y Alturas de Banes-Cacocum. This subregion borders to the south and to the east with the Llanuras y Alturas de Maniabón subregion, and it is made up of block small-mountains, tilted and karstified, and in a greater degree, by tectonic-structural and tectonic-erosive hills, made up of rocks from the ophiolitic complex, and carbonated and terrigenous carbonated rocks from the Paleogene and Neogene.

Their plains, of marine origin, are abrasive and abrasive-denuded, hilly, mainly settled over carbonated-terrigenous sediments from the Paleogene period.

CUBA ORIENTAL [EASTERN CUBA] SUBPROVINCE

This territory is divided into the Noreste [Northeast] district that in turn is subdivided into the Montañas de Nipe-Cristal [Nipe-Cristal Mountains] and the Montañas de Sagua-Baracoa [Sagua-Baracoa Mountains] regions; the Cauto-Guantánamo District, where the Montañas y Alturas de Cauto-Nipe [Cauto-Nipe Mountains and Heights], the Llanura del Valle Central [Central Valley Plain], and the Llanura de Guantánamo [Guantánamo Plain] regions are differed; and the Sierra Maestra District, where the regions Montañas de la Sierra Maestra Occidental [Western Sierra Maestra Mountains], Llanuras de Santiago de Cuba [Santiago de Cuba Plains], and Montañas de la Sierra Maestra Oriental [Eastern Sierra Maestra Mountains] stand out.

Noreste District. It includes the regions Montañas de Nipe-Cristal and Montañas de Sagua-Baracoa.

Montañas de Nipe-Cristal Region. It comprises the Llanura de Sagua de Tánamo [Sagua de Tánamo Plain], the Nipe-Cristal and the Alturas de Mayarí [Mayarí Heights] subregions.

· Llanura de Sagua de Tánamo. It is a northern coastal plain that spreads out from the eastern edge of the Nipe Bay to the western extreme of Moa.

It is made up of abrasive and abrasive-cumulative plains; slightly swampy abrasive-cumulative plains, and fluvial cumulative, low, flat and cumulative plains; and corrosive-cumulative plains, mainly made up over limestone, calcareous marls and sandstone from the Neogene.

The Sagua de Tánamo and de Yaguaneque Bays are among its most important geographic accidents.

· Nipe-Cristal. This unit is located south of the preceding, and it includes the orographic groups of the Sierra del Cristal Range with the Cristal Peak, its topmost height [1231 m], and the Nipe High Plateau with the Pinares de Mayarí Plateau, in which the Loma de la Mensura Hill with 995 m stands out.

It is made up of tectonic-lithologic, *horst* and overthrust *nappes*, tectonic, erosive, low, leveled and dissected mountains systems, and dissected small-mountains, as well as very-small-mountains with an average altitude between 300 m and 750 m.

Serpentinites, serpentinized peridotites, basalt and andesite rocks predominate in this subregion, and also limestone in the edges of the plain.

It is cut through by parts of the riverbeds of the Sagua de Tánamo, Nipe, Levisa and Mayarí Rivers. The Guaro River, one of the tributaries of the Nipe River, has a cascade of about 100 m high. The famous Bitirí natural bridge is in this subregion, a remainder of eroded and destroyed layers in bedded limestone. The Canapú Range is another interesting geographic accident, where there are karstic canyons and caverns in the Farallones de Seboruco; remains of the primitive inhabitants have been found there.

Alturas de Mayarí. It is placed farther to the south than the preceding ones. It is a zone with dissected, folding small-mountains; karstified *horst* low plateaus and block very-small-mountains, constituted in tuffs, andesites, lutites, olistostromes, marls, and so forth.

This zone is historically important, because the headquarter of the II Eastern Front during the Liberation War was located there. The highest hill is 751 m.

Montañas de Sagua-Baracoa Region. It encompasses the Montañas de Moa-Toa-Baracoa [Moa-Toa-Baracoa Mountains], the Meseta del Guaso-Los Montes [Guaso-Los Montes Plateau], the Montañas del Purial-Imías [Purial-Imías Mountains] and the Meseta de Maisí-Zapote [Maisí-Zapote Plateau] subregions.

· Montañas de Moa-Toa-Baracoa. In fact, it includes two types of relief, an abrasive-cumulative and abrasive plain, and hills of considerable altitude for Cuba, known as the Moa, Toa and Baracoa Crests. The latter are low tectonic-lithologic mountains, small- mountains and dissected very-small-mountains, and the Toldo Peak (1175 m) is their topmost point. These mountains are made up of serpentinites, serpentinized peridotites, gabbro-diabases, and gabbros. However, there is the calcareous mountainous area named Farallones de Moa—formed by typical mogotes—that includes the Gran Caverna de Farallones de Moa, a wonderful spelunca, excavated in Eocene limestone, which stands our by a great whiteness, contrasting with the surrounding dark soils and rocks. These mountains have lush tropical vegetation, forests and mighty rivers, such as the Jaguaní, Toa, and Duaba ones, and they are, maybe, the last refuge of the ivory-billed woodpecker *(Campephilus principalis bairdii)*, the largest bird of its genus in the world, and of the "almiquí" *(Solenodon cubanus)*, a paleontologic relic of the Cuban Pleistocene.

· Meseta del Guaso-Los Montes. It is made up of tectonic-lithologic and tectonic-erosive, *horst* low plateau-shaped, karstified mountains; and *horst*, anticlinous and karstified submountains. It mainly includes the hills known as the Guaso Plateau (911 m), made up of hard and recrystallized limestone, and dolimitized limestone from the Medium Eocene, and in a lesser extent, calcareous marls and lutites from the Upper Eocene.

The Guaso, Sagua de Tánamo, and Yateras Rivers begin to flow in the Guaso Plateau; the first one, from the underground drainage that outcrops through several springs in the south side of the plateau. Some of these rivers have carved underground riverbeds, as the Guaso does since it flows through the El Campanario cave, being about 10 km long; others, like the Cuzco River, have caves with a very big gap between their bottoms and roofs, boxed until descending from the elevations for generating electricity by an equipment located in the base. The surface karst of this place has an amazing variety.

· Montañas del Purial-Imías. It includes two well-differentiated geomorphologic regions: San Antonio del Sur with marine abrasive-denuded plains having great aridity and a high degree of karstification of the limestone that made them up, and the El Purial and Imías Hills, where the El Purial Range hills north of the homonymous town are found. The Gato Peak (1181 m) is one of the El Purial Hills.

These are small leveled mountains and also leveled very-small-mountains with hills between 350 m and 500 m, made up of meta-volcanic slates, tuffs, diabases, andesites and other vulcanites, as well as serpentinites in some localities.

The zone—with poor productivity, skeletal soils and xerophitic vegetation much more in the arid coast—, is almost completely devoid of surface drainage. Nevertheless, there are fertile soils in the Caujerí Valley since pre-Colombian times.

The riverbed of the Jauco River is in its eastern extreme—dry except for the rainy season. Its expanse and general circulation of winds cause singular erosion processes in its rough banks.

· Meseta de Maisí-Zapote. It has, just like other physical-geographical units, two differentiated territories: a marine-abrasive and flat abrasive-denuded plain in the eastern coast of the island of Cuba and the Cuban Archipelago, and karstified tilted block small-mountains, and karstified block very-small-mountains.

It is a karstified area as a whole, where limestone and other carbonated sediments from the Neogene and Quaternary predominate, but some hills have been dated from the Jurassic, and are made up of marbles, slates, meta-sandstones and meta-vulcanites.

The marine terraces in several levels stand out in Maisí. The Ameridians left their remains and tools in many caves, like in the La Patana or Los Bichos cave, where the most perfect petroglyphs of the Cuban prehistory were found.

Cauto-Guantánamo District. It includes the Llanura de Guantánamo, the Montañas y Alturas de Cauto-Nipe and the Llanura del Valle Central regions.

Llanura de Guantánamo Region. It comprises the Llanura de Guantánamo [Guantánamo Plain] subregion.

· Llanura de Guantánamo. This physical-geographical unit is made up of abrasive and abrasive-denuded plains of marine origin, and fluvial-marine, deltaic, slightly wavy plains, partly swampy. The subsoil is made up of limestone, calcarenites and marls from the Miocene.

It is a highly populated zone, where bad use or overexploitation of the underground waters caused salinization of soils in some sectors.

The Guantánamo Bay, one of the biggest of Cuba, is in this subregion. It is illegally occupied by a naval base of the United States of America Government and it is a permanent tension focus in the Caribbean.

The biggest salt mines of the national territory are in the Guantánamo Valley, in Caimanera.

Montañas y Alturas de Cauto-Nipe Region. It includes the Llanura de Nipe [Nipe Plain], the Alturas de Báguanos [Báguanos Height], the Llanura del Cauto [Cauto Plain] and the Llanura de Manzanillo [Manzanillo Plain] subregions.

· Llanura de Nipe. They are flat territories consisting of abrasive and abrasive-cumulative plains of marine origin; as well as flat abrasive-cumulative plains, partly swampy, which were developed in Neogene carbonated sediments, having ferrallitic and siallitic soils, where the primary vegetation is nearly completely extinguished because the lands have been used for crops, mainly sugar cane.

It is bathed by the Tacajó and Nipe Rivers, among others, and its most remarkable geographic accident is undoubtedly the Nipe Bay, the bay of the biggest pocket of the Cuban Archipelago that was famous because it had a high shark population.

· Alturas de Báguanos. They are tectonic-lithologic, block, monoclinous, leveled hills being themselves a geomorphologic unit. Marls, clays, calcarenites, and in a less proportion limestone from the Paleogene and Neogene are the prevailing rocks. This subregion is also watered by the Tacajó, Levisa and Mayarí Rivers.

This zone has a good agriculture development, where sugar cane plantations occupy a preponderant place; it means the original vegetation has been notably modified.

· Llanuras del Cauto. This flat subregion is also known as Llanura Cauto-Guacanayabo or Llanura Cauto-Alto Cedro. In this subregion there are deltaic, wavy and flat wavy plains, combined with flat, deltaic plains, partly swampy ones; all of them of a fluvial-marine origin.

Although the plain has a calcareous subsoil on the whole, there is a big thickness of oozes, clays, alluvial sands, varied terrigenous carbonated and marsh peaty deposits from the Holocene and Pleistocene.

This physical-geographical unit is located, as its name indicates, in the valley of the Cauto River—the largest of the Cuban territory. In this valley come together the Buey, Salado, Bayamo, Jobabo Rivers, and many others.

This subregion has highly productive brown humic soils mainly used for sugar cane growing.

It is a territory opened to the Guacanayabo Gulf to which the Cauto River contributes with its fluvial sediments. The ecosystem of the Birama Swamp and the presence, in one of the keys of the river mouth, of large populations of flamingoes nesting there, is an interesting feature.

· Llanura de Manzanillo. This physical-geographical unit, also with coasts in the Guacanayabo Gulf, spreads out along the coast of the Gulf in a southwest direction, and shapes a partially wavy abrasive and abrasive-cumulative plain of marine origin; and an abrasive-cumulative plain, swampy in some places. The chief rocks of this subregion are limestone and calcarenites from the Holocene and Pleistocene, and limestone from the Miocene covered with ferrallitic and fersiallitic soils, and humic soils as well in limited sectors.

The Vicana, Guá and Jibacoa Rivers run across the subregion in different directions, and water the lands sowed with sugar cane and vegetables.

Llanura del Valle Central Region. It includes the Llanura de Palma-San Luis [Palma-San Luis Plain] and the Songo-La Maya subregions.

· Llanura de Palma-San Luis. This subregion is made up of fluvial, erosive, high and hilly plains, and denuded and hilly denuded-erosive plains. It lies in the center of the eastern territory, shaped in terrigenous sediments from the Paleogene and in Quaternary terrigenous sediments in the case of the fluvial plains, in which there is an increasing number of inhabited places; the original natural conditions of these plains are notably altered. It has a secondary vegetation, and sugar cane cropping holds a preponderant place. The Guaninicum River is one of its cheif fluvial streams.

· Songo-La Maya. It is a physical-geographical unit located in the central zone of the eastern territory with plains similar to the preceding subregion, it means, with fluvial and high fluvial-erosive, denuded and denuded-erosive plains; besides, it has block hills, mainly developed in terrigenous and terrigenous-carbonated sediments from the Neogene and Paleogene, and covered with brown soils. In this subregion, there are mainly sugar cane and vegetable growings, the latter for the provision of the population. The Guantánamo, Guaninicum and Mayarí Rivers, among others, water their lands.

Sierra Maestra District. It encompasses the Montañas de la Sierra Maestra Occidental, the Llanuras de Santiago de Cuba and the Montañas de la Sierra Maestra Oriental regions.

Montañas de la Sierra Maestra Occidental Region. It comprises the Llanura y Meseta de Cabo Cruz [Cabo Cruz Plain and Plateau], Alturas de Guisa-Boniato [Guisa-Boniato Heights] and Montañas de la Sierra del Turquino [Sierra del Turquino Mountains] subregions.

· Llanura y Meseta de Cabo Cruz. The Cabo Cruz Plateau is a geomorphologic unit with very especific features that differentiates it from the rest of the territory, aside from occupying the southern extreme of the territory of the island of Cuba. It is surrounded by an abrasive and abrasive-cumulative plain of marine origin, while hills are pseudo-periclinal, block tectonic-structural type.

All these geomorphologic units are shaped in reef limestone from the Miocene and Pleistocene, partial or absolutely devoid of the action of fluvial currents. They also have an unfavorable rain regime, which turn the territory into an arid place, where water is only found in the abundant caverns that drill their rocks. It has, as a general rule, skeletal soils that do not allow for crops. Xerophytic vegetation of dry woodland predominates.

The oscillations of sea level during the Pleistocene and the neotectonic movements have determined the formation of numerous levels of emerged marine terraces, which give a stair appearance to the profile of the place. The caves are remarkable in this territory, like that of Sima de Morlote shaft—with more than 50 m width in its mouth and 78 m deep—, which was discovered thanks to the aviation, because of the difficulties to enter in the location; the El Fustete cave—having a considerable longitudinal development—; and the El Guafe cave, where the Amerindians worshiped their gods sculpting allegorical images in stalagmites.

· Alturas de Guisa-Boniato. It includes the Pilón-Guisa and the III Frente-El Cobre-Boniato geomorphologic units being different between them. The first one is made up of *horst,* anticlinous, karstified submountains, inasmuch as they are made up of notably karstified limestone from the Medium Eocene, and the second one, of *horst* and block mountains, made up of basalt and andesite rocks.

The karstified hills shape the Guisa-Los Negros karstic region, a whole of mogote-shaped hills with poljes, dolines, extensive karrens and caverns that drain part of the volume of the rivers running across its territory, like the Guamá, Bayamo, Contramaestre, Mogote, and others. The La Papelera and Jíbara speluncas are in this subregion. The Jíbara cave is an underground riverbed with various cascades in its inner part, active during the whole year, which has excavated one of the most deep caves of Cuba.

Puerto Boniato, a mountainous port in the western of Santiago de Cuba city is found in the other group of hills. Both groups of hills are located in the north slope of the Sierra Maestra Mountain Range.

Semideciduous forests are still found in the whole subregion, and a part of them has been cleared in order to cultivate coffee.

· Montañas de la Sierra del Turquino. This physical-geographic unit is important because it includes the highest mountains of Cuba, crowned by the Pico Real del Turquino Pike, 1974 m. It is made up of tectonic-erosive, block, massive, deeply dissected medium-sized-mountains with vulcanites from the Paleogene volcanic arc.

Its central axis is parallel to the south coast—from east to west—, and from it, the La Plata, Turquino, and Magdalena Rivers as well as other streams flow southwards; while the Yara, Mogote, Bayamo, Cautillo Rivers, and others, flow northwards.

It presents a hardly altered ecosystem, where several types of tropical vegetation with a certain stratification may be observed, depending on the height. It even preserves pine species endemic of the region *(Pinus maestrensis).* Coffee is the main crop in this lands, which makes this subregion one of the chief coffee-growing territory of the country.

These mountains represented the most important bastion of the revolutionary war developed against Batistas dictatorship that led to the victory of the Cuban Revolution.

Llanuras de Santiago de Cuba Region. It includes the Llanura de Santiago de Cuba [Santiago de Cuba Plain] subregion.

· Llanura de Santiago de Cuba. It encompasses, as a fact, the plain or plains where Santiago de Cuba city —second in importance of the country—is settled, and the buttes having leveled summits that are along the coast, east of the city.

There are fluvial, erosive-cumulative and slightly wavy erosive-cumulative plains with alluvial terrigenous sediments, where the fragments of igneous rocks pre dominate. There are also tectonic-structural, *horst* and block, monoclinous and karstified hills, with leveled summits, like the Daiquirí butte, made up of Neogene limestone. Some lagoons are found in this territory, where even crocodiles may be observed, bordered on the Baconao River, and crossed by the San Juan, Caimanes, El Cobre Rivers and others.

Some remarkable caves are in the karstified zones, like that of Los Majáes,[25] where it may be observed inside the passages and halls a great number of these reptiles, and bats as well.

The Santiago de Cuba Bay is an all-important geographic accident, with an area of 30 sq km, and a narrow mouth that protects it from the open sea.

Montañas de la Sierra Maestra Oriental Region. It includes the Sierra de la Gran Piedra [Gran Piedra Mountain Range], and the Alturas y Montañas de Santa María de Loreto [Santa María de Loreto Heights and Mountains] subregions.

· Sierra de la Gran Piedra. It is composed by low tectonic-lithologic mountains, made up of granites, granodiorites and diorites having a typical morphology, caused by the characteristic exfoliation of the granitoids.

The hill after which the orographic group [1214 m] is named is a well known elevation; it is constituted by a semi-spherical or oval granitic block—which weight is calculated in more than 5000 tons—that occupies the top of a mountain.

The Gran Piedra Range was used as a settlement by many French families that emigrated from Haiti because of the revolution developed in that country in the last century. They built beautiful mansions and took up to coffee growing. The altitude provides a nice though a little wet climate that makes possible the cultivation of some plants, not very common in Cuba.

· Alturas y Montañas de Santa María de Loreto. It is made up of tectonic-structural, monoclinous, little dissected hills with hillsides having steep escarpments. The lower parts of this subregion are made up of granitoids and vulcanites, and the upper ones of limestone displaying a considerable degree of karstification.

The Santa María de Loreto Range is the main orographic group, spanning 12 km long, 2 km in width, and 500 m high.

ISLAS Y LLANURAS SUMERGIDAS DE LA PLATAFORMA SEPTENTRIONAL DE CUBA [ISLES AND SUBMERGED PLAINS OF THE NORTH SHELF OF CUBA] SUBPROVINCE

The following districts[26] stand out: Plataforma Noroccidental [Northwestern Shelf], divided into Llanura Sumergida del Golfo de Guanahacabibes [Submerged Plain of the Guanahacabibes Gulf], and Llanura Sumergida e Islas del Archipiélago Los Colorados [Submerged Plain and Isles of the Los Colorados Archipelago], and Plataforma Centro-Septentrional [Center-Northern Shelf] that is divided into Islas y Llanura Sumergida del Archipiélago Sabana [Submerged Plain and Isles of the Sabana Archipelago], and Islas y Llanura Sumergida del Archipiélago Camagüey [Submerged Plain and Isles of the Camagüey Archipelago].

---

25. The name of this cave means "Cuban boas." *Trans.*

26. Regarding the submerged districts, refer to the epigraph on the subject of Cuban coasts and seas, Chapter IV.

ISLAS Y LLANURAS SUMERGIDAS DE LA PLATAFORMA MERIDIONAL DE CUBA [ISLES AND SUBMERGED PLAINS OF THE SOUTH SHELF OF CUBA] SUBPROVINCE

Llanuras y Alturas del Norte de la Isla de la Juventud Region. It comprises Llanuras y Alturas del Norte de la Isla de la Juventud subregion.

· Llanuras y Alturas del Norte de la Isla de la Juventud. The name of this subregion makes allusion to the plains and hills north of the Isle of Youth; it is made up of karstified *horst* and block tectonic-structural hills, in marbles, calcareous slates from the Jurassic, and leveled *horst* and block tectonic-erosive hills, in slates, meta-sandstones, meta-vulcanites and metamorphic rocks; and also of marine-abrasive and abrasive-cumulative, and flat abrasive-cumulative plains, made up of sandstones, slates and silicites. In the case of fluvial plains having reduced sizes; it may be observed terrigenous sediments which came from the hills and were deposited during the Holocene and Pleistocene.

The territory is cut through the Las Casas River, the main fluvial current, by which the trade and the majority of passengers and all-kind travels arriving to Nueva Gerona, capital of the special municipality is carried out. Also the Medio-Las Nuevas and Siguanea Rivers and small streams run across the territory, many of them dammed in order to allow the watering of the crops.

The karstified marmoraceous hills are the Caballos and Las Casas Ranges that drilled by some gorges and caves, get up with a mogote-shaped profile over the Nueva Gerona Plain. La Cañada, La Daguilla Ranges, and other small hills are slaty.

The territory of the "Isle," as it is commonly named by Cubans, is made up of sandy soil, and there are important citrus fruits and vegetable plantations in it.

Llanuras del Sur de la Isla de la Juventud Region. It includes the Llanuras del Sur de la Isla de la Juventud subregion.

· Llanuras del Sur de la Isla de la Juventud. This name makes allusion to the plains of the south of the Isle of Youth; it is mainly shaped by lacustrine and boggy, cumulative, flat, and swampy plains that form the Lanier Swamp, a natural dividing line between the north and south sectors of the territory, and also by flat marine-abrasive and abrasive-cumulative plains that occupy all the south of that interesting region.

The Lanier Swamp has both terrigenous and marshy peaty deposits that may be gone across by a calcareous bridge named Cayo Piedras. The southern plain is made up of Quaternary limestone and calcarenites. This sector has a very high degree of karstification with many surface karstic forms, but also with small caverns, some of them having great archaeological importance, like the Punta del Este caves. They show remarkable pictographies of the Amerindians that inhabited the zone. Because of their abundance, the De Isla cave [or Número Uno cave] of Punta del Este has been named the Sixtine Chapel of the prehistoric art in Cuba.

CHAPTER VI

THE CUBAN STATE. GOVERNMENT SYSTEM. POLITICAL AND ADMINISTRATIVE STRUCTURES

The Cuban State is ruled by a parliament, denominated *Asamblea Nacional del Poder Popular* [National Assembly of the People's Power], the authority body of this structure that expresses and represents the will of the whole people.

The People's Power, as a nationwide and governmental system, arose in 1976 after a probationary period in the province of Matanzas. This authority body was elected by a great majority of the population (97%) that exercised its right to vote. On February 24th of the same year the Constitution of the Republic of Cuba was aproved by 98% of the citizens that had right to vote. This document gave its distinctive character to the National Assembly, the only one with constituent and legislative faculty.

The members of the National Assembly of the People's Power are called deputies, and they are directly elected from the smallest territorial base (circumscription) for a five-year period. They elect, among them, a president, a vicepresident and a secretary. The deputies to the National Assembly represent all the strata of the population, which freely nominate them according to their personal values, and there is no organization presenting candidates.

The polls of these votings are broach, and they may be attended by anyone. The ballot boxes of the voting are watched over by pioneers.[27]

In the meeting of the National Assembly constitution, in each legislature, the members of the State Council are elected, whose president is in turn the State and Government Head.

The National Assembly of the People's Power has, among its attributions: to approve, to modify or to repeal laws; to discuss and to approve the national plans of the social and economic development and the State budget; to decide the monetary and credit system; to approve the

27. Members of the José Martí Pioneer Organization. *Trans.*

general lines of the foreign and internal policies, and to change the Constitution of the Republic as well.

Also the National Assembly elects the members of the Council of Ministers, the president and the members of the Popular Supreme Court, and of the Attorney-General's Office of the Republic.

All of the national administrative or authority bodies report before the National Assembly in its two ordinary periods of sessions, or in the extraordinary ones if they were convoked.

The deputies to the National Assembly are not professionally trained. They do not receive wages, compensations or any privileges whatsoever. Moreover, they are expected to perform their duties along with their regular jobs.

The Assembly has permanent and temporary commissions. Also there are departaments that permanently work, which must solve internal affairs and those of their functioning in the relationships with the population and the State entities.

The Provincial Assemblies of the People's Power are constitued in each of the provinces of the country, and they are equivalent to the National Assembly in their territories. They are formed also by citizens nominated in public meetings and later elected in popular votings by five-years periods; these elected citizens are denominated delegates. Amongst their members, the provincial assemblies elect a president, a vicepresident and a secretary, that are also members of the Administration Council, the government body in each level.

The Municipal Assemblies of the People's Power are constituted in each municipality of the country with a structure similar to the provincial ones. The assemblies are made up of the delegates elected in the circumscriptions—the smallest cell of the People's Power—for two year-and-a-half periods. The delegates elect, among them,

a president, a vicepresident and a secretary in the first meeting of each legislature; they also have the same responsibilities in the Administration Council, the government body in each municipality.

Some circumscriptions join together, as a flexible way of working, in order to constitute a People's Council, which has proven to be a very valious element in the government and control system in the municipalities, since their members actively work in the control of production and service activities, the most important for the population, among many others.

The Provincial and Municipal Assemblies are known as local bodies of the People's Power; therefore, they perform government functions, manage economic, production and service entities, which are directly subordinated to them, in order to satisfy the necessities of the population of their jurisdiction.

The Provincial and Municipal Assemblies have the following attributions:

· To obey and to make obey the laws and orders coming from the superior bodies of the State.

· To participate in the elaboration of, to approve and to control the technical-economic plan of their respective territories.

· To take agreements about the important subject matters for their territories, and to control their fulfillment.

· To designate and substitute the members of the administration local bodies.

· To propose and to approve or not, the judges of the courts of justice in their territories.

The local bodies help the development of the activities and the fulfillment of the plans of the entities that are located in their territory, but not subordinated to them.

The State Council is the body of the National Assembly of the People's Power that represents it between the periods of ordinary sessions, executes its agreements and fulfills the rest of the functions the Constitution of the Republic of Cuba confers on it. This body is formed by a president, a prime vicepresident, five vicepresidents and a secretary, in addition to other members, up to thirty one.

The State Council has, among its attributions, the following:

· To order the holding of the extraordinary sessions of the National Assembly.

· To decide the date of the elections in order to renew the National Assembly.

· To issue bills between the periods of sessions.

· To give a general and obligatory interpretation to the laws that are still in force, if necessary.

· To exercise the legislative initiative.

· To decree the general mobilization of the whole people, when the defense of the country demands it.

· To assume the faculty of declaring the state of war or of concurring the peace between the periods of sessions of the National Assembly or when it cannot be convoked due to security and urgency reasons.

· To order the holding of referendums, when the National Assembly decides it.

· To substitute the members of the Council of Ministers, between sessions.

· To impart instructions to the Popular Supreme Tribunal and the Attorney-General's Office of the Republic.

The State Council must report about all of its activities to the National Assembly of the People's Power.

The Council of Ministers is the maximum executive and administrative body of Cuba, and constitutes the Government of the Republic. It is formed by a president (who is also the President of the State Council), a prime vicepresident, several vicepresidents, a secretary and the ministers, minister-presidents and presidents of equivalent entities.

The Executive Committee of the Council of Ministers is its most important body. It is formed by the president, the primer vicepresident and the vicepresidents, which control and coordinate, by sectors, the performance of the ministeries and other State central administration bodies.

Among the attributions of the Council of Ministers, there are the following:

· To organize and to guide the fulfillment of politic, economic, cultural, scientific, social and defense actions, decided by the National Assembly.

· To propose the projects of general plans of the economic-social development of the State, which it must organize, guide and control, since they be approved by the National Assembly.

· To guide the foreign policy of the country and the relationships with other states.

· To approve the international treaties in order to submit them for their ratification by the State Council.

· To guide the foreign trade.

· To elaborate the State budget and watch out for its fulfillment, since it be approved.

The Council of Ministers executes the laws and the agreements of the National Assembly, and the bills and dispositions of the State Council.

The Executive Committee may decide about the issues that are attribution of the Council of Ministers, when the urgency of the case demands it.

The president, the prime vicepresident, the six vicepresidents, the secretary, and the 33 administration central bodies form the Council of Ministers, constituting the Cuban Government. From these bodies, 27 are the ministries of: Agriculture; Sugar; Science, Technology and Environment; Foreign Trade; Internal Trade; Communications; Construction; Culture; Economy and Planning; Education; Superior Education; Finances and Prices; Revolutionary Armed Forces; Food Industry; Basic Industry; Light Industry; Fishing Industry; Iron, Steel, Mechanic and Electronic Industry; Interior; Foreign Investment and Economic Cooperation; Justice; Foreign Affairs; Public Health; Work and Social Security; Transport; and Tourism.

Furthermore, the Council of Ministers is formed by the following entities: Cuban Institute of Civil Aeronautics; Cuban Institute of Radio and Television; Cuban Institute of Cinematographic Arts and Industries; National Institute of Sports, Physical Education and Recreation; National Institute of Hydraulic Resources; National Institute of the State Reserve; and also the National Bank of Cuba.

COMMUNIST PARTY OF CUBA AND POLITICAL AND MASSES ORGANIZATIONS

Cuba faced a first half of century distinguished by its political life, where a great number of political parties were linked, in an inseparable way, to an upshot of corruption, abuse, embezzlement, hunger, social abandonment and every kind of discriminations. The victory of the Revolution and the necessity to keep a unique front against the pretensions and aggressiveness of the United States of America Government—that even before the victory used all its resorts to put down the triumphant guerrilla and masses movement—, together with the above mentioned features of the first half of the century, determined the creation of a marxist-leninist party. This party has its antecedents in the Cuban Revolutionary Party, founded last century by the National Hero José Martí, and in the first marxist party founded by Julio Antonio Mella and Carlos Baliño in 1925, and has its most immediate roots in the organizations that arose during the fight against the Batista dictatorship. The Communist Party of Cuba represents the purest interests of every strata of the Cuban population; it strengthens the unity around its unquestionable leader, the Commander-in-Chief Fidel Castro, and around the youngest and historical leaders of the revolutionary process, distinguished by their honesty, courage and total devotion to the revolutionary cause, facing the movement of multiparty system that atomizes and divides the forces, allowing the actions of the declared enemy of the Cuban State.

The Communist Party is the higher leading force of the society and the State that leads the common efforts to the high purposes of the construction of socialism, and the advance towards the communist society (Constitution of the Republic, 1976).

The Party, as it is popularly known, is guided between congresses by a Central Committee elected in its own forum, and which in turn elects, in a secret and direct way, a Political Bureau. The latter has the responsibility for leading the action of the organization in the periods between the plenary meetings of the Central Committee.

The exemplariness principle has always held the first place in the admission process of the citizens to the Party. This principle determines that only those citizens having more outstanding development and more positive positions before the tasks of the country, may compose it. The workers, the members of the armed institutions and the students that wish to go into the Party are elected on this basis in public assemblies, and they are later analyzed by the organization. Definitely, the organization authorizes or not the admission of those citizens. In spite of this severe requirements and the hard economic conditions of the country, after the overthrow of the socialist field, the forces of the Party have increased up to reach more than six hundreds thousands members.

The Political Bureau and the Central Committee do not have an invariable number of members; they are determined in accordance with the membership of the organization. At present, the Political Bureau is made up of 26 members, and of 221 the Central Committee.

Many organizations gather the popular masses in the Cuban civil society, in accordance with their interests, address, political and social aims. They are: the Committees for the Defense of the Revolution (CDRs)[28] created in the first years of the revolutionary process in order to defend the political conquests, and turned into efficient collaborators in all the social tasks; the Federation of Cuban Women (FMC), which gathers all women that wish to join it, and it has developed an extraordinary task in the education of women regarding their rights and duties, in social prevention and welfare, and in numerous fronts. Both organizations have their spheres of jurisdiction in the neighborhoods, the blocks, and the addresses of the population.

The National Association of Small Farmers (ANAP) gathers the independent peasants by themselves, or in cooperatives, do their work. Many of them did not have a piece of land, and the Revolution turned them into land-owners. The Cuban peasantry has a large struggle tradition; they fought in the Independence War against Spain and also constituted the main mass of the Rebel Army.

The Cuban Confederation of Workers (CTC), inheritor of the National Worker Confederation of Cuba (CNOC)—founded by Alfredo López, trade union leader, and Rubén Martínez Villena, general secretary of the first marxist party—gathers 99.4% of the workers of the country, and together with its 20 trade unions it has been in all the struggles of the Revolution.

The Young Communist League (UJC) is a direct inheritor of the Association of Young Rebels, shaped from the integration of several revolutionary organizations in 1960. This political organization comes out itself as a follower of the Party, and as a matter of fact, it has been present in the most difficult tasks, both the productive, and the military ones. In order to work with the students, it rests on the Federation of University Students (FEU), an organization with a rich tradition of struggle and heroism, and on the Federation of Middle Level Students (FEEM), meanwhile it attends the children through the José Martí Pioneers Organization.

Many non-governmental organizations (NGOs) are constituted in Cuba; they have social, scientific, cultural, philantropic, religious, musical, and other interests, and they give great dynamism to the life of the nation, since many of the activities they perform, are interesting to an important part of the population.

POLITICAL-ADMINISTRATIVE DIVISION

Cuba, since the last century, had a political-administrative division that answered to its enslaved nation conditions, where the interests of the Spanish metropolis determined the establishment of 6 provinces and 126 municipalities. The Government of the Republic in Arms decided, since its constitution, not only to keep that division, but also to establish departments with a military character.

This political-administrative structure remained as such during the first half of the twentieth century, even though

---

28. In every organization, you may find between parentheses its abbreviation in Spanish. *Trans.*

some municipalities were added, according to the interests of the dominant classes and to the real development reached by the towns and regions. This structure was changed in 1976 in accordance with the projections and development necessities of the Revolution. Thus, a new political-administrative division was established arranging the country in 14 provinces and 169 municipalities. The provinces, from west to east, are the following: Pinar del Río, 14 municipalities; La Habana, 19; Ciudad de La Habana, 15; Matanzas, 14; Cienfuegos, 8; Villa Clara, 13; Sancti Spíritus, 8; Ciego de Ávila, 10; Camagüey, 13; Las Tunas, 8; Holguín, 14; Granma, 13; Santiago de Cuba, 9; and Guantánamo, 10.

PINAR DEL RÍO

Pinar del Río is the westernmost province of Cuba; it has a territory of 10,924 sq km and a population of 719,000 inhabitants, according to the data of the Multimedia Encyclopaedia *Todo de Cuba-All about Cuba*, published by CEDISAC and Prensa Latina,[29] 1997. It is a predominantly flat territory, but it has the main orographic group of the west: the Guaniguanico Mountain Range. The Pan de Guajaibón, 699 m, is its highest peak, and hence, of the whole west of the country.

Pinar del Río was named "the Cinderella of Cuba" because of the abandon in which its population was before the victory of the Revolution. It is divided into the municipalities: Sandino, Mantua, Guane, San Juan y Martínez, San Luis, Minas de Matahambre, Pinar del Río, Viñales, La Palma, Consolación del Sur, Los Palacios, Bahía Honda, San Cristóbal and Candelaria.

Sandino. It is the westernmost municipality of the country, and it includes the Guanahacabibes Peninsula, a

---

29. They mean: Design Center of Automated and Computing Systems, and Latin Press. *Trans.*

wonderful territory, scarcely subject to the man destructive action. The Roncali lighthouse is in its extreme, a witness of the colonial epoch. It has a surface area of 1711 sq km, and a population of 40,000 inhabitants. Its chief wealth is the forest one, and citrus fruits as well. The new forest areas are a natural refuge for the wild fauna.

Guane. It is located northeast of the preceding municipality, having a surface area of 715 sq km and 36,309 inhabitants. The main fluvial current of the western, the Cuyaguateje River, flows into its coasts. Its chief economic wealth is the tobacco cropping.

Mantua. It has a surface area of 906 sq km and a population of 26,000 inhabitants. Its head, with the same name, is the westernmost Cuban town. The General Deputy of the Liberating Army, Antonio Maceo, in 1896 with expertise, courage and intelligence, led towards this town the invading column from Mangos de Baraguá, expanding the war for the independence from Spain to the whole national territory. Mining is its main wealth.

Minas de Matahambre. It has a population of 36,170 inhabitants, in a territory of 856 sq km, where not only a large part of the Los Órganos Range and some of its most extraordinary geographic accidents are, but also the sink of the Cuyaguateje River, the Hoyo de Potrerito Valley, and the Resolladero cave; all of them linked with the erosive action of the Cuyaguateje River.

Mining and tobacco are its principal wealth. The mines, one of the deepest and most ancient of the New World, are economically exhausted. This municipality has cavern systems like Amistad, Majaguas-Cantera (one of the largest of the Cuban territory), Pío Domingo-Soterráneos and others.

San Juan y Martínez. It has 420 sq km of surface area with 47,000 inhabitants. In spite of part of its territory is mountainous (Alturas de Pizarras del Sur Hills), the largest part of the tobacco of the province is cultivated here.

Viñales. It is a famous territory famous because of its tourist wealth. It has 700 sq km with a population of 26,136 inhabitants. It produces tobaccos and minor fruits. The contrast of its valleys with the calcareous mogotes reveals very beautiful landscapes. In the Viñales Range, one of its orogenic groups, there is the Palmarito cavern system that is the largest of Cuba, being 49 km long nowadays. There is also a big cavern: Santo Tomás, with 45 km of underground passages.

Pinar del Río. It is the head municipality of the province, and Pinar del Río city, the most important of the western, is situated in it. It has a surface area of 684 sq km and 181,185 inhabitants, who mainly live in the city. It is a flat territory where citrus fruits, tobacco, other fruits, and pasture are cultivated; it has some tourist centers.

San Luis. With a triangular shape, it is located in the center-south of the province, between San Juan y Martínez (to the west) and Pinar del Río (to the east) municipalities. It has a surface area of 336 sq km, and a population of 33,705 inhabitants. Its southern part is totally coastal—bathered by the Caribbean Sea—and occupies the section between Punta de Cartas Point, to the west, and Las Cañas Beach, at La Coloma Inlet, to the east. Guamá River flows into this section. Its main wealth are tobacco and minor fruits.

La Palma (former Consolación del Norte). It has a population of 35,185 inhabitants, and a surface area of 622 sq m that includes part of Los Órganos Range, the Alturas de Pizarras del Norte Hills, the intramountainous valleys southwards, and the marshy zones in the north coast. It is a municipality that also has some mining wealth, areas for cattle breeding, and so forth.

Consolación del Sur. Agriculture and livestock are the chief economic staples of this territory of 1125 sq km that has 84,797 inhabitants; it is one of the most populated municipalities in the province. The territory is flat, and it is crossed by the National Highway that favours its communications.

Los Palacios. It has 39,405 inhabitants with a surface area of 786 sq km. The famous spa of mining-medicinal waters named San Diego de los Baños is there, in the north part of the area. The south of the municipality is marshy, fitting for rice growing. There, the rice is cultivated with good productivity.

Bahía Honda. It is a coastal municipality that occupies the northeastern part of the province. It has 47,180 inhabitants in a territory of 796 sq km. El Rosario Range, Biosphere Reserve, is located in part of the municipality. The municipal head is one of the most important towns of the region. The municipality has two ports with good depth: Bahía Honda and Cabañas. It produces sugar and minor fruits; there are also some mines.

San Cristóbal. It is a territory, with flat and swampy zones in the south and mountains of the El Rosario Range in the north. It has a surface area of 918 sq km with 67,365 inhabitants. It produces sugar cane and minor fruits. The Los Perdidos cavern system, with more than 25 km of passage, is located in this municipality.

Candelaria. This small municipality of just 265 sq km and 18,773 inhabitants occupies the eastern and southeastern utmost tip of the province. Its economy rests mainly on minor fruits, sugar cane, tobacco, coffee cropping, and livestock. Remains of coffee plantations belonging to the colonial epoch are found in the mountains of the north part. There are also places of an extraordinary beauty that determined the construction of Soroa tourist center in that area.

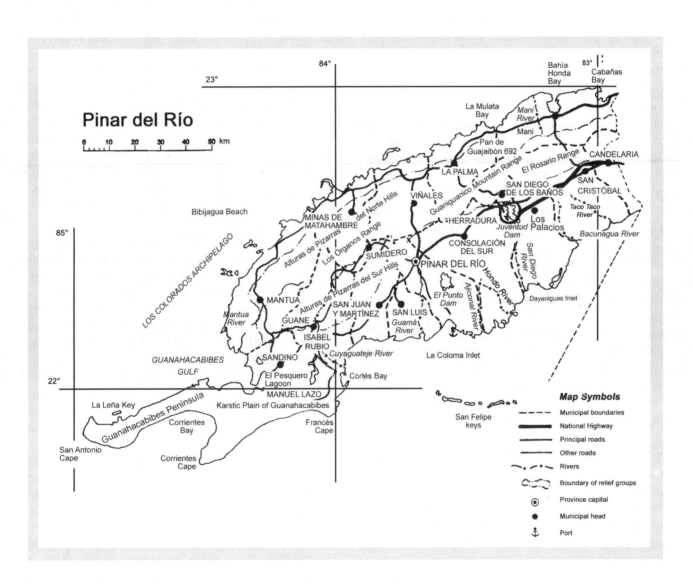

Pinar del Río

0 10 20 30 40 50 km

23°

84°

83°

Bahía Honda Bay

Cabañas Bay

La Mulata Bay

Maní River

Maní

Pan de Guajaibón 692

El Rosario Range

CANDELARIA

LA PALMA

Guaniguanico Mountain Range

SAN DIEGO DE LOS BAÑOS

SAN CRISTÓBAL

VIÑALES

Taco Taco River

Bibijagua Beach

del Norte Hills

HERRADURA

Los Palacios

MINAS DE MATAHAMBRE

Alturas de Pizarras

Los Organos Range

Juventud Dam

Bacunagua River

85°

CONSOLACIÓN DEL SUR

San Diego River

LOS COLORADOS ARCHIPELAGO

SUMIDERO

PINAR DEL RÍO

MANTUA

Alturas de Pizarras del Sur Hills

SAN JUAN Y MARTÍNEZ

El Punto Dam

Ajiconal River

Hondo River

Dayaniguas Inlet

Mantua River

GUANE

SAN LUIS

Guamá River

ISABEL RUBIO

Cuyaguateje River

La Coloma Inlet

GUANAHACABIBES GULF

SANDINO

El Pesquero Lagoon

Cortés Bay

22°

La Leña Key

MANUEL LAZO

Karstic Plain of Guanahacabibes

San Felipe keys

Map Symbols

Guanahacabibes Peninsula

Corrientes Bay

Francés Cape

– – – Municipal boundaries

██ National Highway

—— Principal roads

—— Other roads

–·–·– Rivers

Boundary of relief groups

⊙ Province capital

● Municipal head

⚓ Port

San Antonio Cape

Corrientes Cape

LA HABANA

Although it is a province that stands out for its large agricultural yield, vegetables above all, La Habana is one of the most industrialized provinces of the country. It has a population of 673,392 inhabitants, and a surface area of 5370.5 sq km. It is mainly a flat region, in its southern sector above all, but low-lying elevations like the La Habana-Matanzas and Bejucal-Madruga groups of hills may be observed.

Its distinctive features consist of having the largest number of municipalities (19), even though it has a small area, and that its capital is also that of the neighboring province of Ciudad de La Habana, and in turn, of the whole Republic. The province is divided into the municipalities: Alquízar, Batabanó, Bauta, Caimito, Guanajay, Güines, Güira de Melena, Jaruco, Madruga, Mariel, Melena del Sur, Nueva Paz, Quivicán, San Antonio de los Baños, San José de las Lajas and San Nicolás de Bari.

Alquízar. It is an eminently flat municipality. It has a population of 25,569 inhabitants, and a surface area of 192 sq km. The agricultural yield is its chief economic staple, including sugar cane cropping. It has textile and construction industries, among others.

In its borders with the neighboring municipality, Artemisa, it has a whole of flooded caves where those of Astón stand out, very beautiful caves because of its submerged secondary formations in clean underground waters.

Artemisa. Its municipal capital is the homonymous town, prosperous, one of the largest of the province. It is also the place from where the largest number of young men went away in 1953 to attack the Moncada and Carlos Manuel de Céspedes garrisons, in Santiago de Cuba and Bayamo, respectively, in order to begin the revolutionary war. It has a surface area of 719 sq km with a population of 74,991 inhabitants. Its economy rests on sugar cane, vegetables—mainly banana—cropping, and in sugar and construction materials industries (cement, floor tiles, and so forth). In the former political-administrative division, it belonged to Pinar del Río.

Batabanó. It has an aboriginal name that means "chief's residence." It is a municipality of the south coast, such as those above mentioned, but its coast becomes low and marshy and is covered with mangroves. The municipal head, of same name, is usually flooded by waters in cyclones and rainy periods. Its population comprises 25,329 inhabitants, in a surface area of 186 sq km. Minor fruits, sugar cane and vegetables are cultivated in the lands of this municipality, and there is also livestock. Nevertheless, one of its most important economic staples is fishing, carried out from the homonymous port. The industry related with this fishing (chiefly, lobsters, shrimps and also scale fishes) is the most important one. The island of Cuba is linked by sea with the Isle of Youth from Surgidero de Batabanó by ferries and hovercrafts known as *kometas.*

Bauta. It is a northern municipality, almost totally flat, with a population of 39,816 inhabitants and 157 sq km of surface area. It is one of the most ancient municipalities of the province, moreover it is one of the oldest populated places in the territory of the province (since the sixteenth century). The Laguna de Ariguanabo is one of the most known but less preserved geographic accidents, because this lagoon is practically dry.

Antonio Maceo, General Deputy of the Liberating Army, died in combat against the Spanish colonialists in San Pedro, located south of the municipality. He was one of the most important and popular patriots of the independence wars in Cuba.

The Ariguanabo textile factory stands out in the economic sphere; it is one of the largest and most productive of the country. Also sugar cane and vegetables cropping and livestock stand out.

Bejucal. This municipality bounds with the province of Ciudad de La Habana in its northernmost extreme. It is one of the most mountainous of La Habana; precisely in its lands the elevations of the Bejucal-Madruga group begin and it ends in Coliseo and Limonar, Matanzas. It is also an ancient municipality, and it has the privilege of having been the end of the first sector of the railway inaugurated in Cuba in 1837, first than in the Spanish metropolis. Livestock, sugar cane agriculture, and the existence of some research centers are the chief economic and scientific attractiveness.

It has a population of 22,048 inhabitants and a surface area of 119 sq km.

The monument that stores away the human remains of General Antonio Maceo and his adjutant Captain Francisco (Panchito) Gómez Toro is in the El Cacahual Hill, where the elevations of the Bejucal-Madruga-Coliseo group begin.

Caimito. It is a municipality of the north part of the province that has a population of 31,930 inhabitants and a surface area of 238 sq km. The Mesa de Anafe (or Loma del Esperón Hill), a really two-steps plateau, is located in its central part. Its main production is related to citrus fruits and the industry that processes them; sugar cane, livestock and some industries, like the carbide factory, one of the few of its kind in the country.

Guanajay. It belonged, together with the neighboring municipality of Artemisa, to the province of Pinar del Río before the present political-administrative division. It has a surface area of 112 sq km and a population of 28,018 inhabitants. It is a flat territory, although in its eastern part it includes the Esperón Range that is the last vestige of the Western Guaniguanico Range, together with the Jobo Hills, according to some authors. Its economy rests on vegetables and sugar cane growing, and also cattle breeding.

Güines. It is one of the southeastern municipalities of the province, with a large productive tradition in vegetables cropping, because of its fertile soils and the abundance of the waters of the Mayabeque River that runs across in part, in spite of being a karstified territory. It has a surface area of 445 sq km and a population of 69,647 inhabitants. Villa de Güines, maybe the biggest town of the province, was the last place of the second sector of the Cuban railway, in 1838.

Among the municipal economic staples, mining—with the finding of phosphorites—holds, nowadays, an important place.

Güira de Melena. It is a municipality of the southwest of the province; considered the major producer of potatoes in the country; moreover it is one of the greatest vegetables producers. It is a flat and marshy territory in the south coast, where its scanty beaches, are found among marshy zones. It has a population of 35,187 inhabitants and a surface area of 177 sq km. The submerged cave named Juanelo Piedra, with a flooded passage having more than 100 m and a fauna of blind (anolphthalmic) fishes and shrimps, is found in this territory.

Jaruco. It is one of the municipalities with the most vigorous relief of the province owing to the presence of the Escaleras de Jaruco Range and other smaller elevations that give to this zone a mogote-shaped appearance. This is particularly beauty, with its hills and valleys, some of them hanging, profusely covered with a typical vegetation of this kind of relief. The caves are common in these hills, and because of it and its strategic position, it was a very important place for colonialists and patriots; the latter organized blood hospitals in its caves, and even, in one of them they buried General José M. Aguirre when he died owing to the wounds received in combat. It has a population of 26,310 inhabitants and a surface area of 277 sq km.

From the economic viewpoint, it has characterized by the yield of diverse produce, and the presence of factories of support elements to geological and oil prospecting.

Madruga. It is the central-eastern municipality of the province, having a population of 30,693 inhabitants in a surface area of 463 sq km. It has wavy plains southwards, and northwards, the El Grillo Range and La Gloria Hill, as well as the Pipián Hills that are part of the chain of elevations which starts in Bejucal. It was a famous territory during a span because of the existence of sulphurous waters. Nowadays, sugar cane and vegetables growing, and livestock as well, are its chief staples.

Mariel. It occupies the utmost northwestern extreme of the province, and has an excellent bottle bay, the Mariel Bay, with an intense maritime traffic. The industry of construction materials (cement), the production of electricity and sugar cane growing are its main economic staples. It has 40,110 inhabitants in a surface area of 269 sq km. The Naval Academy, where the officials of the Cuban Marine use to be formed, was in the territory during a lengthy span.

Melena del Sur. It has a surface area of 269 sq km, with 20,065 inhabitants. It is a coastal, southern and flat municipality, with part of the littoral swamp in its coast, though there are the small hills of Guanal northwards. It was the first municipality of the country stated free of illiteracy in 1961, when the Literacy Campaigne was accomplished. The agriculture is its chief income source.

Nueva Paz. It is the southeasternmost municipality of the province, and bounds to the north with Madruga. It has a population of 23,814 inhabitants, and a surface area of 514 sq km. Since it is a southern municipality, has swampy coasts, at such extent that some lagoons of the territory has been inhabited by crocodiles, like the lagoon having same name, and those of Guanamón and Báez. The production of cane sugar, and the sugar cane and vegetable

growings as well, are its economic resources, in addition to factories of food and light industries.

Quivicán. It has a population of 27,275 inhabitants and 283 sq km of surface area. It is part of the southern karstic plain, covered with ferralitic red soils; it has numerous caves, like Insunsa and El Túnel, important phossiliferous beds.

The sugar cane cropping and its production, as well as the vegetables growing and their industrial processing are the most important activities from the economic viewpoint.

San Antonio de los Baños. With 126 sq km, this municipality of the central zone of the province is one of the most prosperous in the territory. With a population of 40,863 inhabitants, it has been stated as the "humor capital," because of the presence of many actors, caricaturists and other people linked to the laugh, native to this place.

The Virginia tobacco cropping and its later processing are the economic activities of the territory, where the yield of vegetables, citrus fruits and another fruits also stand out.

It is a karstic territory where there are plenty of caverns, like those of Sandoval and Paredones that are important paleontological beds. In the latter, mushrooms are also cultivated.

The International Movie and Television School, a laudable initiative of the New Latin American Movie Foundation is located in this municipality.

San José de las Lajas. It is a central territory of the province bordering with the capital, with a surface area of 591 sq km and 61,793 inhabitants. It is an eminently industrial zone, having an important burden in construction materials, basic, food and light industries. Agriculture also holds an important place, and there are research and teaching centers as well.

The Guara Hills and the foothills of the Escaleras de Jaruco are eastwards, where caves like that of El Indio or Los Bichos, located in a dry karstic canyon, known as Boquete de la Jaula, are found.

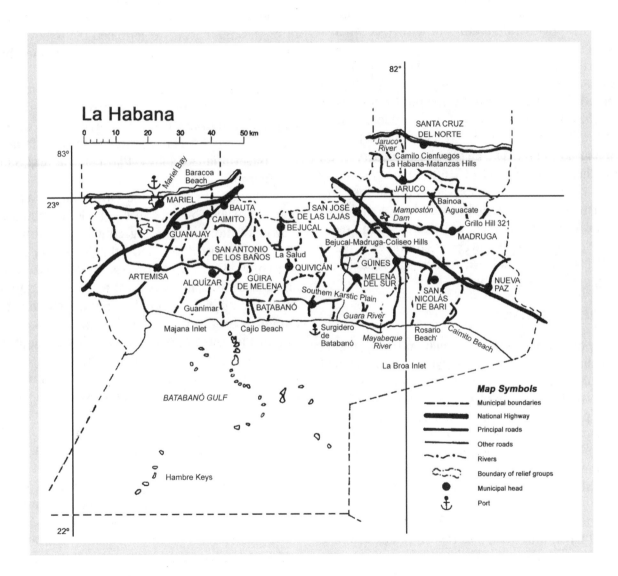

La Habana

0 10 20 30 40 50 km

SANTA CRUZ
DEL NORTE

Jaruco
River
Camilo Cienfuegos
La Habana-Matanzas Hills

JARUCO

Bainoa
Aguacate

Mariel Bay
Baracoa
Beach

MARIEL
BAUTA
CAIMITO
GUANAJAY

SAN JOSÉ
DE LAS LAJAS
BEJUCAL

Mampostón
Dam

Grillo Hill 321
MADRUGA

SAN ANTONIO
DE LOS BAÑOS
La Salud

Bejucal-Madruga-Coliseo Hills

ARTEMISA

ALQUÍZAR
GÜIRA
DE MELENA

QUIVICÁN
GÜINES
MELENA
DEL SUR
NUEVA
PAZ

SAN
NICOLÁS
DE BARI

Guanimar
BATABANÓ
Southern Karstic Plain

Guara River

Majana Inlet
Cajío Beach
Surgidero
de
Batabanó
Mayabeque
River
Rosario
Beach
Caimito Beach

La Broa Inlet

BATABANÓ GULF

Hambre Keys

Map Symbols

– – – – –	Municipal boundaries
▬▬▬▬	National Highway
▬▬▬▬	Principal roads
———	Other roads
–·–·–·–	Rivers
⌁⌁⌁	Boundary of relief groups
●	Municipal head
⚓	Port

San Nicolás de Bari. It is a southern municipality, swampy in the coast, with an important sugar production, in addition to livestock and other industies. It has a population of 21,085 inhabitants in a surface area of 242 sq km.

Santa Cruz del Norte. It occupies the utmost north-eastern extreme of the province, having an important place in its economy because of the industrial production (rums, like the worldwide famous Havana Club; cardboards; electricity, and so forth), and of the presence of a petroleum field, working nowadays. The biggest sugar refinery of the country is there in the Camilo Cienfuegos sugar mill. It has a population of 30,036 inhabitants and a surface area of 373 sq km. In the zones of Boca de Jaruco and Jíjira Point of this municipality there are many caverns registered by speleologists, where diverse archaeological places are found. The Jibacoa and Arroyo Bermejo beaches are places of a great tourist interest.

CIUDAD DE LA HABANA

The territory of this province is very built-up (there are only some agricultural areas in the outskirts), and it is occupied, almost completely, by Ciudad de La Habana—Havana city— that has the triple condition of capital of this province, of La Habana province, and of the Republic of Cuba.

The largest population of the whole archipelago (2,500,000 inhabitants) is concentrated here, and the State and Government central bodies, as well as the national levels of political and masses' organizations are in this province.

It has a reduced surface area (739.9 sq km), most of it having a flat relief, with small hills that do not exceed hundreds of meters in urban zones.

Havana city was located, in its beginning, in the south coast of the current province of La Habana, near to Surgidero de Batabanó town, but the continuous attacks of pirates and corsairs determined the removal in 1519 to its present location in the north coast, bathed by the Atlantic Ocean waters.

The capital is divided, from the administrative viewpoint, into 15 municipalities: Arroyo Naranjo, Boyeros, Centro Habana, Cerro, Cotorro, Diez de Octubre, Guanabacoa, La Habana del Este, La Habana Vieja, La Lisa, Marianao, Playa, Plaza, Regla and San Miguel del Padrón.

Although after 1959, the Government has followed a policy directed towards an equitable distribution of several institutions (regarding education, culture, science, health, administration, and others), certain activities are concentrated in some territories. In that respect, the Plaza and Playa municipalities have a privileged situation, because the majority of the State and Government central administration bodies, theaters, universities and scientific institutions are concentrated there. These two territories are in the littoral of the province, together with Centro Habana, having a large burden in the commercial life; La Habana Vieja—stated Mankind Heritage by UNESCO—, noteworthy because of the preservation of its colonial architecture of many centuries; La Habana del Este; and in part, Regla—showing to the La Habana Bay.

The municipalities of Cerro, Diez de Octubre—the most inhabited of the province—, Cotorro, Guanabacoa and San Miguel del Padrón are the most industrialized, while Cotoro, Arroyo Naranjo, Boyeros—where the José Martí International Airport is placed—, La Habana del Este and La Lisa, have the largest area without urbanizing.

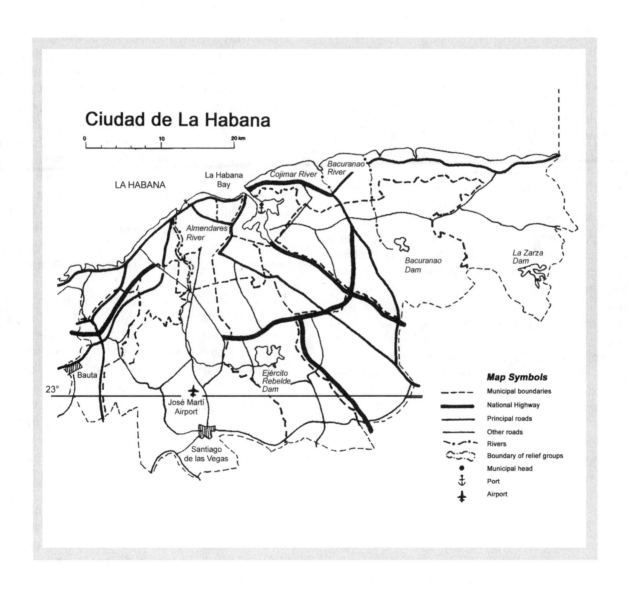

Ciudad de La Habana

0   10   20 km

LA HABANA

La Habana Bay

Cojimar River

Bacuranao River

Almendares River

Bacuranao Dam

La Zarza Dam

Bauta

23°

Ejército Rebelde Dam

José Martí Airport

Santiago de las Vegas

Map Symbols

- - - - Municipal boundaries

━━━━ National Highway

──── Principal roads

──── Other roads

─·─· Rivers

⌒⌒⌒ Boundary of relief groups

● Municipal head

⚓ Port

✈ Airport

MATANZAS

It follows the largest province in the surface area of the national territory, with 11,978 sq km and 635,532 inhabitants. It is one of the territories having fewer population density in the island of Cuba, more plains, and the biggest burden in the agricultural yield, mainly citrus fruits, minor fruits, sugar cane and vegetable production. It is divided into 14 municipalities: Ciénaga de Zapata, Matanzas, Varadero, Cárdenas, Unión de Reyes, Limonar, Pedro Betancourt, Jovellanos, Perico, Colón, Los Arabos, Jagüey Grande, Calimete and Martí.

Ciénaga de Zapata. It has a population of 8267 inhabitants and a surface area of 4230 sq km; therefore, it is the municipality with the largest territorial extension and the smallest population of the country. It is just restricted to the territory of the Zapata Swamp, a zone with a great biodiversity and natural wealth. It is a fragile environment, and this feature impedes the intense exploitation of some of its economic possibilities, like turf, used for the construction of combustible briquettes. Nevertheless, it is a zone of wide tourist possibilities. In this province lies the largest lake of the country: the Laguna del Tesoro with 16 sq km of water area that has an important population of fishes, amongst its attributes, at such extent that it has held during many years the record of the biggest "trout" (16 kg) of the world.

Playa Girón and Playa Larga are two beaches in the coast of the Cochinos Bay, south of this big wetland, that became known in the world for having been the scene of the landing in 1961 of a mercenary brigade—armed, trained and supported by the United States of America Government—that attempted to overthrow the Cuban Government, and suffered an overwhelming defeat in less than seventy two hours.

Matanzas. This municipality shelters a population of 129,702 inhabitants in a surface area of 316 sq km. The municipal head, the homonymous city, is also the provincial capital, and has such a rank since the seventeenth century; it has been denominated "the Athens of Cuba," due to its cultural institutions.

One of the distinctive features of this territory is that it has some caverns in the urban area, like the famous Bellamar cave, probably one of the most ancient tourist centers of the country. The Yumurí Valley is other interesting tourist place because of its natural beauties; the San Juan and San Agustín Rivers flow by this valley through the Yumurí canyon, emptying into the Matanzas Bay. This bay is one of the harbors with bigger trade traffic in the national territory. Near to it, there are some important national factories, like the Rayonera (a rayon factory), a factory of sulfur products, and one of the newly made thermoelectric plants in Cuba. Recently, the installation of a port for supertankers in order to receive the necessary crude oil to local and national economy was finished.

Varadero. It is the tourist place par excellence of Cuba. It has a population of 18,252 inhabitants in a surface area of 22 sq km. It is completely framed in the Hicacos Peninsula that is 18.6 km long, of which almost all are in its north coast of white sand beaches and warm waters. Many investments has been accomplished in lodgings, an international airport and other works that guarantee the reasonable development of this territory for the international tourism. There are consolidated sandy dunes where caves have been excavated; there, the aborigines have left samples of their pictorial art, such as the Ambrosio cave and others.

Cárdenas. It has a population of 91,490 inhabitants in a surface area of 570 sq km with a mainly flat relief. The geological researches proved the existence of petroleum in its plains and submarine shelf; that is why at present, a field of this important fuel is being exploited, and the studies are expanding. Sugar cane is the chief industry in the zone, and it also produces high-grade drinks. Even though it is not a totally karstified territory, there are remarkably caverns.

Unión de Reyes. It occupies a surface area of 856 sq km with a flat relief, and has 42,499 inhabitants. Its chief economic resources are the sugar cane growing and livestock. It bounds to the south with Ciénaga de Zapata.

Limonar. It has a population of 23,747 inhabitants, distributed in a surface area of 449 sq km. It is one of the municipalities of Matanzas presenting highest height, because of the presence of the Guacamaro Range, the end of the Bejucal-Madruga-Coliseo (Limonar) orographic group. The El Jacán Hill, made up of serpentine rocks and other ultrabasites, is found there. In San Miguel de los Baños there are springs of high-grade thermal waters that determined the construction of the spa of same name. Sugar cane and livestock are the greatest important economic staples.

Pedro Betancourt. This municipality receives its name in honor of a patriot, General Pedro Betancourt, who during the Independence War took up arms in this territory and later was officer in command of a *mambí*[30] division that fought there. It has 31,596 inhabitants and a surface area of 387 sq km. The production of cane sugar, cereals and vegetables, and livestock as well, are the main economic resources of the territory.

Jovellanos. It was before named Bemba, and owes its current name to Gaspar Melchor Jovellanos. It has a population of 54,987 inhabitants and its surface area is of 504 sq km. Cane sugar and livestock are its most important economic staples.

Perico. It shelters a population of 1218 inhabitants in a surface area of 267 sq km. It is a territory with scanty fluvial currents, nevertheless the Roque canal brings wa-

30. During the independence wars the Spaniards called *mambises* (*mambí* in singular) to Cuban insurgents, members of the Liberating Army. *Trans.*

ter from another zones to these water-deficit regions. Sugar cane is its chief production.

Colón. It is a municipality that has a great economic importance for being in the center of the extensive Colón plain, of which it occupies a surface area of 597 sq km. Agriculture holds the preponderant staple of its production, where vegetables, sugar cane and tobacco stand out. Its cattle wealth is not negligible, that is why it holds a significant place in the province. It has a population of 68,932 inhabitants. Part of the flow of the Hanábana River, the natural border with the province of Cienfuegos, is in its territory.

Los Arabos. This municipality has a population of 635,532 inhabitants and a surface area of 762 sq km. It is an eminently flat territory, unlike others having karstic character; it is crossed by some fluvial currents, like La Palma, Palmillas Rivers and others. Its chief economic staples are sugar production and livestock.

Jagüey Grande. It is the Cuban territory of the largest yield of citrus fruits of the country, together with the Isle of Youth, to both of which the industry for its processing is associated. Its agriculture is well developed regarding with vegetables. It has a population of 53,527 inhabitants and a surface area of 881 sq km. It borders with Ciénaga de Zapata to the south, and with Aguada de Pasajeros of the province of Cienfuegos to the east. It is an eminently karstic zone, with abundant underground waters, although the Hanábana River that is a natural border, flows across its plains.

Calimete. It shelters a population of 29,716 inhabitants and has a surface area of 957 sq km. Sugar cane agriculture and rice cropping are its most important productions. It borders with the swamp by the south.

Martí. It was before named Hato Nuevo and Guamutas, and occupies part of the north coast of the province, where there are marshy zones like the Majaguillar and Sabanasí

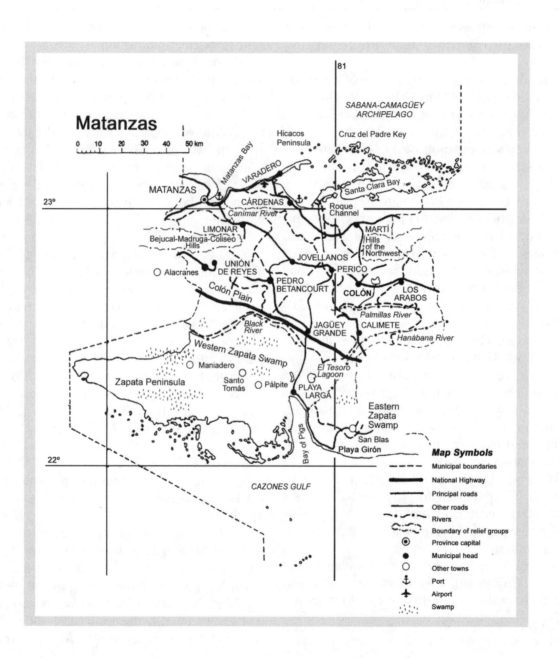

Matanzas

0 10 20 30 40 50 km

SABANA-CAMAGÜEY ARCHIPELAGO

Cruz del Padre Key

Hicacos Peninsula

Matanzas Bay

VARADERO

MATANZAS

Santa Clara Bay

CÁRDENAS

23°

Canímar River

Roque Channel

LIMONAR

MARTÍ

Bejucal-Madruga-Coliseo Hills

Hills of the Northwest

JOVELLANOS

UNIÓN DE REYES

PERICO

Alacranes

PEDRO BETANCOURT

COLÓN

LOS ARABOS

Colón Plain

Palmillas River

JAGÜEY GRANDE

CALIMETE

Black River

Hanábana River

Western Zapata Swamp

El Tesoro Lagoon

Zapata Peninsula

Maniadero

Santo Tomás

Pálpite

PLAYA LARGÁ

Eastern Zapata Swamp

San Blas

Playa Girón

22°

Bay of Pigs

CAZONES GULF

81

Map Symbols

- – – – Municipal boundaries
- ▬▬▬ National Highway
- ───── Principal roads
- ───── Other roads
- –··–··– Rivers
- ⌒⌒⌒ Boundary of relief groups
- ⊙ Province capital
- ● Municipal head
- ○ Other towns
- ⚓ Port
- ✈ Airport
- ⋮⋮⋮ Swamp

Swamps. South of the coastal zone there are some elevations of the group of the Alturas del Noroeste, while the south of the territory is eminently flat. It is gone across by some rivers and streams, among them, La Palma, El Jigüe and Júcaro. It has a population of 25,004 inhabitants and 937 sq km of surface area. Sugar cane agriculture and industry are its chief economic staples.

CIENFUEGOS

It is a province that arose with the new political-administrative division, because in former days its territory was part of the disappeared province of Las Villas. It has coasts only in the south, facing the Caribbean Sea.

It has a high industrial potential, with food products and cement factories, a refinery, a thermoelectric plant, and others. The first nuclear power plant of Cuba (CEN)[31] was placed in its territory, whose works have not been finished even today, because of nonfulfilments of the commercial partner, the disappeared Soviet Union. In each locality of the territory a steady self-supplying agriculture has been developed. It has a population of 383,138 inhabitants and a surface area of 4177.9 sq km with a preponderantly flat relief, but it vigorously gets up in the Trinidad Mountains in the Guamuhaya group, southeastwards. According to the political-administrative division, there are the municipalities: Aguada de Pasajeros, Abreus, Rodas, Palmira, Santa Isabel de las Lajas, Cruces, Cumanayagua and Cienfuegos.

Aguada de Pasajeros. It has a surface area of 680 sq km and a population of 30,521 inhabitants. It is an almost completely flat territory, bordering with some municipalities of Matanzas; Ciénaga de Zapata is one of them, and the riverbed of the Hanábana River separates both mu-

31. It is its abbreviation in Spanish. *Trans.*

nicipalities. Sugar cane agriculture and cane sugar industry are its most important productions (two sugar mills are placed in its lands), together with livestock and the production of construction materials, like the marmorized limestone called Real Campiña, having great demand in civilian buildings because of its diverse varieties.

Abreus. It has a surface area of 563 sq km in a territory flat on the whole, and slightly wavy; it is got over in part by the Damují River, one of the largest of the province. It has a population of 28,664 inhabitants. Cane sugar production is its chief economic staple, although it also has good production of vegetables. The nuclear power plant (CEN) is placed in this territory.

Rodas. It houses 32,697 inhabitants in a surface area of 551 sq km, above all, flat. Its lands are bathed by the Hanábana, Damují and Santa Catalina Rivers, among others. Sugar cane agriculture, the cane sugar production, and cattle breeding, are its main economic staples.

Santa Isabel de las Lajas. It has a population of 23,429 inhabitants in a surface area of 430 sq km of plains. It is crossed by streams and small rivers, among them the Lajas River, that has small waterfalls in its flow. The most important industry in the territory is the sugar one. Lajas has the honor of having been cradle of Bartolomé Moré, more known as Benny Moré, a famous and immortal musician and performer, that took up the Cuban music to international scenes.

Palmira. It is a flat territory of 318 sq km with a population of 32,911 inhabitants. The sugar mills placed in the municipality process the sugar cane planted in its extensive fields. Also limestone and marmorized limestone that are used in the construction industry are exploited.

Baños de Ciego Montero, springs of medicinal waters known since the last century, are located in this municipality. It was here where, for the first time, remains of land vertebrates from the Pleistocene of Cuba, later identified as *Megalocnus rodens* were found.

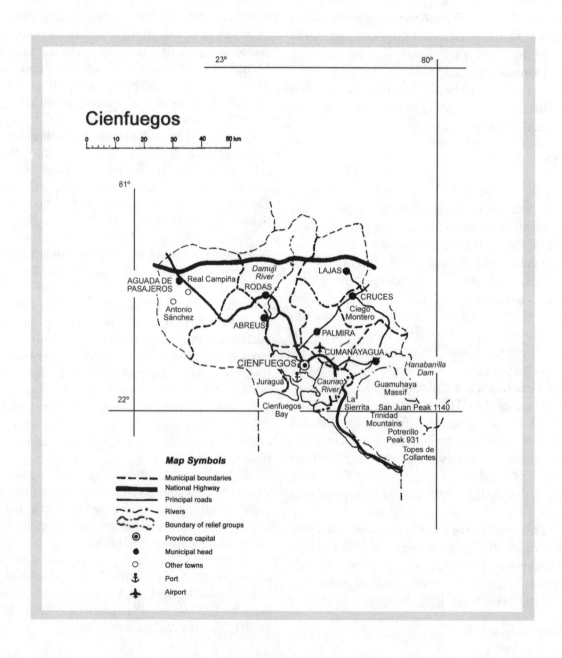

Cienfuegos

0 10 20 30 40 50 km

Symbol	Description
	Municipal boundaries
	National Highway
	Principal roads
	Rivers
	Boundary of relief groups
◎	Province capital
●	Municipal head
○	Other towns
⚓	Port
✈	Airport

Map Symbols

23°   80°

81°

22°

AGUADA DE PASAJEROS
Real Campiña
Damují River
LAJAS
RODAS
CRUCES
Antonio Sánchez
Ciego Montero
ABREUS
PALMIRA
CUMANAYAGUA
CIENFUEGOS
Hanabanilla Dam
Juragua
Caunao River
Guamuhaya Massif
La Sierrita
San Juan Peak 1140
Cienfuegos Bay
Trinidad Mountains
Potrerillo Peak 931
Topes de Collantes

Cruces. This municipality shelters a population of 33,057 inhabitants in a surface area of 198 sq km. It has a completely flat territory, with the exception of the small Chicharrón Hill. Sugar cane agriculture and cane sugar production are its principal contributions to the economy. The Mal Tiempo battle was carried out in its lands; it was one of the bravest victories of the Liberating Army during the invasion to the western territory, a very important military action of the independence wars.

Cumanayagua. It is mainly a mountainous territory having 1096 sq km of surface area. A considerable part of it corresponds to the group of elevations of Guamuhaya that has its topmost point precisely in this province: the San Juan Peak (1140 m). These elevations are known, mistakenly, as Sierra del Escambray Range that are, really, farther to the north. These uneven mountainous areas won fame because here were accomplished the first combats against the counter-revolutionary groups that laid waste during five years this mountainous group. The Martín Infierno cave is found in these elevations; it has a stalagmite of 73 m high, undoubtedly, one of the largest of the world. The municipality is populated with 50,138 inhabitants. Coffee is its chief economic staple, followed by produce.

Cienfuegos. It is a very industrialized municipality, with centers of chemical, iron and steel, food, light, fishing and tourist industries, as well as a thermoelectric plant, among others.

The municipal head, that is the provincial capital, was founded in 1811 by French colonists under the name of Fernandina de Jagua, in a tongue of land that got inside the Jagua or Cienfuegos Bay. It is called "the Pearl of the South," because of the beauty of its architecture, its spaciousness and cleaning; it is, undoubtedly, one of the most important cities of the Cuban southern coast. The municipality has 152,744 inhabitants and occupies 338 sq km of surface area. Cienfuegos Bay, a very shelter and safe bottle bay, has an important trade traffic. The tourist industry supports in the abundance of palaces, colonial fortresses like Nuestra Señora de los Ángeles de Jagua, parks, theatres, churches, hotels and the wonderful Botanic Garden. The latter was created in 1901 by the Harvard University, and has a population of more than 2000 plant species, of which more than 80% are exotic ones.

Cienfuegos was taken on September 5th, 1957 by a troop of revolutionary marines and militiamen belonging to the 26 of July Movement, in an action of a extraordinary fearlessness and courage.

VILLA CLARA

It is one of the central provinces of Cuba that was part of the large territory of the former province of Las Villas, of which occupies its central-western-north portion. It arose as such with the new political-administrative division; it has a population of 824,216 inhabitants and a surface area of 8662 sq km, and that is why it is the sixth province of the country, considering the territorial extension. Its provincial capital, Santa Clara city, holds an outstanding place because of its economic burden, and its scientific and cultural institutions. It is one of the Cuban provinces with greater development in sugar cane production. From the administrative viewpoint, it is divided in the municipalities: Corralillo, Quemado de Güines, Sagua la Grande, Santo Domingo, Cifuentes, Ranchuelo, Santa Clara, Manicaragua, Camajuaní, Encrucijada, Remedios and Caibarién.

Corralillo. It has a surface area of 842 sq km, flat on the whole, although in its lands is located part of the Sierra Morena Range that in turn belongs to the Alturas del Noroeste. It bounds to the west with Matanzas, in a zone where there are plenty of ammonites-rich outcrops from the Lower Cretaceous. Part of the Sabana-Camagüey Archipelago belongs to its jurisdiction.

Villa Clara

0 10 20 30 40 50 km

80°

23°

22°

Elguea Spa
Santa Clara Bay
CORRALILLO
Motembo
Carahatas Bay
Sagua
la Grande Port
SAGUA LA GRANDE
QUEMADO DE GÜINES
Alacranes Dam
North Plain of Las Villas
Fragoso Key
Sagua la Grande River
SANTO DOMINGO
CIFUENTES
ENCRUCIJADA
Yabú River
CAIBARIÉN
REMEDIOS
CAMAJUANÍ
SANTA CLARA
Minerva Dam
Cubanacán Hills
RANCHUELO
PLACETAS
Agabama River
MANICARAGUA

Map Symbols

- – – – Municipal boundaries
- ▬▬▬ National Highway
- ──── Principal roads
- ──── Other roads
- –·–·– Rivers
- ⊙ Province capital
- ● Municipal head
- ⚓ Port
- ✈ Airport

The petroliferous field of Motembo is located in its territory, which produced since its discovering a highly valued natural fuel. Elguea, a spa of mineral-medicinal waters is other estimable natural resource of the municipality; it has a well-earned reputation because of its curative properties. Cane sugar production, and citrus and minor fruits cropping are other important economic activities. Corralillo has a population of 27,667 inhabitants.

Quemado de Güines. It has 23,647 inhabitants in a surface area of 338 sq km having a mainly flat land. Some keys of the Sabana-Camagüey Archipelago and coastal sectors with a few beaches belong to this municipality, since it is a coastal territory; in them the aborigines built palafites. Its lands are crossed by the Sagua la Grande River, one of the largest of the province. It is located between Corralillo to the west, and Sagua la Grande to the east. Industrial production of cane sugar, and sugar cane growing, and cattle rising as well, are its chief economic activities.

Sagua la Grande. It is a territory having a great economic and cultural activity; it had a large native population, as prove the remains found in caverns, near to fluvial currents, and even in cultivation places. Furthermore, it was scene of heroic actions, such as that of the National Liberating War (1953-58), when it was taken by the revolutionary forces during the general strike of April 9th, 1958.

It is inhabited by 60,601 people, who occupy a territory of 712 sq km. Sugar cane agriculture, cane sugar production in its three sugar mills, livestock, fishing, electrochemical industry and trade—the coastal traffic—from the Isabela de Sagua port, are its main economic activities.

Mogotes de Jumagua, a karstic mountainous area, close to the municipal capital, displays numerous regular-size caverns having singular scientific importance, because of its fauna and the archaeological and paleontological remains that are found in them.

Santo Domingo. It is a mainly flat territory, only with small very low-lying hills that occupies 883 sq km. It bounds to the south with the municipality Santa Isabel de las Lajas, of the Cienfuegos province. Rum, beer and cane sugar production (in its three sugar mills), diverse produce and livestock, are the most important economic staples. Also some tobacco is cultivated. It has a population of 55,129 inhabitants.

Cifuentes. It is a wavy territory, where small hills lift up and the Yabú River has shaped a valley with fertile soils. An important amount of diverse produce are produced there for the consumption of the own population that attains 35,862 people, and that of Santa Clara, south located. It has a surface area of 522 sq km. Four sugar mills are the chief industries of the territory; hence, sugar cane agriculture, obviously, has a preponderant role.

Ranchuelo. It has a population of 63,597 inhabitants and a territory of 564 sq km, mainly flat, where the Sagua la Grande River and others flow northwards, from the Cubanacán Hills that constitute a water-parting. It bounds to the south with two municipalities of Cienfuegos —Cruces and Santa Isabel de las Lajas. Four sugar mills determine that sugar production has the greatest burden in its economy.

Santa Clara. This municipality occupies almost the center of the Cuban archipelago. The Cubanacán hills are completely located in its territory; they are small but important elevations, because they constitute the water-parting or dividing line of waters in the central region of Cuba. This municipality has a total surface area of 493 sq km. Geological prospecting in this region has verified the existence of minerals such as gold, copper, iron. The municipal head is in turn the provincial capital, and many industries, such as that so-called INPUD that produces great-quality electrical equipment, are placed here.

The Central University of Las Villas is in this municipality; it is one of the three university centers the country had before 1959. The city was founded in this place in 1689, after moving from its original position—the place that today occupies the San Juan de los Remedios village—, because of the pirates attacks. The municipality of Santa Clara has a population of 222,096 inhabitants.

Manicaragua. With 73,219 inhabitants and 1062 sq km, this is the unique municipality that has no sugar cane in the province. Coffee, and also the famous tobacco cultivated in the Hoyo de Manicaragua valley are its chief productions. This is a mountainous municipality having a recent constitution, where remarkably caverns may be found among limestone and calcareous slates. It bounds, precisely in the mountainous zone, with the municipalities: Cumanayagua, in Cienfuegos, and both Trinidad and Fomento, in Sancti Spíritus.

It has one of the biggest artificial lakes of the country, the Hanabanilla dam, spanning 36 sq km in area and a capacity of 280 million m^3. It is surrounded by singular beautiful mountains, and is, moreover, an excellent place for fishing "trouts."

Camajuaní. It is a municipality of the east and north of the province, with 63,645 inhabitants and 613 sq km, in a predominantly flat territory, but with the presence of the Santa Fé and Cubanacán Hills. Many fluvial currents run across the territory, like the Sagua la Chica and Camajuaní Rivers. Sugar cane agriculture is the most important economic activity.

Encrucijada. It occupies a central position, north of Santa Clara. It has a surface area of 587 sq km in a wavy territory, where small calcareous hills separate the basins of the Sagua la Grande and Sagua la Chica Rivers. It has a population of 35,579 inhabitants, and the majority of the labour active population work in sugar cane agriculture and in the three sugar mills of the municipality, the most important economic activities. One of these sugar mills is named Abel Santamaría, second leader of the revolutionary movement that attacked the Moncada Garrison in 1953; he began the revolutionary struggle, and was born in this locality.

Placetas. It is the central municipality of Cuba, located east of the province, and bordering with Sancti Spíritus. It has a surface area of 601 sq km in a mainly flat territory, though there are the San Felipe, La Cumbre and Cienaguita Hills, south of which the Zaza River, the second longest one of the Cuban territory, springs up. It has a population of 74,074 inhabitants mainly devoted to tobacco, sugar cane and minor fruits croppings. In its lands several sugar mills are placed.

Remedios. This northern municipality has a population of 48,964 inhabitants and a surface area of 559 sq km. It is famous because of the parties held in the municipal head, so-called *parrandas.* Vegetables, citrus fruits, and cane sugar cropping, and livestock as well, are the most important economic activities of the municipality.

Caibarién. It is the last municipality of the northeast of the province, bordering with Sancti Spíritus. It has a population of 40,039 inhabitants in a surface area of 212 sq km. The territory is mainly flat, swampy in the coastal zone. Caibarién port is one of the most active of this region, and it also has a shipyard. The municipality has also eight sugar mills; therefore, this activity is one of the most important for the local economy.

SANCTI SPÍRITUS

This territory was part of the former central province of Las Villas, and arose as an independent province with the new political-administrative division in 1976. It spreads out transversally to the island of Cuba, from coast to coast, bounds with Villa Clara and Cienfuegos to the west, and with Ciego de Ávila to the east. Mountains of the Guamuhaya group, fertile valleys and beautiful beaches are found southwest of the provincial territory, which turn the province into an extraordinary tourist attraction point. A broad agricultural production is developed in the territory.

It has the largest dam of the country (Zaza dam); the most complete health center of the archipelago, the Topes de Collantes Sanatorium; and two of the first villages founded in the sixteenth century by the Spanish conquerors: Sancti Spíritus and Trinidad that preserve the environ and the colonial buildings with a great authenticity.

It has a population of 449,461 inhabitants and a surface of 67,442 sq km. The Zaza River, whose flow of 140 km long makes it the second largest river of the country, runs across its territory, just like other currents, such as the Agabama River. It is one of the greatest producers of sugar cane and rice, and has the biggest paper factory of the country. Its territory is divided into eight municipalities. An intense battle against banditry, known in its origins as *Limpia del Escambray*[32] was accomplished in its lands. Sancti Spíritus was cradle, among other patriots, of Serafín Sánchez, Major General of the Independence War, with a pure time path, who died in combat haranguing his men to continue the march.

Trinidad. It has 71,020 inhabitants in a surface of 1161 sq km. Its municipal head, having the same name, has been declared World Heritage by UNESCO, due to the good preservation of the environ and the colonial architecture. Topes de Collantes, formerly an anti-tuberculosis sanatorium, is the biggest center of health tourism in the country. Livestock, fruits and coffee cropping, and the production of its sugar mill are the chief economic activities. Forest wealth in the mountains is a reason for its preservation. The San Luis Valley, known as Valle de los Ingenios[33] that was also declared World Heritage by UNESCO, is located northwest.

It bounds with Cienfuegos to the west and with Sancti Spíritus to the east; it spreads out to the south coast, where the Casilda port and the Ancón Beach are placed, with well-known tourist attractiveness.

Fomento. It has a surface area of 471 sq km with fertile soils, where coffee, tobacco and sugar cane are cultivated, and cattle is bred; it has a sugar mill. The agricultural yield of the Banao zone is very important for the country, because of its characteristic microclimate. It has a population of 36,184 inhabitants. The Mabujina Hills and the "volcanic necks" southwest of the municipal head, are the preponderant elevations.

Sancti Spíritus. It is, above all, a mountainous territory that is distinguished by the presence of the Sancti Spíritus Range, Guamuhaya eastern massif, with hills being more than 800 m high and large rivers, aside from the Zaza one, that violently flow into the narrow flatland separating the hills from the south coast (Higuanojos, Tayabacoa and Banao). The population comprises 121,501 inhabitants in a surface area of 1150 sq km. The head town, also named Sancti Spíritus, is another of the first villages founded in the sixteenth century. The Yayabo River flows through the town; a quarry stone bridge, a true jewel of the colonial engineering and architecture, was built in 1817 above it. The main economic staples are sugar and food industries (a beer of great demand is produced in a factory there), sugar cane agriculture, livestock, and vegetables yield. Sancti Spíritus also holds an important place because of the volume of its tobacco yield, one of the biggest of the country.

32. In fact, it did not occur in the homonymous range of the same name, but in the Trinidad mountains that are located, in part, in this same province. *Author.* It means the Escambray Mopping-up. *Trans.*

33. It means Sugar Mills Valley. *Trans.*

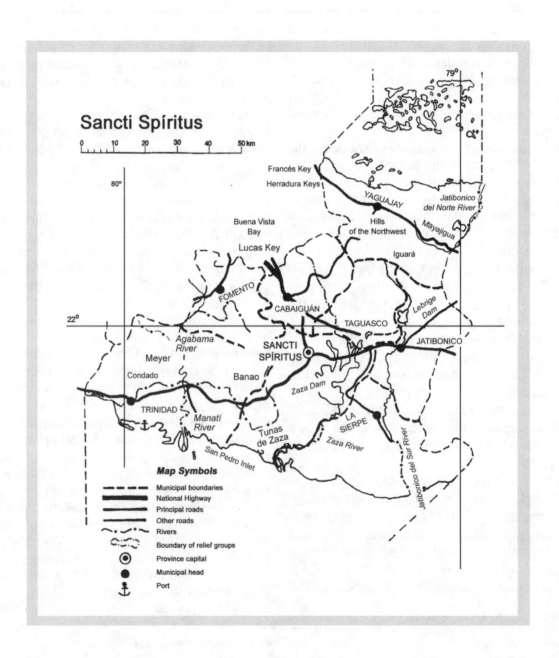

Sancti Spíritus

0 10 20 30 40 50 km

79°

Francés Key
Herradura Keys

YAGUAJAY

Jatibonico del Norte River

80°

Buena Vista Bay

Hills of the Northwest

Mayajigua

Lucas Key

Iguará

FOMENTO

CABAIGUÁN

Lebrige Dam

22°

TAGUASCO

Agabama River

SANCTI SPÍRITUS

JATIBONICO

Meyer

Condado

Banao

Zaza Dam

TRINIDAD

Manatí River

LA SIERPE

Tunas de Zaza

Zaza River

Jatibonico del Sur River

San Pedro Inlet

Map Symbols

- – – – Municipal boundaries
- ▬▬▬ National Highway
- ▬▬▬ Principal roads
- ▬▬▬ Other roads
- 〜〜 Rivers
- 〜〜 Boundary of relief groups
- ◉ Province capital
- ● Municipal head
- ⚓ Port

Cabaiguán. It has a population of 66,798 inhabitants and a surface area of 596 sq km, in hilly lands that are the northern foothills of Guamuhaya. The Tuinicú, Santa Lucía, Manacas, Calabazas Rivers and others from the Zaza basin run across the territory. It has very fertile lands allowing the municipality to produce a remarkably high-grade tobacco. It also has a sugar mill and a petroleum refinery (the only one that is not near the sea), among the main industries. Furthermore, it produces vegetables and minor fruits, in an outstanding way.

Taguasco. It arose as a municipality after the new political-administrative division in 1976. It has 36,335 inhabitants and 517 sq km of wavy and flat territory. Southeastwards, the Zaza River runs across it, skirting the Zaza del Medio and Siguaney Hills (161 m). Sugar cane and tobacco is cultivated in its lands, and cattle is bred, that together with the white cement production—unique in Cuba—are its chief economic activities.

Yaguajay. It is placed in the north coast, and bounds to the east with the municipality of Chambas in Ciego de Ávila. It has a surface area of 1032 sq km, where three different natural regions are clearly defined: the coast, where there are important swampy zones that isolate more elevated areas, in which scanty towns and some cavern systems are located, like that of "Cayo Caguanes" and Judas Point—isolated both from the mainland by the mentioned swamps—; the center, where plains with sugar cane growings are found; and a region with calcareous elevations (Meneses and Jatibonico Ranges), located south of the central part, where many caves have been excavated, which were shelter of partisan groups during the revolutionary war. In the municipal head a historic battle was waged in the last days of the struggle against the Batista dictatorship, headed by Commander Camilo Cienfuegos.

Yaguajay is a land of sugar cane production; it has cropping areas and three sugar mills; moreover, it also has a soft-drink factory and lands for livestock. In the north, there is the San José del Lago spa, a famous center of mineral-medicinal waters. Some of the most beautiful keys of the Sabana-Camagüey Archipelago belong to this municipality that are being or have been communicated with the mainland through stone-roads. Yaguajay has a population of 60,970 inhabitants.

La Sierpe. It is the municipality that occupies the utmost southeastern extreme of the province, with a surface area of 1139 sq km of flat and low lands in the south part, where rice cropping is successfully carried out. Sugar cane agriculture and livestock are also developed. It has a population of 31,916 inhabitants.

Jatibonico. This territory, until 1976, was part of the province of Camagüey, and is the easternmost of all the municipalities of Sancti Spíritus. It has 712 sq km of flat and fertile lands, watered, among others, by the Jatibonico del Sur River, and pond in its high basin by the Lebrije dam, west to the La Estrella Hill (369 m). Its population consists of 41,536 inhabitants. This municipality has the Uruguay sugar mill, the biggest of the country, nearby to which a paper mill was built, whose row material is the sugar cane pulp. Agriculture produces vegetables and all kind of minor fruits, in addition to sugar cane for the sugar mill.

CIEGO DE ÁVILA

This province was created by the new political-administrative division; formerly it was part of the former province of Camagüey. It has 393,527 inhabitants in a surface area of 6910 sq km. Its chief yield is the agricultural one, and stands out the pineapple cropping, of which it is the major national producer. The geological research registered in its lands the presence of petroleum that at present is successfully exploited. Some keys of the Sabana-Camagüey

Archipelago belong to this province, where tourism is developing. The tourists have had the opportunity of knowing a lush nature, almost unchanged. At the south, the very beautiful keys of the Jardines de la Reina Archipelago are still more virgin. The territory has been divided into eight municipalities: Chambas, Florencia, Majagua, Ciro Redondo, Venezuela, Morón, Bolivia and Baraguá.

Chambas. It occupies the utmost northwestern extreme of the province, and bounds with Yaguajay, of Sancti Spíritus, to the west. It has a population of 41,150 inhabitants that live in a territory of 770 sq km, with fertile soils yielding minor fruits, sugar cane, fibers, vegetables, and forest resources.

This territory has very singular caves in the Mabuya Range and other hills; they are unique because of they have been shaped in limestone caps overlying vulcanites, and that is why it has a predominant vertical development with large halls and scanty passages.

Florencia. It is also a bordering municipality with Sancti Spíritus, but located south of Chambas. It only has 21,196 inhabitants and 284 sq km of surface area.

It has a wavy relief that becomes more abrupt in the Jatibonico Range, having a calcareous constitution that is crossed by the underground riverbed of the Jatibonico del Norte River, along a cavern that is known by the name of Los Boquerones or El Boquerón cave. This cavern, having an uncovered riverbed like a hanging fluvial canyon and drained above its flow, was used by forces of the Liberating Army and the revolutionary combatants during the independence and partisan wars. The economy of the region rests on the tobacco and minor fruits cropping, and timber production.

Majagua. It is the third municipality that constitutes the western border of the province, but in this case, to the south. It has 25,786 inhabitants and a surface area of 502 sq km, practically flat, and one of the most important petroleum yield of the country. Sugar cane growing and

the cane sugar production of the Orlando González sugar mill are its main economic activities.

Ciego de Ávila. With 117,110 inhabitants and 444 sq km of area, it is one of the most developed municipalities in regard with the agricultural yield, pineapple cropping— the queen of the fruits—, and with the consolidation of research institutions and industries, mainly, the food one. The municipal head is Ciego de Ávila town, a center of an important cultural and scientific spreading.

Ciro Redondo. This is a municipality that arose with the new political-administrative division, and its municipal head, formerly known as Pina, took its current name from one of the martyrs of the revolutionary struggle, an attacker to the Moncada Garrison and an expeditionary of the Granma yacht: Ciro Redondo. It has 27,294 inhabitants and a surface area of 591 sq km having flat lands used for petroleum yield and sugar cane agriculture, and vegetables as well.

Venezuela. It is also a newly created municipality that takes its name from the homonymous sugar mill, former Stewart. It has a population of 28,397 inhabitants and a surface of 709 sq km, made up of plains, marshes and mangroves to the south. Sugar cane and vegetables are the chief agricultural yield. It has a loading port of sugar in bulk.

Morón. It is a northern municipality that has marshy and flooded areas in the north, near to the coast, and peculiar emergent zones, like the isle of Turiguanó, joined to mainland by one of the first stone-roads constructed in the country. It has 56,115 inhabitants and a surface of 615 sq km. La Leche Lagoon that is, in fact, a coastal pool due to its communication with the sea by three natural channels, is one of the most known geographic accidents. The name of that coastal pool is determined by the marl composition of the aquatory floor, because before natural or artificial movements, the water becomes cloudy and causes that milky appearance. La Redonda Lagoon, the

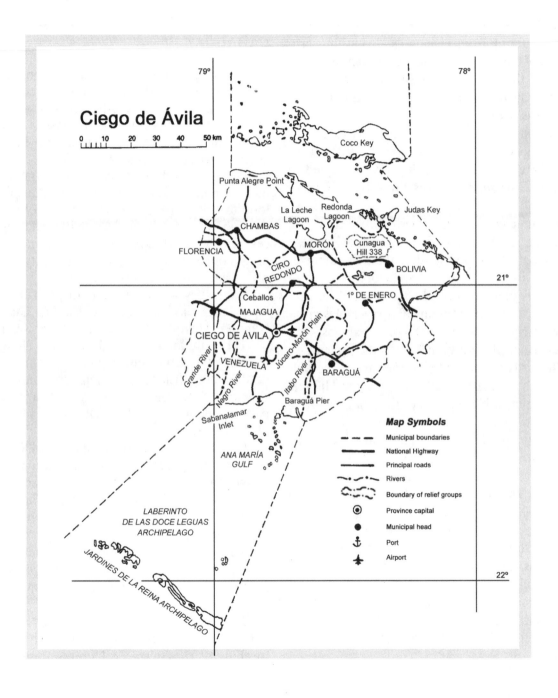

Ciego de Ávila

0 10 20 30 40 50 km

Coco Key

Punta Alegre Point

La Leche
Lagoon

Redonda
Lagoon

Judas Key

CHAMBAS

MORÓN

Cunagua
Hill 338

FLORENCIA

BOLIVIA

21°

CIRO
REDONDO

Ceballos

1° DE ENERO

MAJAGUA

CIEGO DE ÁVILA

VENEZUELA

Júcaro-Morón Plain

BARAGUÁ

Grande River

Negro River

Itabo River

Baraguá Pier

Sabanalamar
Inlet

ANA MARÍA
GULF

Map Symbols

- - - - Municipal boundaries

━━━━ National Highway

──── Principal roads

-·-·- Rivers

Boundary of relief groups

◉ Province capital

● Municipal head

⚓ Port

✈ Airport

LABERINTO
DE LAS DOCE LEGUAS
ARCHIPELAGO

JARDINES DE LA REINA ARCHIPELAGO

22°

79°   78°

International Center of Trout Fishing, is also in this territory. Some keys of the Sabana-Camagüey Archipelago have been joined with the island of Cuba by stone-roads that start from lands of this municipality. Sugar cane production is the chief economic staple.

This municipality reached a sad fame because in it, during the independence wars, was constructed a fortified troche, whereupon the Spanish army attempted to avoid the pass of the *mambí* forces towards the west of the country.

Bolivia. The municipal head, formerly named Cunagua, changed its name for that of the Latin American country, and the municipality adopted it since the new political-administrative division in 1976. Its population consists of 16,165 inhabitants in an area of 917 sq km, used for livestock, and for pasture, forest, grains and vegetables cropping. It is a municipality of the north coast that closes the province to the east, where it bounds with the province of Camagüey. Towards the central-western part of the municipal territory the Loma de Judas de Cunagua Hill lifts up, with two prominent hills in each extreme having 332 m and 338 m each of one.

Primero de Enero. This municipality arose with the political-administrative division in the seventies, and was formerly named Violeta. There inhabit 29,184 people in a surface of 712 sq km of flat lands, where sugar cane and vegetables are cultivated.

Baraguá. It has a population of 31,130 inhabitants and a surface of 724 sq km. It is a newly created municipality, which economy is close linked with sugar production; the Ecuador sugar mill that is in its lands is one of the most important of the province. It is a flat territory that is crossed by several fluvial currents of short and marshy (in the coast) riverbeds. It is the southeast border of the province with Camagüey.

CAMAGÜEY

It is the largest province of Cuba, according to its territorial extension, 15,900 sq km, distributed in extensive savannas—marshy in the south coast—, sowed by sugar cane, and where an important cattle mass is bred; it also has rough calcareous low-lying elevations, but with complex geomorphologic shapes, like the Sierra de Cubitas Range in the north, and the Najasa one in the south. Furthermore, the major keys of the homonymous archipelago belong to this province, some of them joined to mainland through stone-roads, constructed for making easy the access. In the south coast, the Jardines de la Reina Archipelago offers also a fine display of beauty in virgin beaches with white sands and lush nature.

Camagüey was the scenery of great battles during the struggle for the independence, like Las Guásimas, and El Naranjo, where the Cuban military art was revealed.

There are archaeological evidences showing the province was the settlement of native populations that practiced hunting, fishing, and even agriculture. They left their skeletons, tools and other rests of their culture in several parts of the territory; the Tuabaquey Hill (309 m) is one of these places.

Camagüey has a population of 771,400 inhabitants and an important group of cultural institutions that includes a classic ballet company, numerous scientific institutions, industries and teaching centers. It also has one of the ports of major economic activity of the country: Tarafa in the huge Nuevitas Bay.

The most recent geological research has proved the mining wealth of these lands that are being exploited by joint ventures, according to the reorganization of the Cuban economy.

Esmeralda. It is a territory of 1230 sq km of surface, flat, as a general rule, although it reaches to the east, the foothills of the Sierra de Cubitas Range. It bounds to

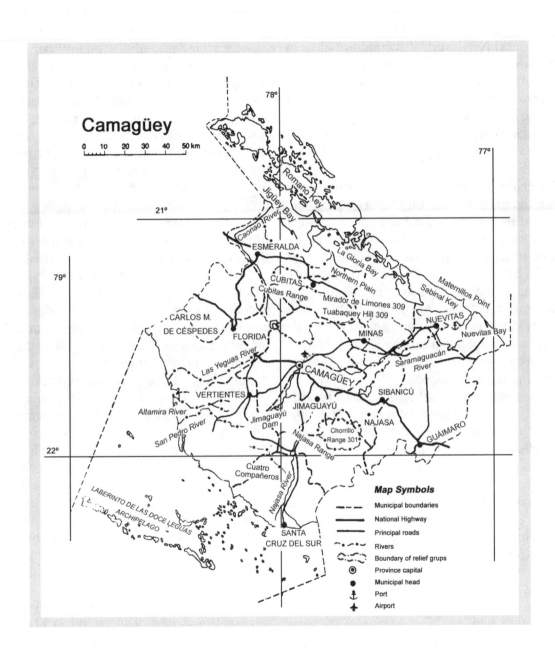

Camagüey

0 10 20 30 40 50 km

78°

77°

21°

Romano Key

Jigüey Bay

Caonao River

ESMERALDA

La Gloria Bay

79°

CUBITAS

Northern Plain

Maternillos Point

Cubitas Range

Mirador de Limones 309

Sabinal Key

Tuabaquey Hill 309

NUEVITAS

CARLOS M.
DE CÉSPEDES

MINAS

Nuevitas Bay

FLORIDA

Las Yeguas River

Saramaguacán
River

CAMAGÜEY

VERTIENTES

SIBANICÚ

Altamira River

JIMAGUAYÚ

NAJASA

San Pedro River

Jimaguayú
Dam

Chorrillo
Range 301

GUÁIMARO

22°

Najasa Range

Cuatro
Compañeros

Najasa River

Map Symbols

LABERINTO DE LAS DOCE LEGUAS

ARCHIPELAGO

SANTA
CRUZ DEL SUR

- – – – Municipal boundaries
- ———— National Highway
- ———— Principal roads
- ·–·–· Rivers
- Boundary of relief grups
- ⊚ Province capital
- ● Municipal head
- ⚓ Port
- ✈ Airport

the west with Ciego de Ávila, and is the northwestern utmost of the province. Northwest of the municipality, in Guaney, an archaeological place was excavated by the researcher A. Núñez Jiménez, consisting of a bat-shaped mound that may be only observed from above. In other places of the territory there are aboriginal remains. Esmeralda holds an important place in the sugar cane production in the province. It has a population of 32,536 inhabitants.

Carlos Manuel de Céspedes. It has the name of the lawyer who proclaimed the independence, on October 10th, 1868. He was threatened by the Spanish colonialists to abandon the struggle in order to save the life of his under-arrest son, and he turned down the offer expressing: "... all the Cubans are my sons ...." That is why he is named the Motherland's Father. In this municipality 23,599 people inhabit in a surface of 653 sq km, with flat relief, low in the south, even to reach the marshy category. It is a southern territory that arose with the new political-administrative division bordering to the west with Ciego de Ávila; it depends on sugar cane agriculture and sugar production.

Florida. It is a very important municipality regarding sugar production and sugar cane research, because it has two sugar mills and a sugar cane research institute. It has excellent soils, where livestock is also developed. It has a population of 75,270 inhabitants and an extensive surface of 1760 sq km, where flat and boggy lands predominate onto the low and swampy south coast.

Camagüey. This municipality lies in the center of the province. It has 309,604 inhabitants, mainly in urban zone, and 1177 sq km of surface area. The flat territory with excellent soils was always characterized by the abundance and quality of the cattle bred, by its milk and cheese production, and by other dairy products. At present the territory has: food, basic, and light industries among others, and also research centers—of genetic and pharmacy, above all—, teaching institutions, and others.

The municipal head is also the capital city. It was one of the first seven villages founded by Diego Velázquez in 1515, but under the name of Santa María del Puerto del Príncipe and with a different geographic location, because it was built in El Guincho Point, in the western margin of the Nuevitas Bay. Frequent attacks of corsairs and pirates forced part of their settlers to migrate to inner territories, up to reach the margins of the Caonao River, in the aboriginal chieftainship of Camagüey or Camagüebax. Then, the simplified name of Puerto Príncipe was taken, whereupon it was known until the nineteenth century, till the current name was popularly imposed.

The "city of the large earthen jars," the name with which it is known because of the abundance of these jars, is one if not the most colonial city, due to the serpentine and labyrinthine layouts of its streets, in order to mislead the pirates that lead waste them. Camagüey was cradle of one of the most distinguished Cuban patriots of the last century, Major General Ignacio Agramonte y Loynaz.

Sierra de Cubitas. It is a new municipality, and it is named after the most remarkable geographic accident of this region; a calcareous mountainous area. The neotectonic accelerated elevation of the hills brought about not only caverns, dolines and lapiez, but also a change in the flow of the rivers, which abandoned their riverbeds in order to flow in another direction, leaving completely dry karstic canyons that cross the mountain from north to south. It is populated by 17,971 inhabitants, and has a surface area of 548 sq km, where citrus fruits and vegetables are cultivated. The municipal head is named Cubitas.

Natives of this territory used the caves of the range to represent their view of the world in which they lived. In the Los Generales cave there is maybe the only Cuban pictography that shows the Spaniard conqueror from the view of an Indocuban.

Vertientes. It is the central-south municipality of the province, and it arose as such from the new political-administrative division in 1976. It has a population of 52,788 inhabitants and a surface area of 1933 sq km. Lands in the south are low and marshy, therefore, rice is cultivated there, while in the north, sugar cane predominates. It has the sugar mill of the biggest milling capacity of the country.

Minas. This municipality arose with the political-administrative division in 1976. It has 39,867 inhabitants and 1076 sq km of surface area. It was named after the boom of mining in this locality during the nineteenth century. It bounds with Sierra de Cubitas to the west, with Nuevitas to the north, and with Sibanicú to the east. The Maximo River runs across the territory shaping the natural pools known as *cangilones* when it crosses over packages of marmorized limestone with beautiful veins. The chief economic activity is related with sugar production.

Jimaguayú. This territory was named after the patriot Ignacio Agramonte, who died in combat in the homonymous cattle ranch. In 1895, the Constituent Assembly of the Republic in Arms was held in its lands, after the independence war was reinitiated. It has a population of 18,350 inhabitants and a surface area of 798 sq km. Livestock, and diverse produce are the most important productive activities.

Nuevitas. It is the smaller municipality of the province that lies around the Nuevitas Bay and south of it, and has 43,170 inhabitants in only 149 sq km. The port of Nuevitas (Tarafa) is one of the most active ports of the country. It is an eminently industrial territory, with factories of wires, electrodes, fertilizers and others. Nevertheless its industrialization, the territory of Nuevitas has important tourist attractiveness: the Santa Lucía Beach, east of the mouth of the bay that is bathed by the Atlantic Ocean waters and it is an important tourist center, and the Sabinal cay with a lush nature and wonderful beaches where live wild species of the Cuban fauna and several foreign hunting species for big game.

Sibanicú. It is a flat municipality with a surface area of 735 sq km, although in part of it there is the eastern portion of the Saramaguacán Range. Livestock predominates in it, but sugar cane also holds an important place. It has 31,086 inhabitants. Its name has an aboriginal origin, and it exists since 1976 as an administrative territory; formerly it was included in the municipality of Camagüey, with which it has borders to the northwest. It bounds to the east with the municipality of Guáimaro, to the north with Nuevitas and to the south with Najasa.

Najasa. It is inhabited by 16,299 people that occupy a surface area of 921 sq km. The second important mountainous group in the province is found in its territory: the Najasa Range, whose topmost point is the El Chorrillo Range (301 m), which has some flora and fauna wealth. The economic activity is centered on minor fruits and vegetables growing.

Santa Cruz del Sur. It is a municipality of the south coast that occupies the southeastern utmost of the province. It has an important fishing port for the province, and it is inhabited by 54,327 people.

Santa Cruz, as it is generally called, is a municipality since the nineteenth century (1871), when a group of fishermen settled in this place. The head town has been hit by repeated destructions, like a fire in 1843, a hurricane in 1850, and a terrible cyclone in 1932 that devastated almost all the town. It was reconstructed 2 km from the foregoing settlement. It has a surface area of 1122 sq km, mostly flat, although to the north is found the Guaicanamar Range, belonging to the Najasa group of hills.

Sugar cane agriculture and sugar production, as well as livestock, are its main economic staples, although fishing is also important.

Guáimaro. Even though it existed as a municipality since the beginning of the Republic, the current territory differs to the former one because it has ceded the region named Amancio Rodríguez to the eastern province of Las Tunas, and it has received lands from Nuevitas. That is why its surface area has been modified, and now is 2112 sq km. The Saramaguacán, Ciego de Molina, and Rosario Rivers to the north, and Sevilla, Tana, Guáimaro and Jobabo to the south flow across its territory. The latter is useful as a border with Las Tunas. It has a population of 57,363 inhabitants.

Guáimaro word has an indigenous root, and this territory is specially important for the Cuban history because there the First Constitution of the Republic of Cuba was proclaimed on April 10th, 1869, as well as the 1940 Constitution. Livestock holds the chief place among the economic activities of this territory that has one of the most numerous cattle mass of the country.

LAS TUNAS

This province occupies the western sector of the former province of Oriente that was divided into five provinces when the political-administrative division was accomplished in 1976. It has craggy coasts, watered by the Atlantic Ocean—the Old Bahamas Channel—at the north, and by the Caribbean Sea at the south, where they are low and marshy, at times. There are important bays in the north coast, like Manatí, Malagueta and Puerto Padre. It is a mostly flat territory with fertile lands, and a predominant sugar cane production owing to its six sugar mills. The second biggest steel rolling mill of the country and other industries were constructed there, and this fact has allowed its economic development. The population of the territory is 516,709 inhabitants and its surface area, 6588.9 sq km. Las Tunas is the "small Motherland" of the Major General Vicente García, patriot of the Independence War, a man of great courage.

Las Tunas (Victoria de las Tunas). It occupies the center of the province with 890 sq km of surface area. The head town, located in the margin of the Hormiguero River, is the capital of the province and it has a great development in the cultural, industrial, scientific and educational sectors. It has a population of 172,223 inhabitants that work in pasture and vegetable crops, and livestock as well.

Amancio Rodríguez. It is a municipality that arose with the new political-administrative division. It was formerly part of the territory of Camagüey and today is bordering to the west. It is also just known as Amancio. Its name is in honor of an outstanding peasant leader of the zone, murdered by landowners and front men of the government. Its municipal head is the little village near to the homonymous sugar mill, former Francisco. It has a population of 44,127 inhabitants and a surface area of 856 sq km, with flat lands, low and marshy coasts, watered by the Caribbean Sea. Yaquimo River, which springs up in the El Chorrillo Range in Camagüey, and the Sevilla River, among others, flow through its lands, used for sugar production and livestock.

Colombia. It is a newly created municipality, located south of the province, between the municipalities of Amancio Rodríguez at the west, and Jobabo at the east. It takes its name from the most important population, a little village near to the sugar mill named Colombia (former Elía) that is its municipal head. It has a population of 33,087 inhabitants and a surface area of 563 sq km. In addition to sugar cane, livestock holds the most important place in its economy.

Jobabo. It has a population of 50,618 inhabitants and it occupies a surface area of 786 sq km. The Jobabo River that formerly divided the territory of Las Tunas from its neighboring western province, cross its lands and flows southwards, together with the Birama River, among others, emptying into the Birama Swamp that occupies the south coast, in the province of Granma.

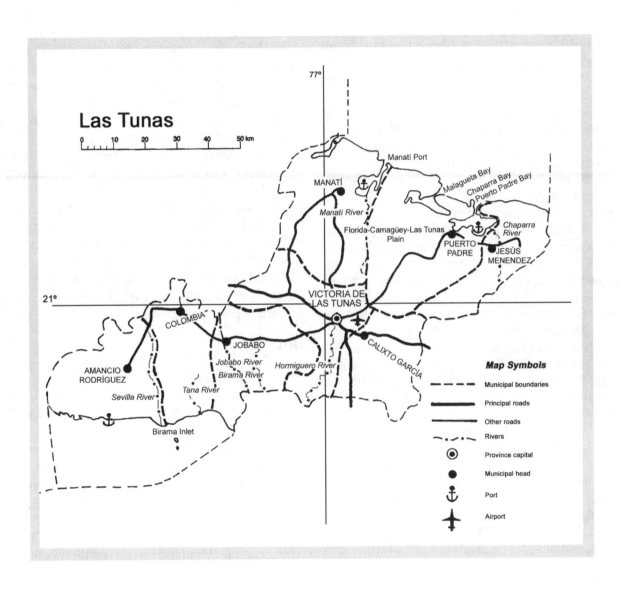

Las Tunas

0   10   20   30   40   50 km

77°

Manatí Port

MANATÍ

Malagueta Bay
Chaparra Bay
Puerto Padre Bay

Manatí River

Florida-Camagüey-Las Tunas
Plain

Chaparra
River

PUERTO
PADRE

JESÚS
MENENDEZ

21°

VICTORIA DE
LAS TUNAS

COLOMBIA

CALIXTO GARCÍA

JOBABO

Jobabo River

Hormiguero River

Birama River

AMANCIO
RODRÍGUEZ

Sevilla River

Tana River

Birama Inlet

Map Symbols

- - - - -   Municipal boundaries

━━━━━   Principal roads

─────   Other roads

─·─·─·   Rivers

⊙   Province capital

●   Municipal head

⚓   Port

✈   Airport

It is a flat municipality, where sugar cane growing is one of the most important economic activities, together with sugar production in the sugar mill named Perú. Its most outstanding industry is a fiber processor plant *(kenaff)*. Vegetables also are successfully cultivated here.

Majibacoa. It is a small municipality that arose with the political-administrative division of 1976, whose territory formerly was part of the municipality of Bayamo. At present, it bounds with the municipalities of Río Cauto of the province of Granma to the south, Cauto Cristo to the southeast and Calixto García to the east. Since it is a southern municipality, it has no coasts. In its 621 sq km live 38,685 inhabitants.

Majibacoa is a flat territory, part of the physical-geographical region of the Florida-Camagüey-Las Tunas peneplane and the Cauto-Guacanayabo plain. This territory contributes to the volume of the largest river of Cuba with the waters of the homonymous river, the Naranjo and the Niguas Rivers, among others. Its outstanding economic activities are the sugar cane, vegetables cropping, together with sugar production in the Majibacoa sugar mill. Calixto is its head town.

Manatí. It is a municipality of the new political-administrative division, with 32,808 inhabitants and 953 sq km of surface area. It lies in the north coast of the province and occupies its utmost northwestern extreme. It is a flat territory, used for sugar cane growing and sugar production in the Argelia Libre sugar mill, although it also produces vegetables and has important forest areas. Manatí Bay is a very sheltered bay for navigation, into which flows the Manatí[34] River, which probably has that name because of the presence of that sirenian. A sugar medium-scope loading port is placed there.

Puerto Padre. It lies east of the municipality of Manatí, with a population of 92,054 inhabitants and a surface area of 1178 sq km, of flat lands, mostly of them with sugar cane growing.

34. It means "manatee." *Trans.*

It is a very important municipality for the province because a large trade traffic is registered through the Puerto Padre and Malagueta Bays, the latter located farther to the west. Carúpano port, in the Puerto Padre Bay, has one of the most intense sugar loading activities of the country.

The Antonio Guiteras sugar mill is a colossus of the sugar industry that together with the textile, footwear and leather industries, are the most important economic activities, as well as the harbor one.

Jesús Menéndez. It is bordering to the west with the municipality of Puerto Padre, and to the east with Gibara, of Holguín. This municipality is named after the most outstanding trade union leader of the Cuban sugar workers. It has a population of 53,213 inhabitants and a surface area of 637 sq km of flat lands that are crossed by the Chaparra and Vega de la Mano Rivers, among others. A sugar mill with the same name of the municipality is also a colossus in sugar production. Furthermore, its livestock has not a great development.

HOLGUÍN

It is the fourth province in territorial extension of the nation, with a surface area of 9300.5 sq km, and second, together with Santiago de Cuba, regarding population, with 1,012,778 inhabitants.

It was part of the former Oriente province, as did the other provinces of the region; that is why it has contributed with territories towards and received territories from other municipalities and provinces. It is one of the most mountainous territories of Cuba, since it is the site of the Sierra del Cristal Range and the Moa Crests to the southeast, and the Maniabón Hills to the north. It has the largest bottle bay of the Cuban Archipelago: the Nipe Bay, and important rivers such as Mayarí, Sagua de Tánamo, Cacoyuguín, Nipe and others.

Holguín

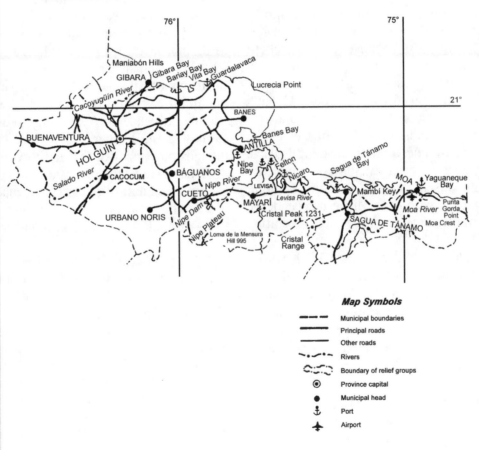

Map Symbols

- – – – Municipal boundaries
- ——— Principal roads
- ——— Other roads
- –·–·– Rivers
- ⌇⌇⌇ Boundary of relief groups
- ⊙ Province capital
- ● Municipal head
- ⚓ Port
- ✈ Airport

Holguín is a province with coasts only in the north, watered by the Atlantic Ocean, in the Old Bahama Channel. It is divided into 14 municipalities, and it is the unique province that has borders with the other four. The exploiting of nickel beds at Moa and Nicaro along with the successful construction and production of the agricultural-machinery factory, the presence of ten sugar mills that are among the biggest and most productive of the country, have given rise to an important industrial and mineral region. Furthermore, it has a great tourist attractiveness because of its excellent beaches; Guardalavaca (or Guardalabarca), northwest of Banes stands out among them.

Formerly known as the "Breadbasket of Cuba," Holguín is recovering its bean production and other crops, and also its livestock is among the most important of Cuba. The mountains of the Sagua-Baracoa group have incalculable natural wealth with great biodiversity, still not completely researched. Holguín was the cradle of Major General Calixto García Íñiguez, a hero of the three independence wars, and a great number of generals of the Liberating Army.

Gibara. This municipality exists since 1822, whose borders were modified by the political-administrative division of 1976. It has a population of 70,910 inhabitants in 630 sq km of surface area. Its territory consists mainly in wavy plains and small hills belonging to the Maniabón group. The Silla[35] de Gibara Hill—an elevation whose shape is similar to a saddle, with a calcareous cap over vulcanites—stands out in this orographic group. It is a notably karstified territory, above all towards its northern region and in the Cupeicillo-La Candelaria Hills, with many caverns, some locally famous, like the Los Panaderos cave, but more important due to the flooded caverns located in

the littoral plain, named Cristalitos de Papaya and Tanque Azul, the largest caves of the whole archipelago.

There is an important fishing port in the Gibara Bay. Playa Caletones is an excellent beach with tourist perspectives, as well as the Maniabón buttes. The Cacoyuguín and Gibara Rivers, that flow into the bay, supply the aqueduct of Holguín.

Its lands produce vegetables, that together with fishing, are the main economic activities of the territory.

Holguín. This municipality lies south of Gibara and bounds to the northwest with Las Tunas. It has a population of 291,755 inhabitants and a surface area of 655 sq km.

Its municipal head is the provincial capital, Holguín, an important city since the eighteenth century. It has kept a relative independence from Santiago de Cuba that was the capital of the former province of Oriente, and hence, the most important of that territory.

It has an outstanding position as a cultural, educational, scientific and industrial place. The machinery, metal-forming, food industries—for instance, the Mayabe beer factory—and the sugar one are an indicator of the economic development of the territory.

Calixto García. This municipality arose with the new political-administrative division and bounds to the west with Las Tunas and to the east with the municipality of Holguín. It has a surface area of 617 sq km, and it is located in a wavy region with the Maniabón group northwards. Its name is in honor of the mentioned general of the independence wars. It has a population of 56,936 inhabitants; the municipal head is named Buenaventura, and the chief activities are diverse produce and livestock.

Rafael Freyre. It is a newly created municipality, and it is named after a revolutionary man who died during the Fulgencio Batista's dictatorship. It has 49,071 inhabitants and a territorial extension of 613 sq km. The reduced bays named Vita and Naranjo are in its north coast, and also

35. It means "saddle." *Trans.*

the small Bariay Bay, through which the admiral Christopher Columbus arrived to Cuba for the first time, after his travel that gave rise to the knowledge about the existence of America for Europe.

Its most important economic activities are sugar agriculture and sugar production in the sugar mill of the same name of the municipality. Its village is the municipal head. Also livestock has a local importance.

Cacocum. This new municipality is important because it is the connection of the province with the central railway. It has 44,026 inhabitants and a territorial extension of 661 sq km. The sugar cane agriculture and sugar production in the sugar mill named Cristino Naranjo—a rebel commander of the National Liberating War, treacherously dead by a traitor—, one of the biggest of the country, are the most important economic activities of the municipality. It is a flat zone, and the rivers and streams that drain it are tributaries of the Cauto River.

Banes. It lies in the north coast, east of the municipality of Rafael Freyre; it has 87,667 inhabitants in a surface area of 779 sq km. Its aboriginal name that is related to the findings of remains of the first settlers of the territory. One of their most important pieces, a gold idol, is displayed in the Bani Museum, the most complete of the world regarding the *Taíno* aboriginal culture. The archaeological site—at present, the Chorro de Maíta Museum—with samples of the funeral customs of these primitive cultures, unknown before now, was found in this territory.

Its wavy territory is part of the Maniabón group, and has a high degree of karstification. In the Yaguaray Range, a group of small and rough calcareous hills, there are numerous caves with remains of aboriginal cultures. Some hypogeum karstic forms of this zone are well known, like Las Cuatrocientas Rosas cave, that during a long time was the largest of the eastern region. The most important economic activities are sugar cane agriculture, citrus fruits and

vegetables, banana above all. Guardalavaca (or Guardalabarca) Beach, a famous tourist jewel of the province, is located in its coast, and the Banes and Samá Bays too.

Báguanos. It is also a new municipality, with 55,025 inhabitants in a surface area of 805 sq km. Its name remembers the victorious combat of Rejondones de Báguanos during the Independence War. Sugar cane agricultue and sugar production are the most important economic activities. The Tacajó River flows across the territory, almost down the middle.

Urbano Noris. This municipality, former San Germán, is named after a trade union leader murdered during Batista's dictatorship. It is a southern municipality that bounds with Cacocum to the west, with Granma to the southwest and with Santiago de Cuba to the southeast. It has a population of 44,588 inhabitants and a surface area of 829 sq km; it is crossed to the south by the Cauto River, the largest of Cuba. It is one of the main sugar producers because of the production of the Urbano Noris sugar mill.

Cueto. It is next to the Urbano Noris municipality to the east, and bounds with Santiago de Cuba to the south. It has a territorial extension of 326 sq km, with flat lands, slightly wavy northwards. The Nipe River runs across through part of its territory, flowing into the homonymous bay. Its population comprises 38,367 inhabitants, who work in sugar cane agriculture and sugar production in the Loynaz Echevarría sugar mill, as well as in livestock.

Mayarí. It is the most extensive municipality of the province, with a surface area of 1303 sq km and a population of 113,616 inhabitants. It is a contrast zone, because includes the low zone around the Nipe Bay—the biggest of the Cuban archipelago—; the elevations of the Nipe highland, better known as Pinares de Mayarí, whose main summit is the Loma de la Mensura Mountain (995 m); and the foothills of the Sierra del Cristal Range, to the east. This is a territory with a tradition of struggles against colonialists and rich landowners. Both aboriginal and run-away slaves findings have been discovered in this municipality, the first ones in the Seboruco caves, on the banks of the Mayarí River. It was also site of the II Eastern Front Frank País during the National Liberating War. Nickel mining in Nicaro, timber, and coffee, tobacco and vegetables cropping, are the most important economic activities. Tourism in the territory have an outstanding development.

Frank País. It is a small municipality located in a flat zone, north of the mountains of the Sierra del Cristal Range and the municipality of Sagua de Tánamo. Its coasts are bathed by the Atlantic Ocean, in which the Sagua de Tánamo Bay stands out, where the homonymous river flows into.

It has a population of 29,754 inhabitants and a surface area of 514 sq km, and arose from the political-administrative division. It is named after who was an experienced leader and an audacious fighter of the clandestine struggle in the cities, during the last revolutionary war. Its municipal head is the town named Cayo Mambí, placed in the inner margins of the bay.

Sugar cane growing and sugar production in the "Frank País" sugar mill, coffee and livestock, are the chief economic staples.

Sagua de Tánamo. It is a municipality of 59,200 inhabitants and 701 sq km of surface area; it is, above all, a mountainous territory, having the Sagua-Baracoa group, with the Cristal Peak (1231 m) as its topmost level. The Sagua de Tánamo River is the main fluvial current, even though it is not the unique; it is navigable in a sector close to the municipality of Frank País. In rainy season, this river has undergone huge floods that have affected Sagua de Tánamo city, municipal head that the river crosses.

Coffee is the chief cropping, although sugar cane and vegetables are also cultivated.

Moa. It has a population of 59,339 inhabitants, although it was an almost uninhabited territory before the revolutionary victory, when it was a neighborhood of Baracoa. The nickel plant was abandoned by the North American capital with the purpose of disappearing it, and the North Americans did not leave either drawings, spares and infrastructure. The unbelievable rescue of the nickel plant and the approval of investments that turned the municipality into a priority work for the country, allowed to attract a large number of professionals and technicians. They grew in number when the Instituto Superior Minero-Matalúrgico [Mining Metallurgical Superior Institute] was created in the industrial city of Moa. The municipality has a surface area of 728 sq km, where there are elevations made up of peridotites and other ultrabasic rocks, over which there are shaped lateritic soils with important reserves of nickel, cobalt and iron. These elevations belong to the Moa crests, of the Sagua-Baracoa group, whose topmost point is the Toldo Peak (1175 m high). Aside from these elevations, the Farallones de Moa Range in Moa is made up of limestone from the Eocene, having mogote-shaped forms that are crossed by the Moa River. The underground riverbed of this river is the large cavern of Farallones de Moa, a true jewel of the Cuban territory.

Antilla. It is a small municipality that occupies the La Torre Peninsula in the northwestern margin of the Nipe Bay, and because of that it has a very reduced surface area, 101 sq km. It bounds with Banes, the territory that closes the peninsula, and has a population according to its territorial extension. Since it occupies a margin of the Nipe Bay, its economic life is related with its trade activity. It has 12,525 inhabitants.

GRANMA

This province of the south coast is named after the Granma yacht that led Fidel Castro and the rest of the members of the expedition towards its coasts, in order to start the partisan fight in the Sierra Maestra. It bounds to the north with the province of Holguín, to the east with Santiago de Cuba, to the west with the Guacanayabo Gulf, and to the south with the Caribbean Sea. With 8371.8 sq km of surface area, it is the sixth largest province of the Cuban nation. It has a flat relief in its north part because of the Cauto-Guacanayabo plain, but it is mountainous in the south because of the presence of the Sierra Maestra.

The Cauto—the largest of Cuba—, Bayamo, Jibacoa, Guamá, Cautillo and Yara Rivers, among others, flow across the province.

It is both an agricultural and industrial province; it produces sugar, vegetables, and fruits. It has ten sugar mills, factories of agricultural equipment, of construction materials, and others. Fishing and livestock also are important activities in its economy. Granma has a population of 820,256 inhabitants, distributed in 13 municipalities.

Niquero. It is the southernmost territory of Cuba, located in the Macaca Peninsula that includes Cruz Cape, the south extreme of the national territory. It is an important territory from the historic viewpoint because the Granma yacht landed in Playa Las Coloradas, located in its swampy coast, and it was the scenery of the first combat of the newly Rebel Army in Alegría de Pío.

The marine terraces are the most remarkable geographical accidents, that just like in Maisí, are elevated hundreds of meters from the sea; they include all kind of karstic and karstic-littoral forms. This zone is arid and inhospitable even at present, but nevertheless long time ago it was inhabited by natives, who left in its caverns (as did in the Guafe and El Fustete caves) unequivocal evidences of their presence through pictographies and idols sculpted in the cavern speleothems. Other caves, like the Sima de Morlote shaft, were discovered thanks to the aviation, because the landscape is too rough, and it has not been possible to access to them; in spite of it, there are more than 50 m width in its entry. Sugar cane is cultivated in its flat zones, and it is processed in the Roberto Ramírez sugar mill. Fruits and vegetables are also cultivated. Eastwards there is a mountainous territory. Niquero has a population of 40,733 inhabitants, and a surface area of 582 sq km.

Media Luna. It is a newly created municipality (1976) of the Guacanayabo Gulf that bounds to the south with Niquero. It is a broken territory that rises southeastwards with the foothills of the Sierra Maestra. The Vicana River, among others, runs across the municipality.

Its economy rests on the sugar production of the Juan Manuel Márquez sugar mill. The name of this sugar mill is in honor of the second leader of the Granma yacht expedition, who was murdered when he was captured by Batista's army, after the Alegría de Pío combat. It has a population of 36,768 inhabitants living in 383 sq km.

Campechuela. It is also a municipality of the Guacanayabo Gulf next to Media Luna northwards. It has a population of 48,926 inhabitants and 577 sq km of surface area, with a wavy territory southwards that turns into a mountainous one in the foothills of the Sierra Maestra, and it is flat northwards. There are two sugar mills: Enidio Leyva and Francisco Castro Ceruto, and that is why sugar production is one of the chief economic activities, together with coffee and fruits cropping.

Manzanillo. It has a territorial extension of 498 sq km, with a population of 134,845 inhabitants that are very proud because in its lands is placed La Demajagua, where the independence of the country was proclaimed by its owner, Carlos Manuel de Céspedes, the Father of the Motherland. Its municipal head, the city of the gulf per excellence, has been a revolutionary center with an outstanding trajectory in the country.

Manzanillo has swampy territories in the coast, flat ones in its center and mountainous in the south, where the Sierra Maestra is. It has fertile lands and numerous fluvial currents that water them, like the Yara River. Sugar cane, coffee and rice are cultivated in its lowlands; livestock products have reached a well-earned fame due to its quality.

Pilón. It is a newly created territory (1976) that was part of the municipality of Niquero. It has a population of 30,633 inhabitants and 462 sq km of surface area. It lies south of the province, bordering with Niquero; it is mountainous to the east and the north, wavy in the center and the west, and bounds to the south with the Caribbean Sea. It produces cane sugar in the Luis E. Carracedo sugar mill, and stands out due to fruits cropping, even grape, having a very good productivity. The Marea del Portillo Hotel, surrounded by excellent landscapes, is linked with Santiago de Cuba by a road that travels through the south of the Sierra Maestra, and it is an important tourist attractiveness. Fishing is also an important economic activity.

Bartolomé Masó. It has the name of a general of the independence wars, the last president of the Republic in Arms. It has a population of 58,166 inhabitants and 635 sq km of surface area. The Sierra Maestra is to the southeast, where the partisan fight against Batista's dictatorship began. The Yara and Jibacoa Rivers and others flow across Its territory. Coffee and vegetables are cultivated here, mainly for self-consumption. Sugar cane is cultivated northwards, where an homonymous sugar mill is placed.

Yara. It has the name of an aboriginal princess, symbol of the national rebelliousness. Formerly, it was part of Manzanillo municipality, until the new political-administrative division (1976). It bounds with Manzanillo to the west and southwest, with Bartolomé Masó and Buey Arriba to the south, and with Bayamo and Río Cauto to the north and northwest, respectively.

In its lands the first combat for the liberty and independence in Cuba was waged. Its surface area is of 575 sq km with a population of 59,386 inhabitants.

The Buey River runs across its flat territory from east to west; tobacco and vegetables are cultivated in its lands.

Río Cauto. It has 45,789 inhabitants and a surface area of 1600 sq km. It occupies the utmost northwestern extreme of the province, being part of the Cauto-Guacanayabo plain. Formerly, it belonged to Bayamo municipality. The Cauto River flows across part of its lands. Sugar production in the sugar mills named José N. Figueredo and Grito de Yara, and rice cropping in the lowest zones of the municipality, are the main economic activities.

Cauto Cristo. It is also a newly created municipality (1976); it was part of the municipality of Bayamo. It has a population of 19,130 inhabitants and a surface area of 550 sq km. It is crossed by the Cauto River; it has easily flooded lowlands. It is a cattle territory, where also vegetables are cultivated.

Bayamo. It occupies the center of the province, with a surface area of 917 sq km and a population of 200,605 inhabitants. It has plains at the north, where livestock is developed; sugar cane and vegetables are also cultivated. The Sierra Maestra is south of it, from which come the Buey, Bayamo, Cautillo and other Rivers.

The municipal head, Bayamo city, was the second village founded by Diego Velázquez in 1513, and has an heroic history regarding adversities of nature, pirates' and corsairs' incursions—who used to go in inland going up the Cauto and Bayamo Rivers, navigable in other times—, injustices caused by the Colony and destructive actions carried out by the governors.

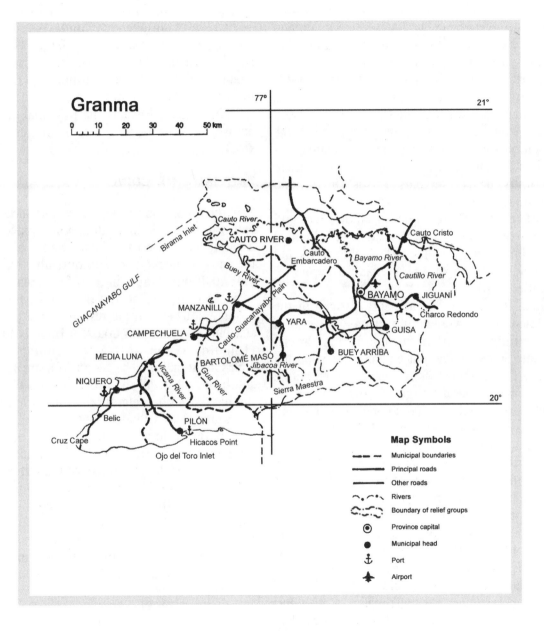

Granma

Map Symbols

- – – – Municipal boundaries
- ····· Principal roads
- —— Other roads
- ∼·∼· Rivers
- ⊂∼⊃ Boundary of relief groups
- ⊙ Province capital
- ● Municipal head
- ⚓ Port
- ✈ Airport

Bayamo was the cradle of Carlos Manuel de Céspedes, Perucho Figueredo—general of the Independence War and the author of the Cuban "National Anthem"—and other notable patriots. It withstood the 1551, 1621, 1624 and 1776 earthquakes and the 1616 and 1693 floods. In 1868, in view of the proximity of the Spanish troops—larger in number and armament and led by the Count of Balmaseda of the Spanish Army—that had the purpose to crush the growing revolution for independence, its inhabitants preferred fire the city reducing it to ashes; later, all of them went to the countryside as insurgents. This is why Bayamo was stated National Monument.

In times of the pseudo-republic, of landowners and front men, the workers of the Mabay sugar mill (named Arquímedes Colina today) took the industrial facilities and neighboring fields, and implanted a socialist "republic" known as "Soviet of Mabay."

Buey Arriba. It is a new municipality, formed at the expense of Bayamo and Manzanillo; it has above all a mountainous territory. Mining production had an special importance some time ago, and place names like Minas de Bueycito, Minas del Frío and others that were used before are abandoned or inactive at present. Coffee cropping is the chief economic production. It has a population of 32,219 inhabitants and a territorial extension of 454 sq km.

Guisa. It is a mostly mountainous municipality, with 596 sq km of surface area and 54,552 inhabitants. It has an aboriginal name, and was part of the municipality of Bayamo, only a few kilometers away from the municipal capital. Its territory is crossed by the Bayamo and Guamá Rivers, dammed up in the Corojo dam, in spite of the karstic features of the mountainous summits they cross. It has typical karstic forms in the hillsides of the north slope of the Sierra Maestra, such as caverns, lapiez, dolines, shaping the Guisa-Los Negros karstic region. Coffee and fruits are cultivated in its lands, and also cattle is bred.

Jiguaní. It has a population of 58,388 inhabitants and 645 sq km of surface area. Santa Rita de Jiguaní was the scenery of the first *machete*[36] charge, a military action of the Liberating Army of the nineteenth century that changed the fighting idea, turning the farm tools into arms in favor of the revolution for independence.

The Jiguaní River is the principal current that flows across the territory, whose economy rests mainly on livestock.

SANTIAGO DE CUBA

It is the second more populated province of Cuba, and a cultural, scientific and educational place. It had, during a span, the second university center of the country and the most important institutions, after the capital. It has 1,017,040 inhabitants in a surface area of 6170.1 sq km. It has a flat relief northwards, and between a wavy and mountainous one in the rest. It is a city that opens to the sea only to the south coast; it bounds to the north with Holguín, to the west with Granma and to the east with Guantánamo. The Sierra Maestra spreads out to the south of almost all the province, and the Turquino Peak, the highest Cuban elevation, is in its territory.

Santiago de Cuba city is the provincial capital, second in importance in the country because of its economic development and population density. It has eight sugar mills, the second crude oil refinery of the national territory, factories of cement, textiles, construction materials, food industry, two thermoelectric plants and other industries. The Santiago de Cuba port is, practically, the only harbor of the province, and has a great mercantile activity.

The zones of fruit trees (for instance, El Caney) are typical of this province, where also poutlry, cattle and pigs are developed.

---

36. It is a large or long knife for cutting cane. *Trans.*

Santiago de Cuba

0 10 20 30 40 50 km

76°

20°

CONTRAMAESTRE

Contramaestre
River

MELLA

MAYARÍ ARRIBA

Guaninicum
River

Maffo

Carlos Manuel de Céspedes Dam

SAN LUIS

PALMA SORIANO

LA MAYA

CRUCE DE LOS BAÑOS

La Bayamesa Peak 1730

Gilbert Dam

Alto Songo

Gran Piedra
Range 1214

Pino del Agua
Sierra Maestra
Mountain Range
Martí Peak 1722

El Cobre

SANTIAGO DE CUBA

Turquino Peak 1974

CHIVIRICO

Santiago de Cuba Bay

Baconao
River

Map Symbols

- – – – Municipal boundaries
- National Highway
- Principal roads
- Other roads
- Rivers
- Boundary of relief groups
- ⊚ Province capital
- ● Municipal head
- ⚓ Port
- ✈ Airport

Santiago de Cuba was the cradle of the General Deputy of the Liberating Army Antonio Maceo Grajales, the highest exponent of the Cuban patriots that fought for the independence of Cuba and were born in a humble cradle, just like Guillermo Moncada (Guillermón), Quintín Banderas, among many other *mambíses* that today are legend and example for current generations.

The province is divided into nine municipalities.

Guamá. This is a mountainous municipality, whose coasts are watered by the Caribbean Sea. It occupies the utmost southwestern of the province. Its municipal head is Chivirico, a town located south of the Sierra Maestra. The peaks of the Turquino massif and the Martí Peak (1622 m) are part of this territory. The municipality has a population of 34,377 inhabitants and a surface area of 951 sq km.

The local economy rests on timber staples, citrus fruits and livestock. Nowadays, tourism is developed in the wonderful landscapes of the Sierra Maestra, thanks to the construction, in its south slope, of a road from Niquero to Santiago allowing the access to beaches and places with extraordinary beauty.

Tercer Frente. It is mainly a mountainous territory, with a population of 40,946 inhabitants and 361 sq km of surface area. It lies north of Guamá municipality, and bounds with Granma province to the west, and with Palma Soriano municipality to the east. It is crossed from north to south by the Contramaestre River, which springs up in the Sierra Maestra at heights of more than 1000 m and later ponds in the Carlos Manuel de Céspedes dam in the municipality of Contramaestre. The Jíbara cave being 236 m deep stands out among the underground accidents of the limestone hills in this mountainous municipality, and also does the Pipe gorge, with the largest absolute vertical well (155 m) of Cuba. In this territory, in a place known as La Lata, laid the headquarters of Commander Juan Almeida, chief of the III Eastern Front Mario Muñoz, during the revolutionary war.

The municipal head is Cruce de los Baños, a town located in the banks of the Contramaestre River, in the central-eastern part of the municipality. Coffee, vegetables and fruits cropping are the main economic staples.

Contramaestre. It is a newly created municipality (1976) that formerly was part of the municipalities of Jiguaní and Palma Soriano; it has a surface area of 611 sq km and a population of 100,680 inhabitants. Its economy rests above all on the production of citrus fruits and also another fruits, sugar and vegetables. The América Libre sugar mill is placed in this territory.

In the zones of Baire, Los Negros, Matías, and others, Contramaestre has a great development of karstic forms, in the limestone of the Charco Redondo formation that corresponds with the north slope of the Sierra Maestra. Poljes, blind valleys, sinks, lapiez and other forms are frequent. In the first decades of the century, several manganese mines were exploited in the region.

Julio Antonio Mella. It is a municipality that arose from the new political-administrative division, whose name is in honor of a Cuban revolutionary that was founder of the first marxist party. It lies in the northern part of the province.

The municipal head is the little village near to the Julio Antonio Mella sugar mill, former Miranda when it was property of a North American company. The municipality uses a forth part of the territory for sugar production.

Palma Soriano. It has a population of 124,354 inhabitants and 852 sq km of surface area. The municipal head, of the same name, lies near to the banks of the Cauto River. The Gilbert dam, which controls the upper Cauto and supplies Santiago de Cuba city with water is located in this municipality. Its chief economic staples are coffee, livestock, citrus fruits, and vegetables.

San Luis. It lies north of the municipality of Santiago de Cuba, and has a population of 88,241 inhabitants. It has a wavy territory of 763 sq km of surface area that is crossed by the Guaninicum River, with an economy resting on sugar agriculture, minor fruits, vegetables, and livestock as well.

Santiago de Cuba. This municipality bounds to the east with Guantánamo. It has a surface area of 1025 sq km, a mainly mountainous territory with the elevations of the Sierra Maestra to the west, the Gran Piedra Range (1214 m) to the east and other hills.

The municipal head, Santiago de Cuba city, was founded in 1514 by Diego Velázquez. It withstood earthquakes and pirates attacks, but was able to maintain its geographical position. At the beginning of the nineteenth century, the village and its surroundings grew because of the arrival of French emigrants coming from Haiti that devoted themselves to coffee and cotton cropping.

Santiago was cradle of many heroes and martyrs of the revolutionary heroic deeds, and that is why Santiago was designated Hero City of the Republic of Cuba. Patriots such as Antonio Maceo, Guillermón Moncada, Quintín Banderas, Flor Crombet, Emilio Bacardí, Frank País, José Tey and many others were born in Santiago. The unbelievable attitude characterized by an exceptional generosity of mothers like Mariana Grajales, María Antonia Figueroa and others, extols the memory of Cuban woman. Santiago de Cuba has a tourist zone with a remarkably development, located in the banks of the Baconao River, named precisely, Baconao National Park.

Songo-La Maya. This municipality arose when the Alto Songo and La Maya neighborhoods—northeast of Santiago de Cuba, bordering with Guantánamo—were joined. It has a population of 99,532 inhabitants and 720 sq km of surface area. It has played an important role in the independence and liberation wars because of its strategic position.

The territory of this municipality occupies the upper basins of the Guaninicum, Guantánamo and Baconao Rivers, which water the lands that produce fruits, sugar, citrus fruits and vegetables. It has two sugar mills in its lands.

Segundo Frente. This municipality was formed with lands of the former municipalities of Alto Songo, Guantánamo, Sagua de Tánamo and others that after the victory of the Revolution in 1959 achieved such a development allowing to join them and declared the territory a political-administrative unit. Mayarí Arriba is its municipal head, and near to it, in Soledad de Mayarí Arriba lay the headquarters of the II Eastern Front Frank País, led by the current Army General Raúl Castro. It is a territory where both housing and paths are newly constructed. It has a population of 40,946 inhabitants and a surface area of 539 sq km. It produces coffee and vegetables; forest species are planted, and cattle is bred.

GUANTÁNAMO

It is the easternmost of the Cuban provinces, made up at expenses of the former municipalities of Guantánamo, Baracoa and Yateras. It has a population of 509,282 inhabitants, distributed in 10 municipalities, and a surface area of 6,186.2 sq km, where mountains, part of the Sagua-Baracoa group, predominate. The Toa Crests (1011 m) and El Purial Range, in which the El Gato Hill (1181 m) is located, stand out.

It is crossed by the Toa—the mightiest river of Cuba—, Jaguaní, Guantánamo, Yumurí and other rivers. There is a great biodiversity in the Toa basin, where there are unexplored locales, and the unique true rainforest of the Caribbean-Antillean region. It is the last redoubt of endangered species such as the "almiquí" *(Solenodon cubanus),* a true living fossil; and the ivory-billed woodpecker *(Campephilus principalis bairdii),* an endemic subspecies of Cuba, threatened with extinction, whose search have been carried out by many expeditions in the last years, and there are no objective evidences about its presence in this zone of the Toa basin; several expeditions could only find abandoned nests and hear its call.

Six sugar mills, a polygraphic plant, processing plants of coconut oil, cacao and coffee, salines, and others are placed in this province. It has one of the university faculties in the mountains in the Cuban territory, located in Sabaneta, municipality of El Salvador.

The United States of America Government keeps a naval base in Guantánamo Bay since 1902, against the will of the Cuban people. Guantánamo has heroic traditions; the National Hero José Martí together with Máximo Gómez, General in Chief of the Liberating Army and other revolutionaries, landed in Playitas de Cajobabo, in order to join up the necessary war; as well as Antonio and José Maceo, Flor Crombet and other patriots landed in Baracoa.

In its lands is Realengo 18, a historical zone because of its peasant struggles for land possession, always threatened by landowners.

Niceto Pérez. It occupies the utmost southwestern extreme of the province, with a flat territory in the center of its north part, and a mountainous one southeastwards, where a group of calcareous buttes having leveled summits surround the coast. It has a surface area of 639 sq km, and it is crossed by the Guantánamo River and others, some of them ponded in La Yaya Dam.

Its economy rests on sugar cane growing and sugar production, citrus fruits and livestock as well. Its population is 16,159 inhabitants. The municipality and its municipal head is named after of a peasant leader of the region, murdered by henchmen. It arose as a political-administrative unit in 1976.

El Salvador. It has 44,684 inhabitants and a surface area of 636 sq km. It is the municipality of the utmost northwest tip of the province that was born with the political-administrative division of 1976, and took the name of the sugar mill of the region (former Soledad), whose little village near to it is the municipal head. It was renamed out of solidarity with that Latin American country.

Its economy rests mainly on sugar cane, although in its elevations, belonging to the Sagua-Baracoa group (western part of the Guaso Plateau), coffee is also cultivated, and in the flattest zones, vegetables. It is site of one of the university faculties in the mountains of the country.

Guantánamo. It has a population of 245,812 inhabitants, occupying 741 sq km. The municipal head—with town hall since 1860—is also the provincial capital.

In the south, the municipality spreads out through the valley of the Guantánamo and Guaso Rivers. It bounds with the municipality of Caimanera. At the north, the Guaso Plateau and other hills of the Sagua-Baracoa group are found. This flat-topped mountainous area has its highest elevation at 911 m, and works like a water-parting of the rivers of the province in this sector. From this summit, the Santa Clara, Sagua and Cuzco Rivers, among others, flow to the north, and to the south, the Guaso River. The latter sinks beneath the surface in Hondones, travels about 10 km through underground passages—explored by first time in 1988 by Cuban and Bulgarian speleologists—and emerges through the El Campanario cave, increasing its volume with many springs that appear in the southern side of the range. Furthermore, the plateau has a high degree of karstification that determines the presence of numerous surface and underground forms. Guantánamo produces sugar cane, coffee, and vegetables.

Caimanera. It lies south of Guantánamo and around the homonymous bay; it has a surface area of 365 sq km and a population of 10,222 inhabitants. In this municipality the United States Naval Base is placed. It has the biggest salines of the country, and as opposed to the past, it does not rest its economy in doing services to the base, but it has diversified the production of vegetables and other staples.

Guantánamo

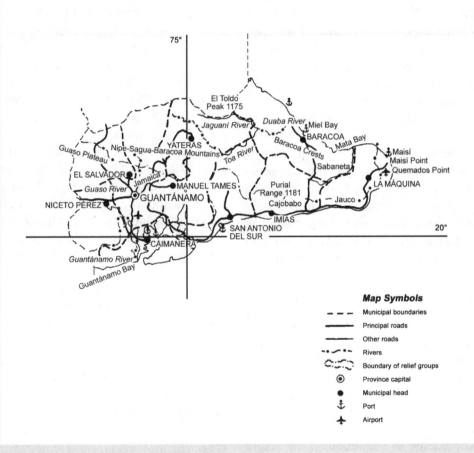

0 10 20 30 40 50 km

75°

El Toldo
Peak 1175

Duaba River

Miel Bay

BARACOA

Jaguaní River

Baracoa Crests

Mata Bay

YATERAS

Nipe-Sagua-Baracoa Mountains

Toa River

Maisí
Maisí Point
Quemados Point

Guaso Plateau

Sabaneta

EL SALVADOR

Jamaica

LA MÁQUINA

Guaso River

MANUEL TAMES

Purial
Range 1181

NICETO PÉREZ

GUANTÁNAMO

Cajobabo

Jauco

IMÍAS

20°

SAN ANTONIO
DEL SUR

CAIMANERA

Guantánamo River

Guantánamo Bay

Map Symbols

- – – –   Municipal boundaries
- ━━━━   Principal roads
- ─────   Other roads
- ·–··–·   Rivers
- ⌇⌇⌇   Boundary of relief groups
- ◉   Province capital
- ●   Municipal head
- ⚓   Port
- ✈   Airport

Yateras. It is a northern non-coastal territory with a surface area of 664 sq km, and bounds with the municipality of Moa in Holguín to the north, and with Baracoa, to the east.

It is a mountainous region with large forest areas, mighty rivers and fertile valleys located in the basins of the Toa River to the north, and of the Yateras River to the south. It is one of the main coffee planter of the province.

Its population consists of 20,146 inhabitants. Palenque de Yateras is its municipal head. The whole region was famous during the nineteenth century because of the presence of Yateras "Indians," a group of individuals with aboriginal features that supported the Spaniards at the beginning of the independence wars, but in the course of the fight, they held the cause for independence. The "Indian" features of many of the inhabitants indicate a clear aboriginal origin.

Manuel Tames. The municipality, as well as a sugar mill, is named after a revolutionary who died in the province in 1958. Although it occupies the central area of a quite mountainous region, it is a relatively flat and wavy territory; that is why its main production is sugar cane, in addition to the forest areas. It is crossed from north to south by the Yateras River. Its population is 15,217 inhabitants and its surface area of 525 sq km.

San Antonio del Sur. It arose with the new political-administrative division of 1976; formerly it was part of the municipality of Guantánamo. It has 27,127 inhabitants in 585 sq km. It is characterized by the aridity of its coast in the south, among Caimanera to the west, Guantánamo and Yateras to the north and Imías to the east, in spite of the Sabanalamar River runs across its territory from north to south, and crosses the Caujerí Valley flowing into the homonymous bay. The Toa River borders and waters the utmost northwestern extreme of the municipality before receiving the Jaguaní River, and the Yateras River drains practically all its territory from north to south. It is one of the municipalities with major forest wealth of the province and the country, in its northern sector (La Redonda, La Ceiba, Rancho Nuevo, and others). There it is frequent to find cultural remains belonging to primitive inhabitants of this region, even in the open air, which would prove a large population judging by their abundance.

Imías. Just like San Antonio, it is a municipality that arose with the new political-administrative division; moreover, it is historically important because the National Hero José Martí, the officer in command of the Liberating Army Máximo Gómez and another chiefs and officers landed in Playitas de Cajobabo, in order to join the *Mambí* Army in 1895. In 523 sq km, it has large forest wealth, and a growing cattle development. The most arid and dry landscapes of the country are in its coastal zone. It has a population of 19,923 inhabitants.

Baracoa. It is a municipality of a considerable surface area: 976 sq km where 80,636 inhabitants live; it holds an important place in the history of Cuba because its municipal head was the first village founded by the Advanced Diego Velázquez in 1512. The General Deputy Antonio Maceo landed in Duaba Beach, together with the generals José Maceo, Flor Crombet and others, in order to join to the necessary war, in 1895.

The Yunque[37] de Baracoa Hill, a singular flat-topped elevation is in this municipality; it is the emblem of the city and the region. Baracoa has an extraordinary wealth of its forests and wild biota, specially in the basin of the Toa River, threatened—until not much time ago—by the construction of an hydroenergetic work that menaced to flood part of the best-preserved rainforest of the Caribbean. An ecological solution would be a scheme of hydropower mini-plants. The fauna that inhabits its remote

37. The elevation had such a name because it is an anvil-shaped hill; "yungue" means "anvil." *Trans.*

mountains must be preserved; one of the species of that outstanding fauna is the *"almiquí" (Solenodon cubanus),* a true historic relic.

The economy of Baracoa rests on coconut, coffee and cacao cropping, from which it is the biggest producer of the country. Among other industries, a chocolate factory is placed in Baracoa city.

Maisí. It has a population of 29,271 inhabitants with a surface area of 525 sq km. The municipal head is named La Máquina. It has many evidences of aboriginal presence in this zone, including petroglyphs, such as those of La Patana cave, taken away by the North American archaeologist Mark Raymond Harrington for their exhibit in the Museum of the American Indian at New York. The region is characterized for having numerous levels of marine terraces, similar to those of Cruz Cape. The economy of the municipality rests on forest exploitation, coffee and cacao. It is the easternmost part of the Cuban archipelago, and its eastern extreme, the Quemados Point, is the end of the Republic of Cuba.

THE SPECIAL MUNICIPALITY
OF THE ISLE OF YOUTH

It has a surface area of 2397 sq km, from which 2199 belong to the Isle of Youth in strict sense; its population consists of 76,713 inhabitants. Its former name was Isle of Pines, and it was stated as a special municipality by the political-administrative division of 1976. It is a very flat territory, with hills to the north—Las Casas Range (261 m) and Caballos Range (235 m)—, and in the center—La Cañada Range (803 m). All of them have very different features: the north part of the isle is a metamorphic complex, and it notably differs from the south that has a marshy character, then arid and karstic in the littoral plain. In the buttes of the north, in the south plain above all, there are caves with aboriginal furniture. The De Isla cave in the southeast, in Punta del Este Point, has pictographies, whose significance and cultural far-reaching are still today in discussion.

The fluvial net is controlled by numerous dams in the northern part that allow the irrigation of the productive and extensive citrus fruit plantations. Those fruits have great acceptance in the international market.

Tourism is developing quickly, supported in the facilities of the Colony Hotel in the western coast, in the virgin beaches of the southern littoral and in the international diving center of Francés Point.

The municipal head, Nueva Gerona, is a picturesque town and a fluvial port on the banks of the Las Casas River.

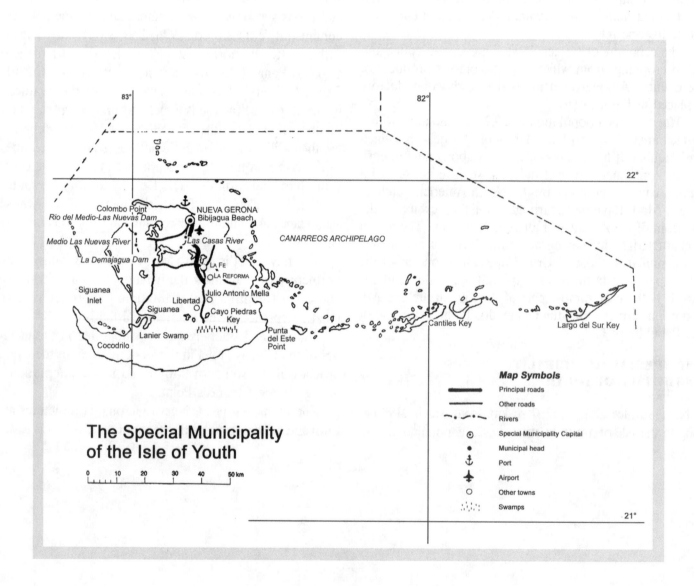

The Special Municipality
of the Isle of Youth

0   10   20   30   40   50 km

Map Symbols

	Principal roads
	Other roads
	Rivers
	Special Municipality Capital
	Municipal head
	Port
	Airport
	Other towns
	Swamps

POLITICAL-ADMINISTRATIVE DIVISION

Pinar del Río

La Habana

Ciudad de La Habana

Matanzas

Cienfuegos

Villa Clara

Sancti Spíritus

Ciego de Ávila

Camagüey

Las Tunas

Holguín

Granma

Santiago de Cuba

Guantánamo

Municipio Especial Isla de la Juventud

[The Special Municipality of the Isle of Youth]

In the background, the Tetas de Managua, twin hills located south of Ciudad de La Habana. They are part of the Bejucal-Madruga-Coliseo Hills, spreading out from the eastern half of the province of La Habana to the western part of the province of Matanzas. Photograph by Maurilio Ávila Estopiñán.

Bordayo Inlet, in the north slide of the San Carlos Range, Pinar del Río; it is a depression that, from the geological-structural viewpoint, is a tectonic window. The huge entry to the Gran Caverna de Dos Anas of the Majaguas-Cantera cavern system, having about 30 km of underground passages, may be observed at the back. Photograph by Roberto Buzzini.

Mouth of the sink of the Resolladero cave of the Cuyaguateje River, Pinar del Río, seen from the Hoyo de Potrerito. The river reaches the San Carlos Valley after a short section, having crossed this cave. Photograph by Manuel Rivero Glean.

Typical landscape of the Cuyaguateje River during the winter or dry season in the Pica Pica Valley, hundreds of meters before entering by the famous homonymous sink excavated in the Sumidero Range in Pinar del Río. In the photo, explorers of the Martel Speleological Group of Cuba. Photograph by Gabriel Barceló Carol.

La Ermita stream, typical small current that cuts and drains in an ortogonal way the confines of the El Rosario Range in Pinar del Río. Photograph by Manuel Rivero Glean.

In the foreground, mushroom-shaped cavern formations made up of zinolite—unique in the world—among other secondary cristalline forms (speleothems) in the Gran Caverna de Santa Catalina, one of the biggest speluncas of Matanzas. This cavern is found in a thick coastal forest north of the current highway from Matanzas to Varadero. Photograph by Roberto Buzzini.

Scene at the Almendares River, main fluvial current that cross Ciudad de La Habana. This river is unfortunately polluted with sewer waters, and that make easy the proliferation of water hyacinth *(Eicchornia crassipes),* an aquatic plant, indicator of the eutrophication of tropical aquifers. This photo was taken from the 23 Street.

Mouth of the Cojímar River, notably affected fluvial current owing to the pollution with industrial residual and sewer waters from the east of the capital of the Island. In the foreground, the organogenic limestone that form practically all the coastline of the provinces Ciudad de La Habana and La Habana. Photograph by Maurilio Ávila Estopiñán.

Valley of the Yumurí River, an emblematic landscape of the province of Matanzas; it is found in the east extreme of the Habana-Matanzas eroded anticline, among the hills having the same name. Photograph by Gabriel Barceló Carol.

Typical small mogote at the Escaleras de Jaruco Range belonging to the natural region named Alturas La Habana-Matanzas, in La Habana province. It is a locality of cupole karst, similar to that of the Los Órganos Range in Pinar del Río, made up of rocks ranging from the Paleogene to the Neogene. Photograph by Gabriel Barceló Carol.

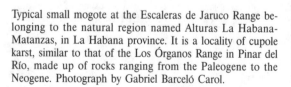

Typical landscape of the Florida-Camagüey-Tunas central plain, with its grassy savannahs where palms belonging to the *Coccothrinax*, *Copernicia* and *Saba* genera grow. Photograph by Antonio Núñez Jiménez.

El Caletón Inlet located in the back of the Cochinos Bay, south of the province of Matanzas. In the foreground it may be observed the organogenic limestone, typical from the Zapata Swamp, bellow which the very dark and reddish water may be seen owing to the presence of mangrove tannin. It is a considerable hydric volume—preferable drainage of the swamp—, organized along a fault. In the background, students and professors of the Geography Faculty of the Instituto Superior Pedagógico Enrique José Varona. Photograph by Manuel Rivero Glean.

Speleo-divers from the Martel Speleological Group of Cuba, preparing to explore the XXXV Aniversario kamenitza (75 m deep), one of the flooded caverns of the speleolacustrine system of the Zapata Swamp. Photograph by Manuel Rivero Glean.

Waterfall of the Caburní River in Topes de Collantes, Trinidad Range, in the Guamuhaya Mountains. In these mountains abound cascades similar to those, shaped because of a family of concentric faults that have transversally broken off the nearly radial drainage of this metamorphic massif. Photograph by Julian Jean Pierre.

Partial view of the famous Viñales Valley located in the central part of the Los Órganos Range, west of the Guaniguanico Mountain Range in the province of Pinar del Río. To the left in the foreground the Feita mogote is observed, and behind it, also to the left, the Viñales Valley mogote; the limy mogotes of the La Guasasa Range are at the background. All of them are practically hollowed by numerous caverns and underground rivers. Photograph by Eugenio Pérez Ferrer.

Typical sugar mill in the Júcaro-Morón Plain, surrounding by sugar cane crops and fallow lands. Photograph by Eugenio Pérez Ferrer.

Black-sand (tuffaceous) beach in Marea del Portillo, Niquero, Granma province, in the western coastal extreme of the Sierra Maestra. Photograph by Manuel Rivero Glean.

Moon-like landscape, as a result of the exploitation of polymetallic crusts. The Moa Crests are observed at the background. These extensive laterite areas that nowadays are one of the biggest nickel reserves of the world are in a rehabilitation process. The new mine zones are being studied taking into account the environmental impact, according to the effective law, in order to reduce the soil, biota and landscape damages. Photograph by Manuel Acevedo González, courtesy of Jorge Macle Cruz.

High coast of Farallones Point in the western coastal extreme of the Sierra Maestra, where it may be observed areas of developed coastal xeromorphous bush (coastal secondary woody vegetation) with abundant column cactaceae from the *Pilosocereus* genus, short-stems cactaceae like the *Melocactus* with endemic species, and those from the *Consolea* genus. Photograph by Gabriel García Pulpeiro.

Coastal section of the southern slope of the Sierra Maestra Mountain Range, where the fluvial action has carried along hundreds of thousands of boulders from granitoid and volcanic rocks, some of them remodeled *in situ* by marine abrasion, and others by the exfoliation of outcropping rocks. Photograph by Manuel Rivero Glean.

Pico Real del Turquino, Sierra Maestra, seen from the Cuevas del Turquino in its south side, dryer than the north one. (The highest summit may be observed in the right extreme of the photo.) Photograph by Manuel Rivero Glean.

CHAPTER VII

SOCIETY AND ECONOMY

If a briefly characterization of the Cuban economic society is attempted within the natural conditions of the Antillean Archipelago, it arises the risk of generalize and use labels in order to identify that which is Cuban, and thus evaluate so subtle categories such as the cultural ones that usually escape from the mechanical determinism exerted by the geographical circumstances.

It is an indisputable fact that being Cuban is a second nature, the cultural nature of this exceptional Caribbean island. The Cuban society arises as a result of not only economic and cultural events, framed in not much more than five hundreds years of prehistory and history, but also conditioned by its natural reality: landscapes, flora, fauna, water, soil and sun; above all the sun that illuminates and heats and colors everybody during the day, and leaves traces in the *cubanícolas*[38] that stay up late at night.

38. A slang; it has been used as a resemblance with the word *terrícola*, that means "earthling." *Trans.*

Since the natives from the eastern north coast, about five hundreds six years ago, received the three caravels of Christopher Columbus feeling astonishment, fear and merriment, the unmistakable peculiarity of the Cuban society began to form. Then, the Caribbean Island and its inhabitants would leave off being the harmonic (ecological) whole land-men in order to go entirely in the distressed history of the *Homo economicus.*

Since then, the fast and definite extermination of Cuban natives began. The natives left us a beautiful toponymy like a legacy that the colonizer could not substitute: legends about their hopeless resistance and about their pottery, sculptural art and cave painting. Nowadays they are not only in the museums, but also in labels, logos and in diverse displays of culture, trade and sports. These are the roots; they are scanty, dispersed, maybe weak, but they are one and ours.

Afterwards followed the fury of the genocide; the Spaniards, together with the Jews (fearful and perjured from its faith); mestizoes as a result of the mixture between Spaniards and Moors; Canary Islanders; Europeans from the four corners of the Old Continent; and later, in huge surges, still with native ground in their fingers and nails, the Amerindians and Africans, both practically killed. The melting pot was filled, but it did not overflow. Black Africa was added to that which was Amerindian and predominantly from Iberia, so early as in 1512, according to the first document that give evidence of the import of 300 Africans to Cuba, recorded by José Antonio Saco in his excellent work *Historia de la esclavitud* [Slavery History].

At the beginning of the seventeenth century the Island was still half-uninhabited. In 1608 it had about 20,000 inhabitants, and 92 years had to go by to see this figure multiplied 2.5 times; in 1700 the population reached 50,000 inhabitants. In that time, the slaves wrenched from the black continent and the Spanish, French, English and some Dutch enslavers settled in the Island (The latter did not take roots).

As of 1688, important surges of Canary Islanders arrived; they settled inland of the country as peasants.

It did not take a long time to the black population to constantly grow. The Real Compañía de La Habana[39] imported 4986 African slaves between 1740 and 1760; sugar was tinged with red African blood, the air was filled with new songs, rumbling drums and strange religions.

According to Ramón de la Sagra, a Spanish geographer who liked statistics, the first census of the colony in 1768 showed 172,620 inhabitants; from them, 96,540 were white people and 76,620, mestizoes and black ones —among free men and slaves—the 44% of the population.

39. Havana Royal Company. *Trans.*

Marquis de Casa Enrique introduced in Cuba 14,000 slaves from Africa between 1773 and 1779. The English men, active dealers then, moved to the Caribbean Island 5786 negroes in the span between 1786 and 1789.

The Island received a singular population and cultural contribution between 1790 and 1810 because of the immigration of some 30,000 French men from Haiti. They were hurled from their country by the insurgent negroes, protagonists of decisive rebellious events in this western territory of the Hispaniola.

Half of this surge of refugees dispersed in Santiago de Cuba, and an important part of it made possible the beginning of a brilliant coffee culture in the wild mountains of the Sierra Maestra. Today, the so-called "French coffee plantations", now in ruins in the middle of the mountainous forest, talk about the creative determination of their owners. The surnames, translated to Spanish language, but with a French nuance, and the bright eyes of many eastern mestizoes speak about this cultural mixture.

The most important immigrations of the eighteenth century in Cuba, without any doubt, were those of the Canary Islanders, who arrived from the Atlantic Canary Islands to work the Cuban land; in popular slang they are named "Islanders."

The immigration of about 29,000 Spanish citizens from many places of the Iberian Peninsula was recorded in 1809. A group of French persons, coming from the northern Louisiana, was settled in Cienfuegos in 1819. Immigrant traders from Catalonia began to arrive in 1830; they founded an important association of the wholesalers and retailers.

About 227,000 slaves were imported from Africa to the Island from 1790 until 1830 coinciding with the expansion of the sugar industry. A new nation was being created. "The negroes—in Fernando Ortiz's opinion —should feel, not with a bigger intensity, but maybe earlier than the white people, the emotion and the conscience of being Cuban ..." (DP-FAR, 1983).

In 1841, 436,500 slaves were 43.3% of the population. As of 1847, important surges of Chinese and Yucatan workers were introduced, and they had to work in semi-slavery conditions. The melting pot of the nationality was diversified.

The armed struggle against the Spaniard colonialism joined races and nationalities. Cuba turned into a land of internationalist combatants: former officials of Bolívar, North American patriots, Spanish deserters, Antilleans and Chineses, and to a great extent, black slaves, white natives and Cuban mestizoes made up ranks in the *mambí* troops.

A culture of unusual mixtures, regarding to religion, the alimentary habits, popular argot, and art and culture, built up together with the nationality and the patriotic sense. This happened in the *mambí* camps, in cities and towns or in the dungeons where the patriots were confined. The rebellious wars finished with the population and wealth of the Island.

Cuba had 1,572,797 inhabitants in 1900, according to the voting register carried out for the municipal elections that would be on June 16th of that same year. The Spanish politic and military power was replaced by the North American economic power. The renascent sugar industry needed laborers; in 1907 2,048,980 inhabitants were registered; from them 228,477 were foreigners (11%), from which 185,393 (81%) were from Spain; 11,217 from Asia; 1948 from Africa; 6713 from North America; 2918 from Puerto Rico; 4280 from the Antilles; 1476 from France, and 1442 from Central and South America.

The statistics of the Ministry of Treasury of Cuba (its Section of Statistics, Immigration and Passengers' Movement) recorded between 1906 and 1931 the arrival to the capital of 336,916 Antillean immigrants, among them: 190,255 from Haiti, 121,520 from Jamaica, 12,133 from Puerto Rico, and the rest, from Dominican Republic and other isles (Álvarez, 1988).

When considering the *fin-de-siècle* decreased Cuban population, it is understood the populational and cultural importance of immigration. To that, it must be added the small colonies of Hindus in the province of Oriente, the arrival of Antilleans from the British West Indians, the Iberians from the regions of Asturias and Galicia, Jews from the center and east of Europe (the so-called "Polishes" in the popular argot); and Syrians, Lebaneses, Palestinians, Chineses (from the United States of America), North Americans, Mexicans from Yucatan, Japaneses (to the Isle of Pines), Irishmen, Italians, and so forth.

The majority of the Antillean laborers directly arrived to the provinces of Camagüey and Oriente, in order to work in sugar labors. The most cultured or less poor immigration arrived to La Habana province and worked in retail trade.

The Cuban population and culture eagerly nourished from this immigrant army; this economic and cultural phenomenon definitely marked the racially mixed condition of the Cuban nation.

The Cuban population grew until 1940 at the expense of the immigration and its own natality. After that date the migratory phenomenon towards the Island dropped.

After 1959, with the victory of the Cuban Revolution, an economic, political and cultural relationship began with the countries of the so-called socialist block formed by the Soviet Union, Eastern Germany, Poland, Bulgaria, Czechoslovakia, Hungary, Romania, Yugoslavia, China, North Korea and North Vietnam. As a result, there were a varied interchange and influence; no changes or marked trends in the cultural level, but Cuban cosmological philosophy was fulfilled. In that same period, about 350,000 traveled to Angola, Ethiopia, Congo, Guinea and other African countries in order to collaborate in national liberation wars, and in the post-war restoration.

Thousands of teachers, constructors, physicians, sports trainers and other specialists of the Antillean Island worked in Latin American and African countries. Other thousands of young pupils from Third-World countries have studied and study in Cuba. All this wide historical phenomenon of economic, political, scientific and cultural interchange of the Island with the rest of the world marked the current Cuban society, and makes it tributary of varied racial, religious and national cultures. Cuban athletes and artists successfully perform in varied disciplines. Cuban music is nowadays one of the most spread of the world, and it shows the character of a nice, cultured and happy people that assimilate without reticence the foreign influences, and give back them to the world with the hallmark: "the most beautiful land that human eyes have ever seen," Christopher Columbus, Cuba, Bariay, October 27th, 1492.

POPULATION

In Chapter 6, Political and Administrative Structures, in the paragraph corresponding to the political-administrative division, are given the figures of the population of provinces and municipalities, until December 31st, 1996.

The Cuban population grew up to 11,094,000 inhabitants in December, 1997; it has its greatest concentration in the capital, with 2,200,400; Santiago de Cuba with 1,020,900; and Holguín with 1,118,200 inhabitants.

HEALTH

Despite the huge economic difficulties the country has gone through as a consequence of the collapse of the socialist block, where there were the first trade partners of Cuba under favorable conditions of trade interchange; the strengthening of the economic blockade, even to the most subtle issues—sale prohibition of medicaments—by the United States; and the logical influence of the preceding facts have had upon the budgets for health, the Cuban Government, based on the political disposition of its social program, not only has kept, but also improved the main health indexes.

The life expectancy rate was 74.7 years in 1997, a typical index of a developed country. The population has one physician per 176 inhabitants, and one dentist per 1124 inhabitants. The Family Physicians (primary attention system promoted by Cuba) take care of 97.6% of the population. In that same year, the country had 2013 units of medical services, 723 hospitals, 166 stomatologic clinics, 220 mother's homes and 196 senior citizens' homes.

The children's mortality indexes are one of the most impressive achievements of the Cuban health system. In 1997, the index was 7.2 per each thousand born alive children (one of the lowest of the world), a figure that is almost the same in the whole regions of the country, even in the mountains.[40]

EDUCATION

The national system of education is another aspect that characterizes the Cuban society today. It could develop in spite of the unbelievable economic above mentioned limitations.

In September, 1997, 2,224,100 students entered in the schools in order to receive education from 198,600 pro-

40. *Estadística Seleccionada* [Selected Statistics], Oficina Nacional de Estadísticas (ONE)—Statistics National Office—, 1997.

fessors, teachers and other teaching staff, which used 9487 elementary institutions, 1943 of secondary education, and 35 of university education. The 10% of the gross domestic product (GDP) is earmarked for education.

BRIEF PANORAMA OF THE CUBAN ECONOMIC SITUATION

Since its constitution as a Republic in 1902, still under the rule of the North American Government—even without doing reference to the colonial times—, Cuba had to pass along diverse stages in its economic development, marked by *sui generis* features and conditions. Until 1959, the economy was subordinated on the whole to the North American capital that found in the archipelago a safe market for its numerous products, whether necessary or not for the development of the country, and a mild and cheap supplier of cane sugar and other row materials. All the technology of the few industries that could flourish or keep themselves—among them, transportation and communications—came, almost exclusively, from the United States of America. The North American investments, from 106 million dollars in 1906, amounted to 1200 million dollars just in 1923. In that year, the North Americans owed the three-fourth parts of the sugar industry, and more than 100,000 *caballerías*[41] (1,342,000 ha), among others. In the first quarter of the century, in order to obtain cheap laborers and to make easy the sugar expansion, about 250,000 Antillean agricultural workers were introduced in Cuba. The investment's structure by the end of the first half of the century had changed because of the sugar price, among other reasons, and it concentrated in hotels, casinos, banks, and so forth.

41. It is an agrarian measurement unit used in Cuba, equivalent to 1343 areas. *Trans.*

After the victory of the Revolution, the United States of America Government decided to blockade Cuba with the consequent reduction and the later suspension of the consignment of equipment, spares, and even medicines and food. Then, the Cuban Government had to turn the economy round, and look for suppliers and new markets with reasonable monetary valuations; they were found in the countries of the vanished socialist block, above all, in the formerly Soviet Union.

The First Law of Land Reform, among many others, was one of the internal measures necessary to promulgate, as a pressing need to break the obsolete structure of land possession, the main cause of population hunger and poverty. The property of lands was handed to those who worked them, such as the squatters, sharecroppers and other peasants that were not land owners. So as to discourage the small farmsteads, which would have spurred disorderly production, consequently preventing the implementation of technological advancements, large latifundiae were transferred to the state agricultural sector, which meant to guarantee the intensive use of fertilizers, agricultural machineries, and other inputs in nearly 40% of the land, as well as the elimination of middlemen and the disappearance of the unemployment in the countryside. The Second Law of Land Reform had a marked socialist character, because it looked for the elimination of the capitalist production relations in the countryside. Many credit and service cooperatives were created in this stage as a way of associating the landowner-peasants; the State gave very favorable credits to the farmers, who in a common agreement and in an oriented way, cultivated certain products having governmental interest.

The Cuban Government needed both to recover from foreign hands the national economy, and to maintain the necessary production levels before the growing sabotage to the economy by foreign capital. For instance, the petroleum refineries denied to refine the Soviet oil that had had to be acquired from the USSR before the negative of the United States of America to supply it. Then, the Cuban Government enacted the Nationalization Law that gave to it the control of the refineries, sugar mills, electricity enterprises, banks, processing mineral plants, and many other institutions.

Cuba paid in exchange 60 million dollars to the impaired countries because of the nationalization from 1967 to 1986. It was not possible the payment to the United States of America due to the obstacles set by the own North American Government.

The banditry stage (1960-1965) seriously affected the Cuban economy, not so much because of the direct losses brought about by the terrorist attacks, but for the number of workers and peasants mobilized in the avoidance or repression of bandits, as well as also for the necessity to spend a considerable part of the national production to the support of this revolutionary campaign.

The global social product (GSP) grew 51.8% at a rate of 6.1% a year between 1963 and 1970. Sugar production had an important burden in this increase; it grew 38.7%. The relative failure in doing a harvest of 10 million tons of sugar was a far-reaching fact in that time. The efforts of a considerable part of the Cuban workers engaged in that task, who in spite of not achieving their objective, obtained the biggest crop of the agriculture history of the country.

The favorable conditions to impel the economic activity were created as of 1970, and laid the basis for a thorough restructuring of the economy management system that began at a breakneck pace taking measures in all the productive and budgeted institutions, diversifying the agriculture and the industry, and having the support and material aid of the socialist block.

The economic management system rested on the centralized planning shared with the relative autonomy of the enterprises in their operative-economic management, the effective use of the monetary-mercantile relations and the value law, the use of the finances and their categories—state budget, credits, prices, costs, profits, profitability, and so forth—, and on the principle that the enterprises must replace their expenses with their incomes and at the same time they must create an excess or surplus that would be used in social aims, or in the maintenance of necessary but unprofitable productions.

In 1972, Cuba became a member of the Economic Mutual Aid Council (EMAC), in which it took part as an observer from 1964. Then, important investments were accomplished in almost all the industrial branches, roads, constructions, and services, adapting the production structure to the socialist block market. It caused a sustained increase of the populational standard of living between 1972 and 1989.

During the 1st Congress of the Communist Party in 1975 was aproved the continuation and the improvement of the institutional process that was being carried out in the Cuban economy were approved, in accordance with the favorable conditions that have been created. The establishment of a new political-administrative division was one aspect of this process, which would allow the rational application of the necessary measures and regulations. Thus, in 1976, the People's Power bodies were constituted, and on February 24th of that year, the Constitution of the Republic of Cuba was passed with voting of more than 98%; it was previously discussed by the whole population in (local) assemblies at neighborhoods.

Since the end of the eighties, the economy began to have a deep crisis owing to the cracking and subsequent collapse of the socialist block and the disintegration of the USSR, aggravated by the increase of the United States Government blockade against Cuba. This situation became worse with the approval by the congress of that country of the Torricelli Law, and later, the Helms-Burton Law, having a worldwide interventionist character.

The blockade has had for Cuba, from a monetary viewpoint, a cost of more than forty five million dollars, which has been greater in losses than the aid granted by the socialist block.

In our country, having a high dependence from foreign trade, a loss between 75 % and 80% of this activity and of a considerable part of the large investments accomplished to insert itself in the socialist block market, brought about a sudden fall of the standard of living, and a pronounced collapse of the production (35%) and of nearly 35% of the Gross Domestic Product (GDP) between 1989 and 1993. The Special Period in peace times, a plan of emergency including extreme measures to guarantee the people's surviving, was stated in order to face this situation. Undoubtedly, 1993 was one of the most critical span of the Cuban economy, when the lowest levels of efficiency were reached and the existence of the nation was more than ever endangered. In that year, there was a harvest of just 4.2 million tons of sugar together with the decline of food production with a drift of the farming population towards the cities; a budget deficit—it grew 4.5 times over 1989, reaching 33% of the GDP—; and the fact that the population had increased their money 2.5 times, with reference to 1989 (the base-year), the last one before the Special Period.

In the first months of 1994, the problem worsened (even the harvest of that year 1994-1995 was just 3.3 million tons of sugar), until it was elaborated a plan for stopping and reverting this economic situation. That plan included, among others, the following measures: decriminalization of the tenancy of foreign currency (the Penal Code established sanctions for those who handled that currency) and free circulation of both foreign and Cuban currency; creation of shops for collecting foreign currency (TRD in Spanish); revitalization of taxes; opening to tourism; transformation of state farms into cooperatives; self-employed expanse; opening of agricultural markets, where in same conditions came together private and state producers, promoting a good productive emulation.

In 1994 the descent curve came to a halt, and some slight changes were achieved at the end of the year, such as the stopping of the production depletion that had an increase of 0.7% over the foregoing year, a 0.2-percent GDP growth, and others. A reorganization process in the economy was accomplished from this year, that is why in 1995 the GDP grew in 2.5 regarding to 1994; also a progressive reactivation of the internal finances was carried out.

Despite the difficulties in the sugar harvest, an economic growth of 2.5% was recorded in 1995, and the budget deficit was set to 3% of the GDP, even though the financial liquidity of the population grew in 3%.

In 1996, although the production was still more than 25% fewer than in 1989, Cuba was the country of the greatest economic growth in Latin America—7.8%—in spite of the increase of the North American pressures against every nation or enterprise that would trade with the Island. Positive advanced signs were showed with a harvest of 4,450,000 tons of sugar and the continuos increase in food production, such as the recovery of the national currency value, the price-cutting in the national market (10.4% over 1995), the 11.4-percent increase in populational global incomes over the previous year, among others.

The Foreign Investment Law (Law number 77) was enacted in September 1995, in order to propitiate foreign capital investments for development national economy. Nowadays, the foreign investments are in 34 sectors and branches of the cuban economy; 56 belong to the industrial sector; 34 to tourism; 28 to mining and 25 to petroleum, just to mention the most representative sectors.

Forty three nations take part in joint ventures with the Cuban Government. The most important are those regarding nickel, hotel management, telephone, petroleum exploration and exploitation. Nevertheless, these enterprises generated only the 3% of the net incomes of the country in 1995.

CUBA'S FOREIGN DEBT

Cuba's foreign debt was 10,504 million dollars at the end of 1995 (it includes the mature contractual interests); in that same year, it surpassed in 1,412.2 millions the 1994 debt, it means that it grew 15.6% due to changes in the types of currency exchange and to a dominant "Cuba risk" coefficient in the loans (never soft, and always near-term), which increase the interest. The external debt reached 48% of the GDP value in 1995, and the relation to the exportations, 710%; it indicates the country would have to totally earmark the incomes for the current value of its exportations during 7 years in order to pay it.

The main foreign creditors of Cuba are: Japan, 21.4%; Spain, 13.0%; France, 12.18%; Great Britain, 7.8%; Argentina, 7.7%; Italy, 5.7%; Mexico, 4.0%; Switzerland, 2.7%; and Germany, 2.3%.

Cuba's foreign debt slightly decreased in its total value at the end of 1996, over 1995, down to 10,400.5 million dollars despite in this year, just like in the foregoing since the collapse of the socialist block, the stringent credit conditions and the limited or null access to international financial institutions prevail.

STATE BUDGET

There is a policy of maximum austerity in public expenditure that is based on the increase of the incomes from the increase of the fiscal discipline and the reduction or disappearance of the aid to state enterprises. The permissible budget deficit was fixed in 2% of the GDP, and in 1996 it was 2.4%, a rate corresponding with the levels of developed countries. For instance, the State assigns from the budget: 3.5% for education; 7% for health; 8.5% for housing and communal services, among other spheres.

The income in 1995 were 11,600 million pesos that means a 3-percent increase in relation to the foregoing year. The net outcome of state enterprises in 1996, for the first time since 1986, was 1% favorable to the budget, exceeding in 756 million pesos the contributions to the granted aids from the profits.

The incomes in that same year (1996) reached 12,242.7 million pesos, it means, 642.7 millions more than in the previous year. In 1997 they decreased in little rate to 12,143.0 million pesos, with a profit value of 2345 million pesos, which represents a deficit of -468,000 million pesos, even though it has been able to verify that the costs of the enterprise activity decreased.

It has been possible to keep up the contribution to education, health and social security; they have had more rationality and efficiency in their management. The GDP rose in 1997 to 14,572.4 million pesos, which means 102.5-percent increase over 1956.

EMPLOYMENT AND WAGES

The work in the state sector diminished 10% in 1995, due to the decrease of the employment volumes in state entities (owing to the reorganization and the best use of the labor force), meanwhile it grew in 22% in the non-state sector.

A considerable number of public employees were not abandoned to their fate since "shock therapies" were not put into effect and many aids were conferred, and also the reorganization of the self-employed work allow them to reach acceptable standard livings. The mean wage was 190 pesos in 1995, and grew to 203 in 1996. The work productivity grew in 8.5% in 1996, when important growths were registered in some branches such as 31 in construction (hotels and housings); 17.5% in agriculture; 16% in mining and quarries; 36% in nickel, and so forth.

MAIN ECONOMIC FIELDS OF THE STATE

FOREIGN INVESTMENT

The Law number 77 for Foreign Investment, passed on September 5th, 1995, promotes the foreign investment in the territory of the Republic of Cuba, in order to carry out profitable activities that contribute to the increase of the economic capacity and sustainable development of the country, on the basis of respect to national sovereignty and the protection and rational use of natural resources. This opening process is intended to solve the main problems of the economy, such as: the diversification of exportations regarding their quantity and quality, the acquisition of raw materials, the necessity of new capitals, the insertion in new markets, the acquisition of advanced technology, the introduction of advanced practices of economic management, and others.

This behavior allowed and still allows, in first place, a greater exploitation of the inactive capacities and the available resources that were created during the stage of integration to the socialist block; and the exploration (it is carried out at risk) and extraction of petroleum and solid minerals. In second place, it was later extended to services and pre-financings in sugar cane and non-sugar cane agriculture, and other industrial productions, attractive for the investors. Associations for the expansion and construction of new facilities for tourism were created.

The investments increased, from less than 100 million dollars in 1990, to more than 2100 million dollars in 1995; they played an important role in the search for market, technology and financing, that have disappeared together with the socialist block. It represented 3% of the GDP and about 5% of the labor force employed in this sector.

The existence of an important industrial basis, high tourist potential, qualified work force, political stability and a real environ of security and seriousness are factors that have contributed to attract foreign capital.

Bilateral agreements about promotion and reciprocal protection of investments have been subscribed with Argentina, Barbados, Bolivia, Chile, China, Germany, Great Britain, Greece, Italy, Lebanon, Romania, Russia, South Africa, Spain, Switzerland, Ukraine, Canada and Laos, to attain twenty two. Significant groups of North American businessmen in several opportunities have asked their government to stop the blockade and the hostile attitude towards Cuba, as a way to accomplish investments in the Cuban territory, which represents a natural market for their products and services, according to their statements. These capital groups have even signed letters of intent for the businesses that would be established at the ceasing of the blockade.

Until 1993, before the enactment of the Law of Foreign Investment, the capitals were less important, and in the framework of little and medium enterprises, sixty economic associations were constituted. Capital volume grew from 1994 on, and after the law, it rose at a breackneck pace to reach in 1996, 260 associations of the state sector with foreign capital.

The policy of the Cuban Government towards the foreign capital investments rounds off with the Law of Duty-Free Zones and Industrial Parks which improves the conditions in the Cuban territory to any kind of foreign investments.

TOURISM

The denominated "smokeless industry" or "leisure industry," endowed with numerous and varied interesting landscapes, has meant for Cuba a net contribution to the economy that grew 50% in 1996 with regard to the preceding year.

In 1996, for the first time in the history of the tourism in Cuba, came one million tourists more (30%) than in the foregoing year. For this concept, Cuba received one thousand three hundred million dollars, and Canada, Italy, Spain and Germany continue—since the tourist opening started—as the main tourists' emitter countries to Cuba.

The gross incomes grew 29,4% in 1995 in relation to 1994, by increasing to 1400 million dollars. The number of foreign visitors rose, just a year later (1997), up to reach 1,170,000, which meant an income of 1500 million dollars.[42]

SUGAR

Sugar was always one of the main exportable staples for Cuba. It reached, in 1981, 70% of the incomes in foreign currency from exportations. Meanwhile in 1939, 118 of the 174 sugar mills belonged to the North American capital, in 1959 there were 29 sugar mills belonging to North American enterprises that had 33% of the industrial capacity of this branch.

The United States of America Government decreed the suspension of the sugar quota that Cuba sold in its markets in 1960, which caused that urgent negotiations were undertaken. The consequence was the trade agreements with the USSR and other socialist countries; they were a safe market, not submitted or influenced by the

world-wide market fluctuations. From 1963-64, a rearrangement of the sugar industry was carried out; Cuba received the USSR collaboration regarding mechanization and market guarantee.

Certain assessments favored the goal of producing in the 1970 harvest 10 million tons, although there were only really milled in the sugar mills 8.5 million tons with a high efficiency of 55.3 ton/ha. A necessary recovery and restructuring of the industry and agriculture was carried out again between 1973 and 1975; even some sugar mills were constructed on the basis of Cuban projects. In 1985, 156 sugar mills milled sugar cane in Cuba.

The conditions that caused the production collapse were created since 1990, with the loss not only of the main suppliers of inputs, such as fertilizers, tires and spares, but also of efficiency; low productivity; and agricultural and industrial indisciplines. Nevertheless, in 1991-92 within the Special Period, having Cuba resources coming from the socialist collaboration yet, the production of 7 million tons was feasible, that figure continued its fall down to 4.2 million tons in the 1992-93 harvest, until the 1994-95 disaster, during which only 3.3 million tons were produced; it caused losses of about 2000 million dollars.

An intense review of the main deficiencies of the harvests gave as a result that in 1995-96, with a provision of anticipatory finance that guaranteed the tires and batteries for the agricultural machineries and spares for the factories, the sugar mills made 4455 million tons of sugar, 1,117,000 tons more than in the foregoing harvest. Each million tons of sugar was produced with 9% less of sugar cane than in 1994-95, and with 85% of recovery, the greatest of the last years. The struggle for recovering the discipline in the agriculture and the industry caused the increase of the agricultural efficiency, meanwhile the industrial one grew in 8.3%.

Nowadays, sugar is responsible of 50.3% of the incomes from exportations, and it is still the most sensitive point of

42. *Estadística Seleccionada* [Selected Statistics], Oficina Nacional de Estadísticas (ONE)[Statistics National Office], 1998.

the economic reanimation; such as a Cuban old proverb says: "without sugar there is no country."

In the 1996-1997 harvest, 4,155,800 tons of crude sugar were produced. The 1997-1998 harvest turns up very influenced by the irregularities of the climate, which do not allow to estimate good outcomes.

AGRICULTURE

Tobacco always has been a crop linked to the economy of the country; it traditionally depicts like the second agricultural staple and the third industrial one. It is an important source of foreign currency income for its exportation.

Tobacco production in 1957 was 50,500 tons, and in 1958 fell to 42,165 tons in 1958. With the victory of the Revolution and the enacting of the First Law for Land Reform, the production rose to 51,244 tons in 1962, continuing an upward trend until to reach a 1000-tons increase in the 1975-76 harvest. It was possible because with the introduction of technological reformations and plague killers, the efficiency got better. The years having the highest indexes were 1966 and 1968; over 45,000 tons were produced, though in 1971 down to 24,757 tons.

The suspicious appearance of some diseases and plagues, such as the blue mould and others, caused that yield tragically declined, at such an extent that in 1979-80, it was only 6700 tons, down from the peak (after 1959) of 54,600 tons in 1981.

Nearly one third of tobacco production in Cuba is used in cigarette production (*cigarros* in Cuba), meanwhile the remainder is used to manufacture Havana cigars (*tabacos* or *puros* in Cuba), for national consumption and exportation.

Private sector has always had the largest part of tobacco plantations, because it is a family-type and full-time yield. In the '60s, private peasants produced 81.5% of the production; working alone or associated in credit and service cooperatives; state farms produced only the remainder 9.5%.

The increase in production was in 1984 and 1985 when nearly 44,600 tons were produced, even though it was damaged by the loss of the socialist market and the economic support the yield had. After a decline, the tobacco production rose 30.1% in 1996, to 33,100 tons. Manufacture industry growth was projected at 9.7%, still below the worldwide demand, since Cuban tobacco classifies among the best of the world, and it only reached 7.8%. The annual demand of cigars is 114 million; Cuba exported 50 million in 1995, and 70 million in 1996. It is expected the upward trend of cigar production continues, reaching 200 million pieces in 1999.

The traditional tobacco producer zones in Cuba were denominated: Vuelta Abajo zone, where the best leaves for manufacturing Havana cigars grow, and Semivuelta zone, both in Pinar del Río; Partido zone, in the province of La Habana, where tobacco is cultivated under cover, and as a result, there are high-grade leaves, also very appreciated to the manufacture of Havana cigars; Remedios or Vuelta Arriba zone, in the provinces of Villa Clara, Sancti Spíritus and some municipalities of Ciego de Ávila, where the biggest tobacco production was achieved during the sixties; and Oriente zone, now included in the municipalities of Granma, Holguín and Santiago de Cuba provinces.

At present, Pinar del Río has 60% of the total agricultural production of tobacco of the country, and Sancti Spíritus, Villa Clara, Las Tunas, Ciego de Ávila, Camagüey, Cienfuegos, Holguín and Granma follow it; it is also cultivated in La Habana, and probably, even though in a lesser amount, in Matanzas that during a period, it was the only tobacco non-producer province. Nowadays, it is a governmental policy that all the lands with an acceptable agricultural efficiency must produce it, and that is why nearly

14,000 hectares have been given to 7000 families interested to and well-disposed for the aromatic leaf cultivation.

Cuban tobacco demand, specially the *puros,* has been adequately supplied in the last years, and has notably encouraged agricultural production and manufacture of the famous Cuban tobaccos to reach 100 million of Havana cigars for exportation in 1998.

Coffee and Cacao. Cuban coffe is considered one of the best in the international market. Although it began to be cultivated since the 18th century, it was not until the 19th century that it reached the present boom. It has been cultivated in all the provinces, both in flat and mountainous zones, but regarding quality, the one that is cultivated in the mountains has proved to be the best.

Coffee crop has been damaged by the peasants' exodus from the mountains to the flatland looking for more favorable life conditions, and also because of the state educational policy, which has given the chance to study to all peasant's children.Once they are graduated, they prefer to settle in towns and cities, inasmuch as often their careers are not similar to the agricultural environment. The Turquino Plan takes some industries and material possibilities typical of urban concentrations to the mountains, besides these zones have priority for the supply of consumer goods, cultural and recreational facilities, and so forth. This plan has stopped emigration, and even favored some people come back; many of them receive lands for coffee cultivation.

Although part of the coffee production is earmarked to international trade, the largest part is consumed by the Cuban population. The fluctuation in the exported coffee amount has been kept between 9 tons and 19 tons. Nowadays, private sector produce much more than 50% of the coffee production; it will be extended to give lands to peasants for coffee cultivation. The largest production is concentrated in just the eastern provinces of Santiago de Cuba, Granma and Guantánamo. Also Cienfuegos and Sancti Spíritus are important producers, cultivating coffee in the mountainous area of Guamuhaya.

The cacao crop is much more restricted to the territories of Baracoa, in Guantánamo, where the 80% is cultivated; the rest, in the Sierra Maestra and Sierra Cristal Ranges, in Santiago de Cuba, Granma and Holguín.

Citrus Fruits. Cuba is among the first worldwide producers of citrus fruits. Since the Citrus Fruit Development Plan started in 1966, farmlands planted in citrus fruits has more than a tenfold increase: from 10,000 ha to more than 100,000 ha. This plan took a breakneck pace since 1973 when 21,700 hectares were planted, given the favourable conditions arosen in some territories where the School in the Countryside Plan began, whose students guaranteed the work force for the harvest.

Because of the value of this production, 85% of it belongs to the state sector. Orange holds the first place, followed by the grapefruit. Both of them has wide industrialization possibilities, and during a large period they had a safe and avid market in the socialist countries.

In 1985, the production was 406,400 tons oranges, 241,400 tons grapefruits and 60,400 tons lemons, for an average of 747,500 tons in the 1981-85 period. In 1989 an efficiency of 9 tons per hectare was reached.

The largest citrus fruit producers in the whole history of the country are the "Victoria de Girón" Plan, mainly placed in the municipality of Jagüey Grande in Matanzas, and the "Camilo Cienfuegos" in the Isle of Youth.

Associations with foreign capital have been accomplished in order to introduce significant technological advancements and to set the Cuban product in the international market.

Citrus fruit production in 1996 was 662,201 tons, increasing in 1997 to 808,312 tons.

LIVESTOCK

This important economic activity have deeply affected owing to the difficulties as a result of the socialist block's collapse taking into account the reached levels.

Cattle held the first place among all, with a mass of 5 million heads; remaining steady beef production with 300,000 tons, and milk production with 920,000 tons. These figures were achieved by means of a racial change to improve the genetic potential, in order to get a priority milk production. Then, races like Holstein tropical, Mambí, and Siboney de Cuba were obtained, with a productivity between 9.7 kg and 11,5 kg per day. All of this was based on a steady supply of imported forage that allowed a high concentration of the cattle mass (in this case, not only cows). The State owned 75% of the cattle; an important part of the fodder came from countries of the socialist block, with the subsequent affectation when it collapsed. In spite of being the largest part of the cattle (22%) in the eastern provinces and Camagüey, the biggest volumes of milk were produced in the western provinces (35% *vs* 13%), above all in La Habana (10% of the cattle mass).

Pigs had the same situation. Initially there was a non up-to-date production and it was only for peasant self-consumption, then it increased, and many state farms reached important head volumes; this upward trend finished in 1989 when production quickly declined before food shortage, diseases appeared or were introduced, both of which strongly hit litters. It was necessary to turn into small and medium-sized enterprises that should produce food for its cattle using technological advancements together with peasant expertise and traditional methods. The majority state sector produced 16,000 tons of pork beef, increasing it to 89,000 tons in 1985.

Poultry activity, with 359 farms in the Cuban territory—the greatest burden in the west—and 40,934 laying hens produced 2524 million eggs and 113,000 tons of meat in 1985. Egg production increased eightfold, and meat, in more than twice. From 1989, important deficits in food for poultry changed it. The major attention was payed to laying hens, but there were also goose and turkey breeding farms.

Sheep-goats production has never been important, although many efforts were done in order to increase it. Private sector owes the largest part of sheep, while State breeds only in large farms. In the 1981-85 period, average production reached 3236 tons, while in 1970 it was just 342 tons. Rabbit breeding had similar features and very low volumes, lower than sheep.

Private owners also have the largest part of horses, which structure is fairer in the country. Horses have the main burden, although donkeys have a special attention due to their importance as beasts of burden in the most mountainous and intrincate zones.

Animal production does not contribute to foreign trade, except for some good equine stallions and fighting cocks; it attempts for reaching the levels before the Special Period.

Cattle breeding as a whole has not achieved an appropriate recovery, even though some productions are getting better.

In 1997, milk production increased from 437,700 tons to 452,100 tons, a slight increase that should continue.

Nowadays meat production decreases. (The production of the Credit and Services Cooperatives and of private peasants are excluded.) State meat production in 1997 totalled 135,200 tons, down from 136,800 tons in 1996, completely unsatisfactory figures for national demand. In the same years state pork beef production also shows a downward trend; it was 42,300 tons and 45,200 tons, just like poultry meat with 31,200 tons and 32,000 tons respectively.

FISHING

Ships for fish capturing and processing increased notably in number and capacity since a well-conceived development plan for fishery was applied; it favored significant advancements after 1959. In this same year, fish catch was 41,900 tons, and in 1985 it rose to more than 70,000 tons. Also exportable staples showed an important growth: lobster (17.6%) and shrimp (6.2%), just to mention the main products.

On account of the contraction of trade relations, through which an important part of food resources came from import trade, fishing is a very important staple of the economy, because of its possibilities for supplying animal protein to the population and to exports.

· Fishing resources are divided into the following ecological complexes: littoral estuarine, having marine grasses and coastal reefs, and in oceanic waters.
· Ecological Littoral Estuarine Complex. It refers to coastal zones nearby the mouths of large rivers; shrimp is 46.7% of the captures in these regions.
· Ecological Complex Having Marine Grasses and Coastal Reefs. It refers to zones having bottoms covered with submarine grasses and reef banks, where lobster is 38.4% of the collected species.
· Ecological Complex in Oceanic Waters. It includes the big oceanic depths, where the species have a markedly migratory character, and where fish catch must be paid or agreed, because they sometimes are fishing zones located in the 200-miles territorial space fixed by many nations. Skipjack Tuna and Blackfin Tuna are the main preys in these places.

In 1994, there was a 10-percent decrease in gross fish catch, but in 1996 it grew 21% over the previous year, reaching 123,900 tons. In 1995, the value of exportation s increased in 25.5% over 1994, which means 20.5 million pesos.

Fishing structure, carried out in 1995, is the following:

· 53.3% was captured in the economic zone (territorial waters and national fishing zones, the ecological littoral estuarine complexes and those having marine grasses and coral reefs).
· 23%, in waters outside the 200 miles or in zones agreed with other countries (the ecological complex in oceanic waters) such as Canada, Mexico, among others.
· 22.5% in aquaculture (fish farming), in inner waters and coastal zones.

Nowadays, the features of Cuban traditional industry are combined with modern fishing methods, some of them terrible due to the indiscriminate catch level they cause.

Lobsters, shrimps, tunas, oysters, crabs, sponges and chelonians are still the main preys.

Overall gross catch in 1997 was very similar to that of 1996, about 123,400 tons.[43]

MINING

Petroleum. Since the 19th century, with the discovery of the Motembo field in the former province of Las Villas, petroleum is known in Cuba. During the first half of this century foreign companies, North American above all, explored the territory and took away the information when the foreign properties were nationalized and they moved away from Cuba. Nevertheless, in 1959, ten new beds produced 50,000 tons of crude oil.

From the beginning of Cuban collaboration with countries of the socialist block, mainly the Soviet Union, the joint geological petroleum research carried out, and a survey of an important part of the national territory was ob-

43. *Estadística Seleccionada* [Selected Statistics], Oficina Nacional de Estadística (ONE)[Statistics National Office], 1997.

tained. Crude oil exploitation carried out in fields placed in Bacuranao, Santa María, Peñas Altas, Guanabo, of La Habana province, and in Motembo, Jarahueca Jatibonico, Catalina, and Cristales in the provinces of Villa Clara, Sancti Spíritus and Ciego de Ávila during the 1966-1970 period.

In the eighties, an intense investment process was developed with an increase of 32% in the exploitation areas. Many geological and geophysic researches were fulfilled until 1989, and 340 wells were drilled. From 1992 an adjustment in extraction labours in order to improve work conditions was carried out; however, lack of finance had affected the research and exploitation rythm. The first international bidding was performed in 1993, in which 32 place clusters were offered, including the interest areas in the country.

National petroleum extraction broke its historical production record in 1996 when it achieved a volume higher than 1 million tons; in 1997 the upward trend reaching 1,461,500 tons continued.

Nickel. The biggest reserves of this mineral are concentrated in New Caledonia, Australia, Canada, the United States of America, Philippines, Indonesia and territories of the former USSR. Nevertheless, the most important nickel deposits are in Cuba. According to the Bureau of Mines of the United States of America, Cuba has 38% of the reserves of known deposits.

Cuban deposits have more than 800 million tons of lateritic content and 19 million tons of nickel (1000 million tons, according the mentioned source, with a content between 0.8 and 1.5), which guarantees the production in the existing plants in Cuba during two centuries. Nickel is found together with chrome, cobalt and iron, whose separation from the main mass of ore is the greatest challenge that faces the industrial process.

The largest deposits are in Levisa, in the municipality of Mayarí in Holguín, meanwhile the richest ones are in Moa, in the same province. It is an advantage that the exploitation of Cuba ore may be carried out in surface mines, because they are found nearby the surface.

As a consequence of the need to use nickel in the armament manufacturing during the World War II, North American companies accomplished research in prospective zones in the Cuban territory that determined the identification of deposits in Nicaro and Moa, where two plants were constructed before 1959 with U.S. capital. When the tensions between the U.S. and Cuban governments worsened, the U.S. technical staff moved away; they not only took away and dissapeared the technological documents (at least of Moa plant), but also caused the delay, during a period, of the acquisition and delivery of spares for the factories. Only the unbelievable feat of their workers and the scanty technical staff that faced all kind of pressures and stayed in their labour places, allowed the start of the Comandante René Ramos Latour and Comandante Pedro Soto Alba plants, in Nicaro and Moa, respectively.

During the investment process carried out in the 1980's, the Comandante Ernesto Ché Guevara plant was built in Punta Gorda, Moa, Holguín, and it ended in 1984; it costed 600 million dollars. An association with foreign capital was carried out after an adjustment process, introducing some technological improvements that have allowed to increase its efficiency. At present, Las Camariocas plant is being constructed in Moa, which will give to the country 100 million ore yearly.

Sales to 26 nations were carried out in 1994; 80% mainly to Canada, and to another western countries, and 20% to China. In 1996, production grew 36% over 1995, and a volume of 55,800 tons was registered, an absolute production record in the country. Nickel and cobalt extraction grew up to 615.1 tons in 1997, a new productive record.

Gold and Other Minerals. Gold was known in Cuba since conquest times by the Spaniards, when they found it in the hands of Cuban natives. Some places near to fluvial currents in the north side of the Sierra Maestra were discovered in 1514, but in 1538 that ore, easy to obtain by washing, had been already extracted. Later, in the Santa Clara region gold was found in veins, where maybe 150,000 ounces were obtained. But the difficulties imposed by exploitation, harder and harder, determined mining turned aside towards easier-obtention ores, such as copper, nickel, cobalt and chrome. Gold deposits are known in Delita, Isle of Youth, San José, Jobosi, Melonera and Yabazón, where it is natif.

Cuba also produces iron from deposits in Santiago de Cuba and other places; chrome in Merceditas and Calcedonia, among others; manganese in Charco Redondo in the Sierra Maestra, and in Amaro; copper in El Cobre, Santiago de Cuba; copper and molibdenum in Guáimaro, Camagüey and other zones; and other metallic minerals according to the different geological zones of the archipelago.

Non-metallic minerals, such as marble, limestone and marl, used as construction materials, are found in several places. Among many places, marble is found in the Las Casas Range, Isle of Youth; and limestone in El Cacao, Baire and Mariel, in La Habana. Dolomite is extracted in Remedios, and more recently in the heart of the capital; zeolite, which is formed in volcanic rocks with hydrothermal alterations, in Tasajera and Limones, in the central region; silicite, in Amaro, Villa Clara; quartzite in Ceja del Negro, Pinar del Río; sandstone, in Cayajabos, La Habana; kaolin in the Isle of Youth; bentonite in Managua; phosphorite in La Pimienta, both in La Habana; barite in Los Indios, Pinar del Río; talc in Crucesitas, in the part of Guamuhaya region belonging to Cienfuegos; gypsum in Corral Nuevo, Matanzas; and magnesite in Redención,

Camagüey. Another smaller productions are carried out in other localities.

Law number 77 for Foreign Investment made possible that companies of several countries interested in mining exploitation in Cuba, may reach agreements with the Cuban enterprise Geominera S.A., representative of the government for these activities. Generally, the agreements have equal-share profits, or a 51-percent profit for the Cuban State and 49% for the companies; they are carried out at risk, but firmly supported in the wide and accurate knowledge about the geology of the Cuban territory, one of the best known and modified of the American continent, thanks to the extensive research developed by Cuban specialists—with scientific degrees, high educational level and proved work expertise—in cooperation with the Ministeries of Geology and the Academies of Science of the former socialist countries.

With the use of technological advancements in geological prospection for solid minerals (just like petroleum), it has been possible to go deeply into the study of marked and promising interest zones; but they are "frozen" because of the lack of appropriate equipments and instruments for subsequent research.

Canada holds the preponderant place in this kind of agreement, with a special interest in gold. The U.S. Government has attempt to apply the sanctions stated in the Helms-Burton Law for the executives of some Canadian companies, even unknowing the Free Trade Agreement (NAFTA) signed by them and Mexico. But the Canadian Government has been steady in the defense of its interests and the worldwide accepted and sovereign practice of free trade; it continues developing their investments in Cuba.

Some of the interesting zones for gold and silver production are Descanso-Melonera and San Fernando, in the central region of Cuba; Dora-Francisco and Sombrero de

Hierro, in Pinar del Río; Gaspar, in Ciego de Ávila; El Jagüey, Tres Antenas and others, in Camagüey; Tamarindo, in Las Tunas; El Purial, in Guantánamo and others that show great perspectives for Cuban economy and good profits for the involved companies. The North American aggressiveness oblige us to be discreet about predictions and plans, and about the identification of foreign enterprises working in Cuban territory, not only the Canadian ones.

MEDICAL-PHARMACEUTICAL INDUSTRY AND BIOTECHNOLOGY

Even though in the first half of the century some specialized laboratories were settled, mainly in the capital, in 1959 there was not a national developed pharmaceutical industry, since the international pharmaceutical monopolies controlled the market, and the settled enterprises were almost all of foreign capital.

Confronting extreme situations, caused by the fierce economic blockade and at the same time, facing the challenge to obtain significant advancements in farming production, and to supplement the lack of medicines, the development of the pharmaceutical and biotechnological industry became a priority for the government.

In view of the planned development in these branches, modern scientific institutions were built that turned into prestigious centers, such as Instituto Finlay [Finlay Institute], Centro de Ingeniería Genética y Biotecnología [Center of Genetic Engineering and Biotechnology], Centro de Inmunología Molecular [Center of Molecular Immunology], Centro Nacional de Investigaciones Científicas [CENIC - National Center of Scientific Researches], Laboratorio de Inmunoensayo [Laboratory of Immunoassay], plants of (synthetic) antibiotics, of blood by-products, of oral liquids, and others, producing several products like vaccines, natural interferons, recombinant interferons,

having recognized worldwide high-grade and demand. PPG, a drug that eliminates the cholesterol; the vaccine against hepatitis B; recombinant streptokinase that favors the elimination of the heart attack causes; the vaccine against meningitis, to name just a few, are examples of advancements in this field in Cuba.

Although the lack of basic medicines for the population (about two hundreds are lacking) in the country, Cuba produces a great number of the pharmaceutical forms that are dispensed from the worldwide known medicines, and there are more than one thousand in the market; such forms cover a far from negligible part of drug taking in the country.

ENERGY

Energy generation in Cuba is expensive owing to the absence of important energetic sources, since the country has neither fluvial currents featuring considerable unevenness where hydroelectric powerhouses could be built, nor enough amount of petroleum to supply thermoelectric stations, even though the latter are the main electricity sources at present. All of this has not prevented that more than 90% of the Cuban population is supplied with electrical energy. When the country had socialist cooperation, thanks to the Soviet petroleum supply, and during the Special Period, to the expenditure of large amounts of foreign currency, the priority the State gave to electrical generation, above all for supplying the population, and the implantation of a saving policy with the consequent increase of electrical tax rate, have been some of the most important measures taken by the Cuban Government.

In the 1970's, the construction of a nuclear power plant (NPP[44]) in Juraguá, Cienfuegos, with the USSR collaboration was projected, and in order to solve the problem of

44. It is commonly named CEN, its abbreviation in Spanish. *Trans.*

electricity generation, in the eastern region began the research of another one. The NPP of Juraguá will have 4 Russian VVER-type nuclear reactors, having pressurized water, each one of a 417 Mw capacity. This plant complies with all the worldwide safety and exploitation indicators approved by the specialized international agency. Its construction would implicate to leave off consuming 2.4 million tons of petroleum, which would double the current volumes of Cuban crude oil extraction. In 1983 began the building of the first reactor and the second one, in 1985; but delays in supply of the components slowed down the execution plan, and after the USSR disintegration, its suspension have paralyzed them. The United States of America Government has attempted by all means to hold up and definitely stop the construction of this plant. Now the Cuban and Russian governments try to find another partner to begin again, end and run this nuclear plant that is, undoubtedly, one of the most important works of the century in Cuba.

In 1996, 8 million tons of available petroleum, between 41% and 47%, were used to the electrical generation. (*La Economía Cubana* [The Cuban Economy], 1997). The electrical generating capacity in this same year was 13,235.8 Gwh (*op. cit.*). The residential sector increased its consumption level 2.5%, and in 1997 were generated 14,146.5 Gwh. In 1998 the Cuban Government designed the Cuban Program of Energy Saving, which has allowed not only reductions in consumption levels, despite the inclusion of new electricity consumers, but also the decrease of blackouts, brought about in hours of maximum electrical demand.

CONSTRUCTION

The Ministry of Construction registered a steady growth and a productivity increase until 1989.

Production value in this sector at the beginning of the sixties had annual average rates ranging from 200 and 300 million pesos, meanwhile in the 1981-85 five-year period, it exceeded 2054 million pesos. Productivity per worker grew from 2080 pesos in the 1971-75 five-year period to 7119 pesos in 1981-85. These outstanding increases were reached thanks to the unquestionable efforts made about typifying, rationalizing and normalizing the projects with which the material basis for the accelerated development of prefabricated systems was created. In 1984, the prefabricated panel production was 1 million m^3, meanwhile in 1995 it was only 550,000 m^3.

Distribution of these investments highly changed in the different stages, having priority from 1959 the productive, social and housing constructions in localities outside the capital. In that period, 89 localities were considered the main industrial investments outside the capital city.

Hydraulic works had a dam capacity of 47.8 millions m^3 in 1959, and later they had a geometrical growth up to attain 5986.5 million m^3 in 1985, with more than 102 finished dams.

Farming constructions, only regarding cattle raising, reached 4300 units and 2236 minor works in 1985; there were also built 155 centers having several categories for pigs, and 359 centers with 6200 naves for poultry.

Regarding the social sector, in the eighties it was registered an increase in housing building, with a potential capacity of 40,000 houses on annual average; from these, a considerable part corresponds to developing zones nearby the province capitals (including the capital of the country) and 335 to rural townships.

Construction of schools began with the transformation of garrisons into schools, since 1959. In the 1970's, with the application of the study-work system and the School in the Countryside Plan, the number of classrooms in the secondary educational level was notably increased.

An important part of social constructions are those for health. In the sixties, seven large hospitals were built, and twenty-nine urban and sixty-eight rural hospitals were later finished.

Since the implementation of the Physician for 120 Families Plan (later known just as Family Physician) constructions for health increased even more in order to build the consulting room-houses.

Until 1985 another group of constructions were made in regard with hotels repairing and construction, sport works. Later the Olympic Stadium was built as well as other facilities for Havana Pan-American Games held in 1991.

Inherent difficulties due to the lack of domestic fuel for the industry and the production of arid materials, cement, and other materials, caused by the suspension of the socialist collaboration, in whose market part of that production was sold, brought about serious shortages.

The reanimation of the investment process and the priority given to the tourist activity brought about a reactivation in this branch of the economy, above all in the building of hotels and stone-roads that join the territory of the island of Cuba with the small isles (keys) of the Sabana-Camagüey Archipelago, which have made possible the use of beautiful and nearly unknown spots of the Cuban geography for the vigorous tourist industry. The projection and development of these stone-roads over the shallow bottoms of those places with many keys, an exclusively Cuban idea, must continue considering, without any excuse, the preservation of the natural environment through taking the necessary measures for minimizing the damage caused by those works. The construction of the Turiguanó-Cayo Coco stone-road and of high-grade hotels in the Coco cay are an example of the success achieved in this respect.

Housing construction, although it is still affected by lack of materials, registered a slight increase in the last years of the Special Period, because of the use of low-cost materials and the possibilities to locally manufacture them.

The production of Portland cement in 1996 reached 1437.9 tons, and in 1997 it increased up to 1702.2 tons. The production of ground stone grew from 2878.0 m³ to 2919.6 m³.

In 1996, 43.2 millions of concrete blocks were manufactured, and its production increased to 45.3 millions in 1997. The building of tourism works reaches a plateau, and finished works increase in 1997; among them, 15 primary schools, 8 hospitals, 46,886 housings.

TRANSPORTATION

There have been good possibilities for developing automotive transportation in Cuba, when considering the construction of 12,132 km of paved roads, with a 0.109 km/sq km index, the best of Latin America.

The main way for the interprovincial transit is the Center Road, constructed in the 1930's; it extends from Pinar del Río to Santiago de Cuba. Nevertheless, the traffic increase and the type of vehicles made necessary the construction of the National Highway that extends from Pinar del Río, in the western of the country, to nearby Taguasco, in Sancti Spíritus, with some built sections in the nearness of Santiago de Cuba.

Since 1959, Cuba had against itself that maybe it has been the unique nation with the necessity to change its equipment twice in thirty years: as of 1960, because of the establishment of the blockade that cut off the supply with equipment and spares, and from 1990, owing to the socialism collapse in the Eastern European countries.

Decrease of fuel volumes for vehicles determined the drastic reduction of vehicular traffic, although in 1996 it was registered an 8-percent growth over the previous year. Railroad holds, in view of these circumstances, a preponderant place in transportation; it has 14,800 km of railways. Merchant navy transported 1,160,700 tons of dead weight in 1989; it includes general load ships, container holders, tankers, grain-carriers, ferryboats and instruction ships. The Special Period caused that in 1993 the merchant navy reduced its ships down to 107 with just 1222.1 tons of dead weight.

Air transportation registered a remarkable increase since 1959, when Cuba only had Britannia airplanes and others that quicly became obsolete. Cubana de Aviación [Cuban Airlines] in 1985 covered 22 air routes with 62,362 km; 89.9% of this rate in kilometers correspond to 9 international itineraries.

Nowadays, the Instituto de Aeronáutica Civil de Cuba [IACC, Cuban Institute of Civilian Aeronautics] also has another enterprises: Aerocaribbean and Aerogaviota, and a number of DC-10 aircrafts in use. Development of the aeronautics has been favoured by the construction of some airports and the conditioning of others with an international character in Varadero, Camagüey, Santiago de Cuba, Holguín, Ciego de Ávila, Cayo Largo, Nueva Gerona, and the capital, as well as other landing strips in other province capitals.

COMMUNICATIONS

Communications showed a revolution since 1959, with the application of technological advancements in all its branches. As an index of that, it may be pointed out that 73% of the telephones of the country were in the capital, and in the whole territory there were 153 localities with non-automatic telephone exchanges. In 1985 in the capital there were 52.9% of the telephone equipment, showing the increase of them in other provinces; even in 1984, 289 automatic telephone exchanges were registered outside the capital. Nevertheless, telephony underwent a strong blow in the eighties because it was a fire in the Dragones telephone exchange (one of the main of the country) that put it off duty.

The Law 77 for foreign investments allowed Cuba to have the necessary capital for renewing the equipment in the framework of an economic association with foreign enterprises, which led to a sensitive improvement of the service. At present, this service is almost totally automated.

In the last years, encouraged by tourism development and with foreign collaboration, the digitalization of the telephone system has began, which has led to greater and better eases for domestic communications and with foreign countries. The inclusion of Cuba in the INTERNET system, as well as the cellular telephony will allow the country to be on line with the most up-to-date advancements in national and international communications.

Regarding radio-communications, there is an installed capacity of 2159 kw that contrasts with 148 kw in 1959. Referring to television broadcasting, in 1959 there were 25 transmitters with a power of 50.5 kw that covered only 25% of the national territory; in 1989, 80 transmitters and boosters covered 90% of the territory with a power of 197.6 kilowatt.

The Estación Caribe [Caribbean Station] was inaugurated in 1973 for the communications by satellite, and more recently, in 1979, the Standard B of the Intersalt system was acquired.

EXPORTS AND IMPORTS

Cuban trade interchange in 1995 grew 27% over 1994. In these years, the number of countries with which Cuba had trade relationships was higher than in former periods, even though it did not reach the figure before the Special Period. Trade distribution by continents is as follows: Europe (Spain, France, Italy, Netherlands) participates with 42% of the overall interchange, and America with 40%, mainly Canada, Mexico, Venezuela and Netherlands Antilles.

Exports grew 33% in 1996 over 1995, meanwhile the imports (33.3%) were slightly bigger. Relative burden of sugar in foreign trade was 47.6% in 1995, much lesser than in 1990 (73%). Although in 1995 exported sugar decreased 6%, the overall exports value grew in 11% because of: mining (67%), where nickel products stand out; tobacco industry with 39%; and other products (6%) such as scrap, cements, fruit juices, coffee, rum and liquors, steel bars and billets, bee honey and others.

The 1995 imports reported increases in all the groups of products, among them foods, fuels and lubricants, chemical products stand out. America holds the first place regarding imports with 49%; Europe follows it with 39%.

UPDATED INFORMATION ABOUT NATIONAL ECONOMY

1999

Gross Domestic Product grew 6.2% in this year. This fact determined this year turned into the second best one regarding the growth of Cuban economy, in spite of the negative behavior sugar price had.

Investments increased in 9.4%, mainly because of tourism, prospecting for oil, modernization of energetic units and systematic improvement of telecommunications.

Work productivity augmented in 5.4%, while the efficiency of investments, in 8.8%.

Energetic intensity decreased in 3.45%.

Expenditure per dollar of gross income diminished in 2.8%.

Fiscal deficit was 2.4%, although a 2.9% (720 million) was planned.

Pay increases reached 620 million pesos.

Liquidity (9781 million pesos) grew 0.7%.

Unemployment rate was reduced to 6%.

The agriculture and fishing sector augmented in 15.1%.

The 1998-1999 sugar harvest meant an increase of 554,000 tons (12.5%) respect to the last one.

Nickel production was 66,503 tons. With that level of production, Cuba became the sixth exporter of this metal and is supplying 12% of cobalt to the world market.

Gas and oil production was increased from 0.5 to 2.6 million tons and from 0 to 650 tons respectively between 1989 and 1999. The combined use of both allowed the country to cover 41% of the necessity of oil for generating electric energy. Moreover, a program of massive gasification began in two main Cuban cities: Ciudad de La Habana and Santiago de Cuba.

In this year, 1,602,000 tourists arrived to Cuba, which represents a 26.5% increase. By way of this, gross incomes increased in 11% (1954 million).

2000

Gross Domestic Product grew 5.6%.

Work productivity augmented in 4.6%.

Energetic intensity coefficient decreased in 3.4%.

Investments attained more than 3100 million representing a 16% growth in relation to 1999, while their efficiency increased in 5.8%.

Constructions grew 9.3%.

Non-sugar industry throve in 5%.

The generation of 51% of electric energy was done with Cuban oil.

The sugar harvest was 4059 tons, which represented a 7.3% growth.

Nickel production was 72,000 tons and steel's, 344,000 tons.

Productions with a high added value advanced, linked to computer services and biotechnology.

CHAPTER VIII

THE ENVIRONMENT IN THE CUBAN TERRITORY

The environment, according to what is stated in the *Nuevo atlas nacional de Cuba* [New National Atlas of Cuba], is conceived as an open system having a historic formation, made up of bilateral relations among the following systems: nature, economy, and population, and their inner relations within society and nature; it includes biotic, abiotic and social-economic elements, at which man, through its action, gets in contact, modifies and uses them to satisfy his necessities, and he also adapts to them.

The current environmental features of the Cuban territory are conditioned by the particularities of its historical, economic and social development, and by the negative influences they have exerted upon their natural conditions. The irrational exploitation of natural resources, the degradation of some components, and the disorderly use of the space of the territory, mainly by human settlements, are their chief negative effects. The agricultural expansion, the industrial development, the overgrazing of cattle and the sugar industry spreading are responsible of the accelerated destruction of forests through their clearance for growing crops, and in a lesser degree for fuelwood.

At the triumph of the Cuban Revolution in 1959, some measures were issued for the environment protection, such as forestation plans and the statement of protected areas —Jaguaní, Cupeyal del Norte, Corrientes Cape and El Veral natural reserves—, among others.

Difficulties caused by the necessity of the impetuous growth of the economy, aggravated by a certain degree of overall ignorance in the society regarding preservation and use of nature were joined to existing environmental problems. Nevertheless, broadly speaking, the environment status at a national level do not have a critical situation, although some of its components have been damaged.

The scientific and institutional development reached by the country, and its planned economy allow to take the decisions to rectify the environmental damage condition, and to guarantee the harmony in the social and economic development; likewise, those actions must answer to the demands and the measures about the environmental protection and improvement, from a rational use of natural resources.

In 1975, the first lines related to the policy for the environmental protection and improvement were laid down as well as the rational use of natural resources were laid down. The Comisión Nacional para la Protección del Medio Ambiente y los Recursos Naturales [COMARNA, National Commission for the Protection of the Environment and Natural Resources] was created.

In its article 38, the Constitution of the Republic points out: "The State looks after the conservation of the cultural patrimony and protects the national monuments and outstanding places for its natural beauty or its recognized artistic or historical values." On August 4th, 1977 the laws number 1 and 2 about the national and local monuments were passed. In 1981 the law number 33 about the Environment Protection and Rational Use of Natural Resources was enacted; this law, having a general character, states the main principles in which the environment protection rests on, and identifies the different protection spheres in order to make possible the elaboration of complementary orders with a more specific character.

The development of the economic activities modifies the environment. It is an example that 60.5% of the national territory is modified by the agricultural activity, and from it, 22.6% is strongly damaged. More than half of the croplands (59.6%) are notably damaged as a consequence of the burden having sugar cane cropping within the agricultural activity, in which are used very high doses of chemical fertilizers and in large expanses, a high%age of mechanization. Croplands are also damaged by other factors, such

as the increase of towns and the construction of hydrotechnical works and roads that have occupied productive lands (5.7% of the croplands).

At present, about 18% of the national territory is covered with forest. Territories having a greater potential for forestry are located, above all, in the mountainous areas of the country: the Sierra Maestra Mountain Range (60% of its territory was cleared), the Nipe-Sagua-Baracoa Mountains (40%), the Guamuhaya Mountains (30%) and the Guaniguanico Mountain Range (15%). Deforested areas on the whole are occupied by natural pastures or minor crops.

The hydric resources are also damaged, mainly by the discharge of residual materials coming from urban townships, and from factories into water masses; half of them come from sugar cane and food industries, and the rest from agricultural activity; all of them on the whole are poured without treatment. Villa Clara, Ciudad de La Habana, La Habana, Sancti Spíritus, Holguín and Camagüey are the most highly damaged provinces. Furthermore, these resources are sensitively degraded owing to the deforestation level in the majority of the hydrographic basins, and as a consequence of it, there are serious erosion problems.

Likewise, the exploitation of underground aquifers for irrigation crops, for supplying farms, or for both, have led to the penetration of salt water in zones like the south of La Habana, Juraguá in the south of Cienfuegos, and in the southern plain of Pinar del Río, just to mention some examples, which causes the water quality diminishes and maybe, soil salinization.

Industrial activity damages the environment quality, above all due to the emission of liquid, solid and gaseous residual materials. Sugar cane and food factories are the industrial branches that affect more the environment, owing to their nationwide distribution, and because their facilities do not have on the whole treatment systems for residual materials, or they work in a deficient way.

Extraction of construction materials also have caused important damages in some areas; 0.3% of the national territory has been modified by this activity. The greatest modification corresponds to the stone quarries (27% of the territory having mines of construction material), sand quarries (11%), clay for construction (10%) and raw materials for cement production (11%). Thus, mining activity, above all when it is carried out in surface mines, works negatively over the environ; it is considered that not only affect the dug area, but also the sector where the slags are poured or the dams where the liquid and semi-liquid residual materials are dammed.

Towns have also contributed in a large extent to the modification of the environment and its pollution, by changing the relief, the soil and the biotic elements with the construction of housings and the necessary infrastructure for satisfying the population necessities.

Briefly, the environmental problems are given, as a whole, for water pollution; soil erosion and salinity; predominance of deforestation in potentially forest territories; natural vegetation degradation, mainly the mangroves; status of the towns, that though there are not a high percentage with drains, they do have a satisfactory status as compared to other countries of Latin America; and air pollution, notably influencing in some points and affecting some areas in La Habana, Nuevitas, Cienfuegos and Matanzas. In the last years, the solid garbage collection in the largest cities has turned into a problem having a hard solution, specially for the necessity of its rational recycling with up-to-date technologies.

NATIONAL POLICY OF ENVIRONMENTAL PRESERVATION AND PROTECTION IN CUBA

The environmental protection is organized by a national system comprising State entities and People's Power local bodies, developing global actions regarding the environment and natural resources protection.

The environment protection program passed for the 1986-1990 five-year period took into account the institutional strengthening in this sphere, as well as a significant increase of the state financial allowance. The Cuban State elaborated its program for complying with the Agenda 21, and because of that, it was one of the first countries in answering this international call. According to this program, several measures were taken, such as:

· Technological solutions for diminishing or eliminating the pollutants from water bodies that receive them, along with the integral cleaning-up of the fluvial basins.

· A priority watchfulness over supply sources to the population, and the establishment of the corresponding needed hygienic-sanitary protection zones.

· Improvement of the eroded-saline, bad-drained and strongly-acid soils.

· Rehabilitation of the territories devastated by mining in surface mines, specially in the eastern zone of Nicaro and Moa.

· Technological solutions to diminish the volume of gaseous emissions.

· Reforestation increase in the cleared territories, and the adequate application and management of reforestation methods.

The establishment of the National System for Protected Areas (SNAP is its abbreviation in Spanish) for the preservation and management of natural resources in Cuba is another of the important measures adopted by the State. These natural and semi-natural spaces cover, in the broadest sense, about 22% of the national territory (1,331,900 ha); in its most strict sense, the protected areas cover about 6% (665,952 ha) of the archipelago.

Stated ecological management categories, and also those that are relying on their approval, according to the proposal of the Centro Nacional de Areas Protegidas belonging to the Agencia de Medio Ambiente,[45] of the Ministry of Science, Technology and Environment are:

Management Categories (Cuba)	Number
1 Natural Reserve	8
2 National Park	14
3 Ecological Reserve	23
4 Outstanding Natural Element	4
5 Fauna Refuge	10
6 Managed Flora Reserve	11
7 Protected Natural Landscape	2
8 Protected Area of Managed Resources	8
Total	80

Note: Natural monuments are not included in the figures and categories.

Biosphere Reserves are another special category for ecological management that has international recognition, stated by the "Man and Biosphere" (MAB) international program, organized by the UNESCO. Cuba has proposed several biosphere reserves that have been approved by the MAB; they are the following:

1. *Península de Guanahacabibes* [Guanahacabibes Peninsula), in the western extreme of the province of Pinar del Río.

2. *Sierra del Rosario* [El Rosario Range], in the western part of the Rosario Range, Pinar del Río province.

3. *Cuchillas del Toa* [Toa Crests], in the top basin of the Toa river, north of Guantánamo.

4. *Baconao,* in the eastern utmost tip of the Sierra Maestra Mountain Range, southeast of the province of Santiago de Cuba.

Furthermore, it has been recently proposed for its approval to the MAB program the fifth biosphere reserve in Cuba: the *Ciénaga de Zapata* [Zapata Swamp], one of the most extensive and best-preserved wetlands of the Caribbean.

Safeguard of the national heritage wealth and monuments is another important aspect of environmental protection, because they are the expression and testimony of human creation or nature evolution. Wealth declared monuments are objects; urban historical centers; buildings, either they have civil, commemorative, domestic, industrial, military or religious character; as well as places with natural, archaeological, historical, or even urban character that due to its exceptionality they deserve to be preserved by virtue of their cultural, historical, social or natural significance.

Cuba was one of the signatory nations of the Act of Rio de Janeiro in the International Environment Year, in 1992. This act states a significant commitment in taking all the necessary measures for the environmental protection and preservation, domestically and abroad in the region. In accordance with this decision, an important group of measures have been carried out, such as the creation of the Agencia del Medio Ambiente, belonging to the Ministry of Science, Technology and Environment, which was organized on the basis of a ministerial restructuring, and its

45. National Center of Protected Areas, belonging to the Environment Agency. *Trans.*

antecedents are in the former Academia de Ciencias de Cuba [Academy of Sciences of Cuba], after the United Nations Conference on Environment and Development holding.

Likewise, practical and popular measures have been taken, such as the implantation and promotion of a reforestation plan, the Plan Manatí [Manatí Plan], which has allowed that workers, students, housewives, pensioners, in fact, all the population, as volunteers, may plant fruit trees and others for fuelwood during their working day and free time.

The economic opening undertaken by the Cuban Government since 1993-94 has not been free of regulations respect to the environmental preservation, that is why corresponding laws and orders have been enacted. According to these, the environmental impact studies previous to the fulfillment of investments must be done in fields like mining, industry, constructions, and others, as well as also needed measures for protecting, preserving and improving ecosystems must be taken. ·

Inherent difficulties due to the lack of household fuels, generated by the hard economic situation and the upsurge of the North American Government blockade against Cuba, have brought about, however, compromising situations by increasing the use of fuelwood in many houses.

The programmed and rational use of this resource is one of the main concern of many local governments in the archipelago, inasmuch as this is only achieved with watchfulness and increasing the knowledge level of the population about these aspects, as well as using another sources. The use of vegetal coal was promoted for rural communities, because it may be obtained from plants having poor benefit for the economy like widespread thorny shrubs.

Scientific commissions have studied the possibility of using the energetic capacities of turf, present in swampy zones, considering that the extraction of this resource would imply necessarily a severe affectation to the marshy ecosystems.

The accelerated expansion of the tourist industry is another challenge, which in searching for attractive proposals, goes about, more and more, into less transformed areas, where the natural resources are better preserved and Nature in itself is more virgin. It requires to state adequately the load-capacity for each place in order to avoid its degradation.

The construction of stone-roads in some places of the territory, above all in the north coast, to facilitate the access to the beautiful landscapes of the Sabana-Camagüey Archipelago and others, and the construction of hotels there, have, at least, three concerns: the first is related to mangrove ecosystems in which temperature, salinity and other conditions have been transformed, because the stone-roads create artificial barriers preventing or modifying the natural movement of marine currents and waves, if enough bridges or passages that facilitate water interchange are not built. Furthermore, it must take into account that mangroves are the base that support the existent ecosystem in the Cuban submarine shelf. The second refers to the control that must be exerted so that the ecological stress on the lives of the animal population—fauna that during milleniums inhabited these places without being damaged by sudden and maybe massive presence of man—may be at a minimum. In third place, it must consider the location of the garbage produced by tourists and constructed facilities, inasmuch as the inadequate management of residual materials may have a negative character, and even, may be irreversible.

The Centro de Investigaciones y Monitoreo del Medio Ambiente Costero [Center of Research and Management of Coastal Environment], constructed in the Coco key, one of the most requested places by foreign tourism, is a symbol of the government concern bout preservation and protection of this resource, that, undoubtedly is a valuable heritage of the nation.

Slash pine grove—(*Pinus caribaea*) a conifer endemic of Cuba—in the Alturas de Pizarras del Sur Hills, in the southern side of the Los Órganos Range, Pinar del Río province. Photograph by Manuel Rivero Glean.

Colony of arborescent ferns in the nearness of the Cuba Pike in the Turquino Range, Santiago de Cuba province. Photograph by Manuel Rivero Glean.

White-tailed deer *(Odocoileus virgineanus)*, introduced in Cuba in 1850; it was adapted and spreaded quickly throughout the wildest places of the country, specially in the mountainos zones and littoral swamps. These specimens were surprised in Mil Cumbres, El Rosario Range, Pinar del Río. Photograph by Jesús Pajón Morejón.

Cuban boa *(Epicrates angulifer)*, the largest Cuban snake. It belongs to the South American family of the boas, and is like its smallest relative. This completely harmless animal is part of the autochthonous and endemic fauna that have adopted the biological control above the pests of rodents introduced in Cuba by the colonizers. Photograph by Gabriel Barceló Carol.

Chameleon or *chipojo blanco (Chamaeleolis barbatus)*, exclusive species from the western region, and one of the three species inhabiting in Cuba. Specimen photographed in Ceja de Francisco, northeast of the Mesa Range, Pinar del Río. Photograph by Manuel Rivero Glean.

Cuban crocodile *(Crocodylus rhombifer)*, a reptile endemic of Cuba belonging to the Crocodylidae family. It differs from the *C. acutus* (bad-named alligator or American crocodile), for having blunt protuberances behind the eyes, a shorter snout, a more elevated head that is broader in its base, and six longitudinal lines of little shields-like in its back. It may have up to 3 m long. It is not an aggressive animal, except for the female when is taking care of its nest. It has semi-aquatic habits and only inhabits in the fresh waters of the Zapata Swamp. Photograph by Gabriel Barceló Carol.

Iguana *(Cyclura nubila)*, the largest lizard of Cuba. It is a pacific herbivorous reptile that may attain 1.85 m from the tip of the tail to the extreme of the snout. It inhabits in rocky enviroments in the whole country, preferably in coasts of small isles of the insular groups. The photo was taken in the Zoo Park of Ciudad de La Habana. Photograph by Manuel Rivero Glean.

Cuban Emerald *(Chlorostilbon ricordii)* in its nest. It is one of the hummingbirds that live in Cuba, relatively abundant even in the gardens of wooded neighborhoods of Ciudad de La Habana. This photo was taken with an approach lens in the nearness of the entry to the La Pluma cave in the northern coastal zone of the province of La Habana. Photograph by Manuel Rivero Glean.

Camaleón azul —blue chameleon—*(Anolis allisoni),* native to the central regions of Cuba. It owes its common name to the change of color happening in part of the male bodies during its excitation; it turns into blue. This specimen was surprised in the surrounding areas of the Marea del Portillo Hotel, Niquero, Granma province. Photograph by Manuel Rivero Glean.

Jutía conga (Capromys pilorides), the biggest autochthonous rodent of Cuba. This hutia has a robust appearance and short tail; it lives in caves and fissures, among rocks and roots. It is one of the most typical mammals of Cuba. This scene was taken in the Zoo Park of Ciudad de La Habana. Photograph by Manuel Rivero Glean.

Almiquí (Solenodon cubanus), an insectivorous mammal, endemic of Cuba. Nowadays this odd animal, which is believed extinct, inhabits the mountainous forests of the Sierra Maestra Mountain Range, of the northeast of Holguín, and of the north of Guantánamo. It is considered an endangered species. This specimen is stuffed in the Museo Nacional de Historia Natural [National Museum of Natural History] of Cuba.

GLOSSARY

Ammonites: Cephalopod mollusks (it means with the foot in the head), related with squids and octopuses. They are extraordinary abundant in the seas from the Mesozoic Era, although specimens from the Paleozoic Era are known.

Angiosperms: Phanerogamous plants with seeds enclosed in a fruit.

Aquifer: Body made up of rocks or sediments that stores water.

Autochthonous flora: A whole of plants typical of a given region.

Basins: Depressions or large abysms that are found in the submarine bottoms, also denominated troughs.

Blind valleys: Karstic valleys, closed by one extreme, in which the waters that superficially have entered by the open part are submerged.

Briophytes: A group of plants to which the mosses and hepatics belong. They are very ancient land plants.

Caducifolious: Trees and shrubs that do not remain green the whole year, because they lose the leaves in the unfavorable season.

Cormobiontes: Vascular plants with stems, roots and leaf system.

Cryptogamous: Group of vegetables without apparent sexual reproduction.

Dicotyledoneous: Plants with two-cotyledons seeds.

Dolines: Closed karstic depressions, circular or semicircular, working as funnels. There are different types, according to their main formation factor.

Endemic flora: A whole of plants that inhabits only in a given region.

Epiphytes: Plants that live on other ones, without parasiting them; for instance, the orchids.

Epiphyllous: Plants that live on the leaves of other ones.

Evaporites: Rocks and sediments shaped in confined environments, as a general rule, where the evaporation predominates. Gypsum and anhidrite are examples of evaporites.

External geodynamics: Modification processes of the earth surface opposing to the internal geodynamics; they are brought about by the abrasion or action of the waves; the erosion; the fluvial, winds or rains action; the ablation or erosion of the ices, and so forth. It may be established that there is a trend to the levelling in the terrestrial surface; everything that stick out tends to level and the hollows, to refill.

Fanerogamous: A group of plants to which the sexual organs may be observed. As a whole, plants with seeds.

Faults: Fracture of the earth crust that brings about the movement of the edges of the rupture line and causes a discontinuity of the strata. These movements bring about earthquakes and earth tremblers.

Flora: A whole of plants of a region.

Flyschoide: It is said about the sediments that display similar to a flysch, it means, with rhythmic alternation of sediments with different composition and affected by tectonism, which determines a great development of faultings and microfaultings.

Gimnosperms: Fanerogamous plants with naked seeds, outside the fruit.

Gneiss: Ancient metamorphic rocks, where the primary components of the rocks have been completely substituted by the metamorphism process.

Graminaceae: Family of herbaceous plants with cylindrical and hollow stems, narrow leaves with pods. They colonize meadows and savannas, for instance, the cereals.

Hepatic: Bryophite plant with a very simple vegetal body (thallus) that constitutes the vegetative and reproductive apparatus of the simplest plants, without true roots, stems and leaves.

Canyons: Defiles, dry as a whole, caused by the karstification operating along the natural fractures.

Internal geodynamics: Geological transformation processes of the earth surface, caused by forces fom the inner of the globe, such as tectonism, vulcanism, magmatism and others.

Karst: Kind of geomorphological, hydrogeological, and other features that have the soluble rocks: salt, gypsum, chalk, limestone, dolomite, under the action (corrosion) of acidulated waters. Its name comes from the Karst plateau, which lies between the former Yugoslavia and the north of Italy. It is characterized by a rough landscape, where the rock appears generally naked, or with a scanty thickness of soils, with plenty of caverns and negative closed forms of the relief; predominating the infiltration of the waters instead of surface drainage, and where a specific vegetation and fauna is developed.

Lapiaz: Typical form of the limestone in karstified zones, with sharp edges and closed depressions. In Cuba it is popularly known as *diente de perro*.

Micranthia: Trend of the flora of a region to display small flowers.

Microphyles: Trees and shrubs of small leaves.

Mogotes: Very karstified lime hills, with rounded summits covered by vegetation, and vertical or subvertical walls, frequently crossed by caves.

Monocotyledoneous: Plants with one-cotyledon seeds.

Nappes: Overturned folds, individualized as scales owing to tectonic overthrusts, where the stratigraphic sequences are turned upside down.

Olistostromes: Bodies of rocks having different origins and compositions, grouped by tectonic causes.

Perennifolious: Trees and shrubs that preserve the greenness and the leaves the whole year.

Petroglyphs: Prehistoric sculptures performed by our aborigins, using generally some irregularity in the rock. Many of them are made in stalagmites.

Phreatic level: Level reaching the waters of the phreatic mantle or level of the underground waters.

Pictographies: Paintings made by the Amerindians in the protected walls of buttes, in rocks or in caverns.

Poljes: Fluvial-karstic valleys, with bottoms of very fertile lands and slides made up of karstified rocks that may have considerable areas. In rainy and stormy seasons, they usually cut off and work as lakes.

Pteridophytes: Group of plants including ferns and similar species.

Pyroclastites: Term comprising the rocks shaped by the deposit of materials coming from volcanoes in marine conditions, such as tuffs and tuffites.

Radiolarites: Rocks of silica composition, made up mainly of radiolarians shells, that are protozoans with silica shell, very abundant in most seas of all the geological periods.

Rudists: Pelecypod mollusks that had a great and fast development during the Cretaceous. Unlike the rest of the components of their group, the rudist had a highly-developed valve, which was buried in the marine bottom; the other one worked as a lid. They shaped true reefs, as the corals do.

Sclerophyllous: Trees and shrubs having very hard leaves.

Sialic aluminum-silicated rocks: Rocks in whose composition the silica and the aluminum predominate.

Sima: Cavern with a vertical profile, whose access is only possible through a vertical passage having craggy walls.

Stenocorous: Very small-area zones, where endemic species inhabit.

Succulents: Plants having thick and meaty stem or leaves, with abundant juice.

BIBLIOGRAPHY

ACEVEDO GONZÁLEZ M. AND R. GUTIÉRREZ DOMECH. "Nuevos reportes sobre manifestaciones pseudocársicas en rocas no carbonatadas." In *Voluntad Hidráulica*, Havana: Instituto de Hidroeconomía, 1978.

ACEVEDO, M., R. GUTIÉRREZ, F. RIVERO AND J. LAMADRID. *The relief Inversion as a Geomorphological Factor in the American Mediterranean*, XXIII International Geographic I Congress. Moskow, Section I, pp. 125-126, 1976.

ACEVEDO-GONZÁLEZ, M. *Geografía física de Cuba*, Havana: Ed. Pueblo y Educación, 2nd edition, 1982.

AYALA CASTRO, N. *Topes de Collantes, Vida silvestre en el Escambray*, Havana: Ed. Empresas Ind. de Comunicaciones, 1989.

BEROVIDES, V. *Protejamos nuestra fauna*, Havana: Ed. Gente Nueva, 1983.

BISSE, JOHANNES. *Árboles de Cuba*, Havana: Ed. Científico-Técnica, 1988.

BONANI, E. G., A. URQUIOLA AND A. BAYRA. *Botánica. Plantas superiores*, Havana: Ed. Pueblo y Educación, 1987.

BUIDE, M. *Reptiles de Cuba*, Havana: Ed. Gente Nueva, 1985.

_____. *Diccionario de nombres vernáculos de vertebrados cubanos*, Havana: Ed. Academia, 1986.

CAPOTE LLANO, S. *Mi tesoro es Cuba. Joyas de la ciencia y la naturaleza*, Havana: Ed. Científico-Técnica, 1984.

CEDISAC-PRENSA LATINA. *Todo de Cuba - All about Cuba*, Multimedia Encyclopaedia in compact disk, Madrid: Indugraf, 1997.

COBIELLA, J. *Sobre el origen del extremo oriental de la fosa de Bartlett*, Havana: Ed. Oriente, 1984.

COLBERT, EDWIND H. "A Jurassic Pterosaur from Cuba," *American Museum Novitates*, 2360:26, 1969.

DAVITAYA, F. AND I. TRUSOV. *Los recursos climáticos de Cuba*, Havana: Ed. INRH-ACC, 1965.

DE ARMAS, LUIS F. *Sinopsis de los escorpiones antillanos*, Havana: Ed. Científico-Técnica, 1985.

DE LA TORRE, SALVADOR L. *Mariposas cubanas*, Havana: Ed. Gente Nueva, 1982.

DEL RISCO, E. *Forests of Cuba. Their History and Features*, Havana: Ed. José Martí, 1999.

DÍAZ, MARTA A. *Las orquídeas nativas de Cuba*, Havana: Ed. Científico-Técnica, 1988.

DUCLOZ, C. *Etude Geomorphologique de la Región Habana-Matanzas, Cuba*. Archives de Sciences. Soc. de Physique et d´Histoire Nat. de Genéve, pp. 351-402, 1963.

FERNÁNDEZ, J. M. AND J. R. MARTÍNEZ FERNÁNDEZ. *Polymita*, Havana: Ed. Científico-Técnica, 1967.

FORS, ALBERTO J. *Maderas cubanas*, Havana: Ed. INRA, 1965.

FURRAZOLA BERMÚDEZ, G., C. JUDOLEY AND OTHERS. *Geología de Cuba*, Havana: Editorial Universitaria, p. 239, 1964.

GARCÍA, F. *Las aves de Cuba. Especies endémicas*, Havana: Ed. Gente Nueva, 1982.

_____. *Las aves de Cuba. Subespecies endémicas*, Havana: Ed. Gente Nueva, 1987.

GARRIDO, O. *Los patos de Cuba,* Havana: Ed. Científico-Técnica, 1988.

GÓMEZ, O. *La naturaleza... y nosotros,* Havana: Ediciones Unión, 1986.

GREGORY, WILLIAM K. "A Jurassic Fish Fauna from Western Cuba with an Arrangement of the Families of Olosteam Ganoid Fishes." *Bull of the An. Museum of Nat. History,* XLVIII New York (1923):223-242, [s. n.].

GUTIÉRREZ DOMECH, M. R. "Condiciones geológicas del desarrollo diferenciado de la carsificación en la cordillera de Guaniguanico, Cuba occidental." Statement of the VI Spanish Congress of Speleology, La Coruña, pp. 97-98, 1992.

GUTIÉRREZ DOMECH, M. R., A. MARTÍNEZ ZORRILLA AND A. ABRAHAM ALONSO. *Curso elemental de Espeleología para guías de turismo.* (Unpublished), Havana: Instituto de Geografía, 1994.

GUTIÉRREZ DOMECH, M. R. AND M. ITURRALDE-VINENT. *Condiciones geológicas de formación del carso en Cuba.* 50th Anniversary of the Speleological Society of Cuba International Congress, Havana, 1990.

GUTIÉRREZ DOMECH, M. R. AND F. RIVERO REYES. "Estudio geólogo-geomorfológico de la zona de Cayajabos, Madruga, La Habana" *Serie geográfica,* (1975): Academia de Ciencias, 12:1-34.

INSTITUTO DE GEOGRAFÍA, ACADEMIA DE CIENCIAS DE CUBA Y ACADEMIA DE CIENCIAS DE LA URSS. *Atlas Nacional de Cuba,* USSR: Ed. No 2, 1970.

INSTITUTO DE GEOGRAFÍA DE LA ACADEMIA DE CIENCIAS DE CUBA, INSTITUTO CUBANO DE GEODESIA Y CARTOGRAFÍA. *Nuevo atlas nacional de Cuba,* Spain: Instituto Geográfico Nacional, 1988.

ITURRALDE-VINENT, M. *Naturaleza geológica de Cuba,* Havana: Ed. Científico-Técnica, 1988.

_____. "Preliminary Report on Distribution of Karst Landscapes in Cuba and Their Relation to Geology." *The Professional Geographer,* (1967) 19, 4:208, 209.

ITURRALDE-VINENT, M., G. HUBBELL AND R. ROJAS. "Catalogue of Cuban Fossil Elasmobranchii (Paleocene to Pliocene) and Paleogeographic Implication of Their Lower to Middle Miocene Occurrence." *The Journal of the Geological Society of Jamaica,* (1996) 311:721.

JENNINGS, J. N. *Karst,* London: M.I.T. Press, 1971.

JUDOLEY, CONSTANTINO AND G. FURRAZOLA. *Estratigrafía y fauna del Jurásico en Cuba,* Havana: Instituto del Libro, 1968.

_____. *Geología del área del Caribe y de la costa del Golfo de México,* Havana: 1971.

LECHA E., L. AND A. FLORIDO TRUJILLO. *Principales características climáticas del régimen térmico del archipiélago cubano,* Havana: Ed. Academia, 1989.

LEIVA SÁNCHEZ, A. "Diversidad y potencialidad económica de la flora silvestre de Cuba." (Lectures), 1994.

LEÓN, H. *Flora de Cuba.* Contribuciones ocasionales, Museo de Historia Natural, Colegio La Salle, Vol. I, No. 8, La Habana, 1946.

LLOPIS LLADÓ, N. *Fundamentos de hidrogeología cártsica,* Madrid: Ed. Blume, 1970.

MARTÍNEZ, R., N. BLANCO and M. GONZÁLEZ. *Diccionario terminológico de Biología,* Havana: Ed. Científico-Técnica, 1989.

MARTÍNEZ ZORRILLA, A. and OTHERS. *Las áreas protegidas de Cuba y su importancia en la conservación de la*

BIBLIOGRAPHY

biodiversidad, Centro Nacional de Areas Protegidas, CITMA, Digitalized Lecture, p. 15, 1996.

MASSIP, S. AND S. YSALGUÉ. *Introducción a la Geografía de Cuba,* Havana: Ed. Fiallo y Hermanos, Vol. I, p. 260, 1942.

MINISTERIO DE RELACIONES EXTERIORES. *Perfil de Cuba,* Havana, 1965.

MORA CASTRO, S. AND R. VALVERDE. *La geología y sus progresos,* Cartago: Ed. Tecnológica de Costa Rica, 1994.

NÚÑEZ JIMÉNEZ, A. *Geografía de Cuba,* Havana: Ed. Lex, 1959.

_____. *Geografía de Cuba,* Havana: Ed. Pedagógica, 1965.

_____. *El Archipiélago,* Serie Cuba, la Naturaleza y el Hombre. Havana: Ed. Letras Cubanas, 1982.

_____. *Bojeo;* Serie Cuba, la Naturaleza y el Hombre. Havana: Ed. Letras Cubanas, 1984.

NÚÑEZ JIMÉNEZ, A., V. PANOS AND O. STECL. *Carso en Cuba,* Serie espeleológica y carsológica No. 2, Academia de Ciencias, Havana, 1968.

RIVERO GLEAN, M. "Biodiversidad para el desarrollo cubano" Handwritten Lecture, 1995.

RUIZ GARCÍA, F. *Anfibios de Cuba,* Havana: Ed. Científico-Técnica, 1987.

SILVA, G. *Los murciélagos de Cuba,* Havana: Ed. Científico-Técnica, 1983.

_____. *Sinopsis de la espeleofauna cubana,* Havana: Ed. Científico-Técnica, 1988.

SILVA LEE, A. *Chipojos, bayoyas y camaleones,* Havana: Ed. Científico-Técnica, 1984.

TABIO, E. *Arqueología y agricultura aborigen antillana,* Havana: Ed. Ciencias Sociales, 1989.

TRUDGILL, S. *Limestone Geomorphology.* Longman Group Limited New York, 1985.

TRUSOV, I. I., A. IZQUIERDO AND L. R. DÍAZ. *Características espaciales y temporales de las precipitaciones atmosféricas en Cuba,* Havana: Ed. Academia, 1983.

VARONA, L. *Catálogo de los mamíferos vivientes y extinguidos de las Antillas,* Havana: Ed. Academia, 1973.

_____. *Mamíferos de Cuba,* Havana: Ed. Gente Nueva, 1980.

ZAMORA, E. *Qué es la Zoología,* Havana: Ed. Científico-Técnica, 1979.

Este libro se terminó de imprimir en los
talleres de Quebecor World Bogotá